John Brotherton

For Shirley,

Best wishes and I sincerely
hope that you enjoy the story.

[signature]

Dec. 2, 2000

A FISTFUL
OF
KINGS

TABLE OF CONTENTS

Author's Note

Because casinos are regulated by state and federal government, it is in the interest of the public that this story has been printed. This story is the sole property of The Shears Group, Limited. Reproduction of the material in this book may only be made by press associations for the purpose of public information and reviews. No portion may be published for entertainment purposes without the express written authorization of The Shears Group, Limited. The Shears Group, Limited reserves the right to edit the material herein as it sees fit.

Dedications
and Acknowledgments

I take great pride in dedicating this book to Eddie Austin, of Lake Charles, Louisiana. Eddie is a shock trooper of a criminal attorney and a true friend on whom I can always depend. Many times in these recent years, I have found myself facing overwhelming odds. Always, I could look over my shoulder and see him with a flashlight of hope, wielding heavy artillery, bearing down on the enemy at hand with the most lethal of strategies. If you find yourself in your darkest hour, you can find him listed in the Lake Charles, Louisiana, phone book.

I wish to express my undying gratitude to two other people who mean the world to me:

- *The Reverend*, who belongs to and inhabits the world at large. Where he is out there is anyone's guess. To him I owe my life and a good deal of my sense of who I am.
- My wife Susan, whom I loved utterly the moment I saw her. Elegant woman that she is, she showed herself to be an amazon in spirit when the time came. To put it simply, she helped save my life in more senses than one.

I congratulate the US government team that accomplished what no one was able to do before—especially US Attorney Eddie Jordan, Assistant US Attorney Jim Letten, Assistant US Attorney Peter Strasser, Assistant US Attorney Mike Magner, and FBI Special Agents Jeffrey Santini,

Dennis Swikert, and Kurt Hemphill. These dedicated men are truly heros in our time.

I also would like to give a heartfelt thank you to my friend Mr. James "Mattress Mac" McIngvale, of Houston, Texas. At a time when Susan and I needed help, he offered a generous hand to get us back on our feet. His advice to me at the time was, "Keep your chin up and keep swinging, kiddo." I surely will do just that from now on. Houston, Texas, is fortunate to have him as its good will ambassador; and I am a very lucky man to have him as my friend.

I am grateful for the support I received from several quarters, many unexpected, during the development of this book.

There is my editor, Tom Wright. As we kept on rucking through my various drafts, he showed himself to the manner of a black hat born and bred.

And there are the several people—some whom I've known for years, some whom I've never met, yet all close friends—who gave generously of their time to read and comment on my drafts. To you all I give thanks in greater measure than I can express.

PREFACE

On June 12, 1998, my wife, Susan, and I walked through passport check and customs into the arms of my waiting parents, in the arrivals area of Bush Intercontinental Airport, in Houston, after having lived and worked in Moscow for eight months. We were exhausted, flat broke, and alive—that, and grateful. Our interests had been looked after. Had it been otherwise, we would have been American dead sleeping cold in the earth that nourishes Birchwood Forest.

On February 22, 2000, in the Federal Courthouse in Baton Rouge, I walked to the witness stand to testify in the trial of former Louisiana Governor Edwin Edwards, who was facing prosecution, under the RICO racketeering and conspiracy laws, for manipulating the casino licensing process to line his pockets. As I passed Edwin, he complimented me on my necktie.

How these two long walks are tied to each other is the story I tell here. It is very much my story, but in telling it I hope to make it yours also.

In the pages that follow, I take you on a roller coaster ride along an unsafe track. In terms pure and simple, you will read of my odyssey through a world where the agents of good and evil contend for my soul. People who have hitched their wagon to achieving success and notoriety in the public eye will find nothing here in the way of validation. Also, I have friends who would have liked to have told their part of this story but, for obvious reasons, have feared to do so.

Few are as fortunate as I am to have descended into the underworld of the casino industry, where everything has its price, and to have emerged, knowing that the bid the devil's advocate makes for your soul is cheap, no matter how high its dollar volume. And few are so blessed as my wife and I to have survived a battle of sheer wits against Russian businessmen on their own turf, with them intent on their special brand of active measures. We survived just barely; and the experience forced me to reshape many of my most fundamental outlooks. In the end, I realized how lucky I was to have had the pearl of greatest price—unbending loyalty and the awesome power of a woman's love—as much as handed to me.

Far more than a kiss and tell account of the low down politics and internecine tactics I witnessed during my years in the casino industry, this book provides windows into several mentalities that are instructive as examples to be avoided. You will, for instance, see the ego-driven mentality that battens to the power residing in public office and appoints itself as unaccountable to the law. There is, of course, assurance and edification in seeing the high and mighty brought to their knees by the legal systems they abused. The spectacle is in the order of Greek tragedy.

You will see abounding in this story the codependent personality that sustains itself by association with power and wealth. Too, you will bear witness to a corporate culture swollen with arrogance, seeking to use political influence to manipulate illegal monopolies and protected markets, abusing the principles of capitalism on which a wholesome economy depends. In this, you will read a story that is told over and over but that cannot be told too often. To the extent that we become tolerant of anticompetitive practices among huge corporations, we allow the competitive, economic vigor of our great nation to be eroded.

In many respects, you will find that my story outstrips fiction in its strangeness, its humor, and its entertainment value. And you will find a deeply woven, elusive mystery in these pages, with the clues carefully laid. You are invited to take up and follow the trail.

Above all else, this book chronicles what I learned by allowing myself to be seduced by the siren song of wealth, prestige, and fame. You will see the prices I paid for having attempted to fly high on wings of fortune that were made from wax: a broken marriage, with certain impacts on two impressionable children, and the near loss, amid violent circumstances, not only of my own life but also the life of my second wife. You will see that in the end I was, out of the raw need to keep Susan and myself alive, brought back to the John Brotherton whom my closest friends had seen and cherished all along but whom I had lost somewhere in the high rolling corporate world of inflated salaries, designer suits, gold Rolexes, and empty job descriptions.

In offering you this book, I start by also offering the following keys to the mystery that lurks herein:

- If you remember well and hold a keen ear, the answer is yours.
- Nobody was really sure if he was from the House of Lords.

And should you take ownership of the answer, I'm sure you will then come to share with me the enlightened state of Coleridge's wedding guest in "The Rime of the Ancyent Marinere":

A sadder and wiser man

He rose the morrow morn.

Major Characters
(in order of appearance)

John Brotherton
The narrator: former US Army Special Forces and 82nd Airborne Division; an executive within Players International; then general manager of the Grand Casino Coushatta Casino; then general manager of the Beverly Hills Club (Moscow) and VP within Chuck Norris Casinos International, Limited.

Ed and David Fishman
From Malibu, California, the founders of and major shareholders in Players International.

Merv Griffin
A major shareholder in and spokesman for Players International.

Kathy Brotherton
The narrator's first wife and mother of his children, Derek and Macie.

Rick Shetler
Edwin Edward's bagman in the Lake Charles, Louisiana, area.

Stephen Edwards
The son of Governor Edwin Edwards (Louisiana), a participant in extortion schemes.

Roland Manuel (the Mallard)
An acquaintance of Edwin Edwards and one of the initial participants in the Lake Charles casino project.

Pat Madamba
From Atlantic City, New Jersey, a lawyer and an executive within Players International.

Howard Goldberg
From Atlantic City, New Jersey, a lawyer and the president of Players International.

Julie Fusilier
A Baton Rouge-based lawyer and lobbyist and a close friend of the narrator.

Robert Wooley
The husband of Julie Fusilier, a lawyer and lobbyist, and a close friend of the narrator.

Edwin Edwards
The former four-term governor of Louisiana and the engineer of schemes to extort funds from casino operators.

Senator Jim Cox
A state senator who represents Lake Charles.

Ken Hagan
The owner of Lake Charles Construction and a close friend of the narrator.

Scott Cooper
An executive within Players International.

Steve Perskie
From New Jersey, an executive within Players International.

Carl Paige
A fishing boat operator.

The Reverend
A retired, senior intelligence operative and a close friend of the narrator.

Steve Labov
From Atlantic City, a close friend and business associate of Howard Goldberg and a consultant to Players International.

Eddie Austin
A criminal attorney, based in Lake Charles, and a close friend of the narrator.

Pat Menche, Lyle Berman, and Tom Brosig
Executives with the Grand Casino organization.

Paul Ruppert
The tribal administrator of the Sovereign Coushatta Nation.

Lovelin Poncho
Chairman (chief) of the Sovereign Coushatta Nation.

Bertney Langley
A member of the Sovereign Coushatta Nation and Lovelin Poncho's rival in an election for chairmanship of the tribe.

Tony Hay
Kathy Brotherton's paramour.

Derek and Macie Brotherton
The narrator's children in his first marriage

Susan Touchette (Brotherton)
The narrator's second wife.

Taylor Touchette
Susan Touchette's son.

Cary Feldman
From New Jersey, an attorney who represents the narrator in his interaction with the New Orleans FBI.

Steve Irwin
The Assistant US Attorney who initially spearheads the prosecution of Edwin Edwards.

Jeffery Santini
The FBI Agent in Charge of the Edwards investigation.

Nikolaj Vissikovsky
One of the three partners in the Beverly Hills Club: A Chuck Norris Enterprise.

Chuck Norris
An alleged operating partner and an investor in the Beverly Hills Club: A Chuck Norris Enterprise and Chuck Norris Casinos International, Limited.

Danny, David, and Huck
American employees of the Beverly Hills Club—A Chuck Norris Enterprise.

Out of all the chaos, still there is love.

– James Webb, *The Emperor's General*

*Few of us can hold on to our real selves long
enough to discover the real truths about ourselves and
this whirling earth to which we cling.*

– J.G. Gray, *The Warriors: Reflections on   Men in Battle*

PROLOGUE
The Game of Existance

I couldn't drive it from my mind—the image of the smashed up white car, blood all over its upholstery. I looked at Susan sitting beside me in the back seat of the cab. She was pale, too afraid to even move. Please, God! Please! I begged. If it has to be someone—me, not her! I didn't have to add that if we made it out of this, I'd be through with casinos. I had already promised myself that.

I looked behind me again. The black Volga sedan that had picked us up almost as soon as we had pulled away from the Sovietsky Hotel was locked onto us, trying to get closer. Susan noticed my face and knew what I was thinking. If they want me, these Russian goons, I'm going to make them work for it. But why does she have to be caught in the middle? It's not fair. All she did was stick by me so they couldn't get me alone. Right! She had made it rough for them. And now? Now they're desperate. Now they'll do what they have to. I know too much.

I reached in my pocket and pulled out all the cash I could get my hands on, and thrust it up to our driver. "Hurry, sir, please!" I urged in Russian.

He looked in the rear view mirror and then, with a jerk of his head, over to his side view mirror. Again, I looked behind me. The Volga had changed lanes and was making a sudden surge to come up on our left flank. Our driver floored the accelerator. We shot forward and passed by a car to our left. He then yanked the wheel sharply to his left and nearly cut the car off.

Behind us the Volga did the same. Ahead I could see the exit to the right, off Leningradeskoye Schosse to Sheremetyevo 2 International. But our driver jerked the cab into the leftmost lane, accelerated even more, then whipped over two lanes to get into the exit lane.

Now the Volga was three cars back, almost riding the rear fender of the vehicle just in front of it. As our driver turned onto the airport exit, tires screeching, I thought of where this had begun, almost five years ago.

CHAPTER 1

THE ASSIGNMENT

✳

I was tired of hearing about the standoff between the feds and the Branch Davidians at their Mount Carmel complex near Waco. I switched off the FM station and inserted one of my tapes. Now, with *Sergeant Pepper* blaring from the stereo, I could enjoy driving east on Interstate 10 on this beautiful March afternoon, relaxing on the crest of the elevated mood you're in when you know your ducks are in harness and moving in the direction you want.

It was just past five o'clock, and the exit for Lake Charles, Louisiana, was only a few miles ahead. I thought about the new project I was taking on for Players International, whom I had joined in '89, as an accountant working in their first venture into the cruise ship casino industry. Soon after, I had been promoted to project director to oversee development of Players' first riverboat casino, located in southern Illinois, on the Missouri River. Now, only three years later, I had made it all the way up to vice president, responsible for spearheading Players' second riverboat casino, here in Lake Charles.

Approaching the exit, I could see the expansive, muddy lake. On its east bank were the elegant mansions that had been built by old oil money and that were now owned by the area's most wealthy families. As a study in contrast, chemical processing plants, their stacks billowing out their emissions, occupied the west bank. To the southwest, the sun was lowering and would soon be setting. Red streams over the iron shore, I thought, noting that the sunlight filtering through the stack emissions created an almost impressionistic effect.

The exit ramp was jammed, backed up with cars all the way to the interstate. I slowed and took my place in line. Up ahead I could see the aftermath of an accident. A small white car had smashed against the guardrail. As I passed the officer who was directing traffic around the wreck, I could see that the car had caught fire and that the fire crew had extinguished the flames. The driver, a young man, was laid out on the pavement, motionless. The ambulance crew wasn't in a hurry, so I assumed that the accident victim was dead. Not the best of omens, first off, pulling into town, I thought. I wondered, Is someone trying to tell me no one's immune to the inevitable?

In Lake Charles, I'd be staying in the Downtowner Motel, located at the north end of the lake, until I could find a house that would be suitable for my family. Owned, from what I had heard, by an older woman who allowed her husband, Bill Woodward, to run it, and ideally located close to the interstate, the motel would be the site of the new Players casino.

Months ago, before I had been charged with spearheading development of the Lake Charles casino, Players' corporate partner in this project, a company calling itself Jebaco, had contracted with Bill Woodward to control the motel site. Jebaco had also broken political ground at the local level by winning the support of the Lake Charles city council, despite public opposition to the casino. The Jebaco partners were supposedly hardwired at the state level as well. Whether that was true would, I thought, remain to be seen. In Louisiana, I knew, your political survival depended on your ability to discern the more of matters than initially met the eye.

The Downtowner, I could see as I pulled up to it, needed a lot of work before it could be expected to attract casino patrons. Right now, it looked rundown—so seedy that I wasn't looking forward to seeing my room, not after my drive from Metropolis, Illinois. First, I'd do an overall recon of the premise; then I'd visit the bar and put a quick drink under my belt.

As I entered the lobby to check in, I noted that it was small and confining, with a mixture of lemon yellow, almond, and chrome furnishings that looked at least twenty years old. The hotel restaurant was off a long hallway. It was large enough to seat maybe one hundred people. The blue carpet was worn. The chairs were the same almond colored, plastic-over-chrome type that I had seen in the lobby.

Farther down the hall, I saw "Bar" handwritten in black felt marker on a large wooden door. It wasn't the kind of place I'd normally go for a relaxing drink, not from what I had heard. In fact, I'd been told it was the sort of bar you'd go to only if you were desperate and had no other choices. I also understood that it was strictly a hangout for locals—the type that didn't warm to out-of-staters.

Inside, the bar was dimly lit and filled with smoke. The only people drinking here this evening were guys, sitting in small groups. No one looked up at me as I stepped in. I pulled a Winston from my pack and lit it. I didn't mind the haze. There'd be little chance of any eye contact here, something that could start the kind of trouble I could live without. Also, I wanted to size up this scene without being noticed.

The door to the bar opened and a man stepped in, stopped, and looked around the room. He was medium in height, casually dressed, and in his fifties, I guessed. His eyes stopped on me. He stood looking at me for a moment; then he approached. "You've got to be John Brotherton," he said. "I know your name, and you're the only guy here I don't know by sight. So I figure one plus one makes you."

"You're right," I said. "And who are you?"

"I'm Harlan Duhon," he answered without offering his hand.

I recalled that David Fishman had told me about this Harlan Duhon; but I didn't expect that I'd be meeting him first off tonight. Nor did I expect him to be here looking for me. I'd heard that he had once been a union strong man and that he had been indicted by the feds for trying to hire a hit man back in 1989. The charges were later dismissed. After the

Right to Work Law had been passed in 1983, hiring union was no longer mandatory in Louisiana. The unions were kept alive by men who weren't squeamish about using forceful tactics.

"You're with Players, right?" he asked.

"I am," I answered. I didn't care to ask how he knew.

"What do you think of Lake Charles, Mr. Brotherton?"

"Been here before, lots of times. I'm from Houston, sir. I've done oilfield work all around this area. I like it here."

"Tell me what you think about the working man," he said in a flat statement rather than a request.

"I'm pro-union, if that's what you're asking. I was raised union; my dad retired from a union."

He smiled briefly. "You planning to use local people for all the building that'll be going on for this casino?"

"I am," I said.

"And you're going to use union people?"

"I intend to see to it that Players uses strictly union, sir."

Duhon engaged me eyeball to eyeball. I held the contact, knowing this stare was some sort of pissing contest or bonding session. I didn't care which. I was familiar with both rituals. Duhon took a pace back from me and looked me up and down. He then stepped back toward me, again looking me directly in the eye. "You'll do okay, maybe," he said.

"I'll do okay, certainly," I answered.

"Hope so. I want you to know that I head the local IBEW union hall. I do my job well."

"So do I. You'll find I mean what I say. And I think you heard what I said. You were doing the asking."

"I was, and I heard," he said, again smiling slightly, perhaps indicating that I had jumped through this hoop in good form. For the moment, I was satisfied. Players would need union support, and I intended to do what I had to make sure we got it.

"Gotta get going," Duhon said, reaching out to shake my hand. "I'll be seeing you again, if you're here for any time."

Before he went out the door, he looked over his shoulder and scanned the bar. The feds have a way of making you do that, don't they? I thought as he stepped out into the hall. I was relieved to see him leave—not knowing at the time that he'd become and remain one of my most trusted friends.

I walked up to the bar, ordered a Jack Daniels, and lit another Winston. As I reached into my side pocket for my wallet, a deep voice behind me said, "I'll get it." Then a huge hand reached around and grasped my arm.

I turned to face a solidly built black man dressed in a polo pullover shirt and neatly pressed, dark gabardine trousers. I noticed the union logo on his shirt. He was at least forty pounds over my two hundred, thick across the shoulders, but otherwise lean. In height, he was over my six feet by at least four inches. If it hadn't been for his friendly expression, I'd have taken him as a professional wrestler. I was impressed but also uneasy. I hadn't been in Lake Charles for more than fifteen minutes, and already I had met two union people who knew who I was.

"John, I'm City Councilman Ken Schexnider," he said and gave me his hand to shake.

I relaxed. How's this for a roll? First unions, now blacks—my two favorite coalitions. And city council, too. I liked working with minorities. Experience had shown I could trust them.

"You like our city?" he asked. His manner was smooth, somewhere between formal and cordial.

I repeated that I was very familiar with the city and the area.

"Oh yeah, you've been here before? When?" He was now openly smiling.

"Back before the oil boom went bust in '83." I paused a moment and then asked, "And what brings you to this wonderful place tonight?"

"I'm here to ask you a few question. Hope you don't mind."

"Of course not, Councilman. Ask anything you'd like."

"For a starter, what do you do for Players?"

"I help get the casino license and build the project."

"You do the hiring or just the construction?"

"A lot of both."

He paused a moment, looking me up and down. "You planning to incorporate the local minorities?"

"I won't disappoint you there," I answered.

"You shouldn't," he replied, in a low voice, his smile now gone. "Around here one thing you need to know is who your friends are."

"I choose my friends very carefully, and I try to make sure I know them. If I have my way, you and I will be friends, sir."

He smiled again and offered his hand. "I need to be on my way. Good to meet you."

"Same here," I replied, impressed by the strength in his outsized grasp.

As he left, I checked my watch. I had about an hour before I was supposed to meet Ed and David Fishman.

I walked out of the bar, down the hall, and out into the hotel parking lot. I stood taking in deep breaths to clear my lungs of the smoke I had inhaled. Night was gathering over the lake, and it was cooler, bracing. The sky above me was perfectly clear, and it was quiet except for the noise of traffic from the interstate. So my welcoming committee had been ready, I thought. No two ways about their expectations. First evening here and already the lines are being drawn.

I walked to my car. Before I opened the trunk to get my bags, I leaned against the driver's door, looked up at the sky, at the first stars emerging, and let my mind slip back in time.

I saw myself as a six-year-old, sitting on the counter of my father's pawnshop, in McAlester, Oklahoma. I was content at this station; from here I could observe Main Street while I played with the small parts that were cast offs from clocks that my father had repaired.

As I was tinkering, a long black limousine came to a stop in front of the shop. I recognized the two black vehicles that followed as Continentals, the ones with suicide doors—the type of car that had exposed J.F.K. to the grassy knoll. I knew about things like that even then. I was growing up in an age of conspiracy, and Stanley Kubrick was painting my mindscape.

The man who stepped from the limo came to visit my dad often. He was Carl Albert, Speaker of the House, L.B.J.'s shock trooper in Congress. For a moment he stood brushing himself off, looking around his hometown and waving to passersby. He carried the air of a Caesar who had returned to dignify his place of birth with his presence.

My dad met Albert at the door and led him into the shop. I continued with my tinkering. When they both stepped out sometime later, Albert was, I saw, holding a package under his arm. Of course, it could have been anything.

As I looked out over Lake Charles, I thought about how politics had run in my blood throughout my childhood, also during my years in the oil industry, just after I had graduated from high school. Then it had been US Army boot camp and after that Fort Benning and Fort Bragg. There had been little of anything political in jump school, Special Forces, or the 82nd Airborne Division: mainly the sort of backbreaking, day in, day out work that forces you to define yourself in terms of new limits.

Now, however, I was back in Louisiana. And tonight, I had made it through one obstacle course. I had no doubt there would be others ahead. But I was confident that I would negotiate them with high marks.

CHAPTER 2

WARM-UP

＊

The Lake Charles casino would be a step forward for Players. At first, Ed and David Fishman, the founders and principals, had busied themselves producing television game shows—*Hollywood Squares, Dealer's Choice, Joker's Wild*, and the like. In short order, they parlayed their contracts and established a tournament enterprise. For a specified fee, they offered gambling tournaments at casinos that agreed to buy into their service. This business line developed into Players Club, a membership company that provided conveniences for gamblers coming to Las Vegas and Atlantic City. Ed, the older of the Fishmans and chairman of the board for Players, recruited his friend Telly Savalas to ramrod promotion.

Although the Fishmans had from the outset wanted to break into the gaming business in a big way, initially they lacked enough capital to buy one of the large hotel casinos on the Las Vegas strip. Their opportunity to act on their ambition came when Illinois passed the Illinois Riverboat Gaming Act into law. Players moved quickly to obtain one of the state's ten available riverboat casino licenses.

In a strategic masterstroke, the company targeted the economically depressed southern sector of the state. While the other applicants sought licenses for sites in highly populated, economically buoyant areas, Players accurately sensed that the intent of the gaming act was to spread development throughout the entire state and to inject new life into economically flagging areas. The state gaming board approved the Players proposal with dispatch. In effect, Players had stolen the gaming license from under the slumbering Vegas big boys.

In a second masterstroke, Players located its first casino in the small town of Metropolis, on a plot overlooking the Ohio River. Although its population numbered only seven thousand, Metropolis was adjacent to Interstate 24, which led directly to Nashville, just two hours away.

It was at this stage that I made my first move up within the Players organization. Because of my previous background in oilfield construction, I was the company's most qualified candidate to develop the Metropolis project. My training as an accountant, moreover, enabled me to deal with the financial end.

Merv Griffin first came into the Players fold as a financial backer for the Metropolis casino. Ed and Merv were long-standing friends, and Players lacked the cash reserves to complete the Metropolis project on its own. In my first contacts with him, Merv came across as genuine and light-hearted. But in short order I learned that he was all business when he saw real money on the table. For starters, he took a huge ownership bite out of Players in return for backing the company's play for the Metropolis casino.

I had developed the Metropolis project under the supervision of David Fishman, the vice chairman of the company. I didn't really dislike him at first—although his tendency to minimize his own exposure to risk by using me as a point man made me nervous. Later, his use of me as a human shield would make me more than nervous. For now, I could see why he was reluctant to step into the front line of the Metropolis project. The local opinion leaders had reservations about a full-blown casino intruding into their corner of the planet, and they mistook David's Malibu airs and graces as effeminate—as gay, even. Fortunately for Players' PR front, my Houston accent and down-home Texan bearing put me in good standing with the townsfolk. In all, I had enjoyed living in Metropolis. I had formed genuine friendships with Mayor Bill Commer and City Alderman "Dude" Little, who had initially opposed the casino. In time, I had been able to win them over as allies.

As the Metropolis project moved on a positive track, Players began eyeballing political developments in Louisiana that augured well for the casino industry. The runoff election between Edwin Edwards and David Duke for the governorship of Louisiana was providing a spectacle for the news media. In one corner was Duke, an extreme right-winger, an overt Nazi sympathizer, and an active member of the Ku Klux Klan. In the other corner was Edwards, long known as "the King of Louisiana." Investigated by the FBI and unsuccessfully tried by the feds twice during his previous three terms as governor, he had established himself as the prototypical Louisiana politician. He had also gathered a reputation as a womanizer. His appetites in this regard were evident in his recent marriage to a stunner who was in her early thirties and aptly named "Candy." Strange as it might seem, Edwards' most formidable weapon was his unabashed admission of his peccadilloes as being only what you'd expect in the wholesome male, political animal. In his election campaign, he was able to manipulate the voting public into endorsing him not as the sacred option but as the profanity of preference. I remembered hearing about the stickers that Edwards supporters attached to their rear bumpers—"Vote for the crook—it's important!"

Of particular interest to Players was the Louisiana Riverboat Gaming Act, which had been passed during the previous term, held by Governor Buddy Roemer, and which had empowered a governor-appointed panel to award fifteen licenses to operate riverboat casinos. Edwards staffed this panel almost as soon as he took office, an initiative that Players saw as indicating Edwards' enthusiasm over the prospect of so many new casinos in his state. The chance for Players to take advantage of opportunities in Louisiana came about fortuitously, through connections between Players and the Jebaco partnership, which had recruited Players at the annual gaming convention in Las Vegas.

Just after the Metropolis casino opened on February 23 (ahead of schedule and with construction costs under budget), Players promoted me to vice president. The next day, they shifted my brief to the Lake Charles casino.

As soon as I walked into my room in the Downtowner, I dumped my bags on the floor and took a quick look around. I was still uneasy that two of the local players in this project had known when I was arriving. Also, both had known my resume cold. I had the feeling I was under surveillance, that perhaps my room was bugged.

First, I checked the most likely places for devices. The large single mirror on the wall behind the TV wasn't two-way. In the center, however, the silver backing was missing over an area about the size of a quarter. As a safeguard, I covered the spot with a "Post-It." Then I swept the room with my hand-held scanner to see if I could detect any electronic signals. The scanner showed no readings—though it did occur to me that the output from a hardwired device wouldn't register.

I turned on the TV at a high enough volume to confound any listening devices. That, of course, wouldn't prevent visual surveillance; but it would let "them" (if, in fact, a "them" there was) know that I was on to their game (if, in fact, a game was in progress).

The newscast drew my attention. The anchorman was on site at the Branch Davidian complex and was playing a tape recorded by David Koresh. Again he was laying claim to being the Messiah, returned for his second coming, as foretold in *The Revelation of Saint John the Divine*. Koresh was also insisting that the end of times was at hand.

I had studied *Revelation* as well as several of its commentaries and was aware of the disputes over how the prophesized events would unfold. I looked in the small bedside credenza, found the courtesy copy of the Gideon Bible, bound in leatherette, and quickly scanned through the text of Saint John's prophetic vision: two witnesses; 144,000 members selected from the twelve tribes; seven seals opened one by one; seven trumpets; seven plagues unleashed on the people left on earth; Satan bound for one thousand years, then let loose, only to be cast into the lake of fire and brimstone; then the new heaven and earth, with the new Jerusalem descending, likened to a bride being presented to her husband. I ran over the pages until I found what I was looking for: "And what shall be the sign of thy coming and the end of the age?"

I wondered about the what and when of the end of times but found it a disturbing thing to be thinking about now, with about an hour remaining before I'd be seeing Ed, David, and the Jebaco partners downstairs.

I felt grungy after my drive and wanted to shower and dress my best, in my favorite suit, a charcoal Armani. First, though, I'd do my miniworkout, which I had missed this morning—the nominal fifty push-ups and sit-ups that had been a physical training (PT) drill at Fort Benning and Fort Bragg.

Before I stepped into the shower, I looked at myself in the large mirror. I would soon be thirty-four years old. I was a bigger than the average six-foot male but not fat. Special Forces had hardened me and I had made sure that I retained my physical edge. When I was well dressed, I knew I presented an impressive image—certainly good enough, I thought, for the Jebaco reps. I thought a moment about the corporate name *Jebaco*. To my ear, it had the ring of the Middle East. Actually, the name had evolved from the mix of the main partners—"a Jew, a black, and a Coon Ass," as I had heard it.

As I was turning on the hot water, the phone rang. I answered, "Yeah!" expecting to hear David's voice. The voice I did hear brought a grimace to my face. It was my wife, Kathy, calling from home. She wasn't happy, which was business as usual for her these days. I braced myself. When Kathy was in one of her black studies, she pushed the practice of sickmouth into the domain of the bizarre.

"What are you doing!" she demanded. I was actually surprised, pleasantly. In this frame of mind, it was rare for her to get through four words without cussing.

"Getting ready to see Ed, David, and the Jebacos. How are your parents?" I asked, trying to offset her foul mood.

"Fine. When are you going to get your ass back here?"

I could sense that she was gathering what would soon become superheated steam. "I thought you all were having a good time. What's the problem, honey?" I asked, still hoping to defuse her.

"I'm fucking tired of playing God damn second fiddle to those motherfuckers at Players. When are you going to stand up to those faggots and make them pay you what you're worth?"

"Kathy," I appealed, knowing from experience that I had nothing to gain by retaliating in kind. "You know I've never made this much money in my life. I'm doing the best I can. Please be patient, will you? You don't have to work. Our bills are paid. Why are you so insistent?"

"Calm down? Fuck you! Fuck you, you hear me?"

Now she had caught her stride and there'd be no toning her down. I could have hung up on her, but that would only start a fight that would go on all night. In that event, I could expect her to call the front desk and leave messages such as, "Tell the stupid motherfucker to call his wife." Worse, she could drive over and put in an appearance that could be embarrassing, to say the least. Back in Metropolis, she loved to walk in on my business conferences. Usually, the meeting came to an abrupt end, leaving me with a liberal dose of egg on my face.

Better, I decided, to face the music now. "Please, Kathy, will you just calm down? I understand that I'm going to get a promotion and a raise if this project goes."

"Project, smoject!" she raged back at me. "You tell that cocksucking David to pay you more money. You are one dumb shit. You can't see that they're taking advantage of you! Wake up and smell the coffee, you stupid motherfucker!"

Truth was, I had just gotten a big raise and a huge bonus, the likes of which I had never seen. Also, I had received stock options for having completed the Metropolis project. But Kathy didn't understand things that were so intangible. The way she saw it, if it wasn't green and in her hot hand, she couldn't spend it now. And if she couldn't spend it now, what good was it?

"Kathy," I pleaded, "I don't own this company. Just a few years ago, we had nothing. We're doing okay now and it's getting better by the day. I'm trying."

"I want your ass back here tomorrow. Don't piss me off. Don't you fucking piss me off!" she warned and hung up. She didn't even give me a chance to talk to the kids.

Kathy certainly had her demons. And we certainly had our problems. But she denied any responsibility and saw the problems as owing to me. She, Kathy, could do no wrong—ever. Thinking of her the way she was now saddened me. She hadn't always been this way.

After I left the US Army back in '86 and returned home (then Huffman, Texas), I looked up a former girlfriend I had known years before. I badly needed a haircut, and she recommended a small salon called The Talk of the Town. It was owned by Kathy.

She remembered me from our high school days and was happy to see me. At the time, she was living with her ex- husband, a situation that impressed me as strange. Kathy insisted that it was an arrangement based strictly on convenience. Soon we started dating.

As I remember her then, she had professionally dyed long blonde hair with bangs—fashionable at the time. She had bright blue eyes, a thin nose, and near perfect facial features. In personality, she was very outgoing, always cheerful. She was about five-foot-seven and ruggedly built, especially in her thighs. Having once been a competition figure skater, she was a physically strong person.

When she came to visit my house, she frequently brought small presents. I began to enjoy the attention and always looked forward to seeing her. But there were two factors that bothered me. For one, she sold cocaine with her ex-husband, a guy named Eddie Strysik—although she claimed she only dabbled in this sort of dealing. Also, she had a four-year-old son, Derek, who lived with her parents. She told me that he was better off with them. Later, after Kathy and I were married, I saw to it that Derek moved in with us.

Once our relationship was in full swing, Kathy told me how she had discarded her first husband. By her account, she set him up for a bust. She knew he was working on a large purchase of cocaine; so she contacted a vice-squad officer (a detective named Ray) and told him where and when the delivery was to take place. When Eddie showed up to receive the merchandise, the officer was laying in wait for him. He was then arrested, convicted, and sentenced to a long term. I should have taken note of her methodology. Later, I would learn that Kathy, once bent on foul intent, was a force to be reckoned with.

Kathy and I married on September 5, 1987, after having lived together for two months. Soon after, she gave birth to our daughter, Macie. From that point on, our relationship steadily degraded.

Just after our marriage, I took a job as an accountant in Baytown,

Texas. But my income wasn't enough to support two children. On the small amount of money we had saved, we moved to Los Angeles, where the job market was very active. We found an apartment in the south part of the city, and I started looking for interviews. I recall that I was jumpy at the time because the move had dwindled our savings and I had no money coming in. It was imperative that I get myself employed; and, in the meantime, I felt that we had to keep ourselves on a Spartan budget. I decided, for example, to forego a new pair of shoes and to spit polish the one, old pair I had so I'd look respectable for interviews. For some reason that I never really understood, however, Kathy saw things differently. One afternoon, she left the house, not saying where she was going. She returned with a brand new Dooney and Bourke leather purse.

When I asked her about her extravagance, she cut loose with the stream of vulgar rhetoric that later became typical of her.

I realize now that I would have acted in the best interests of both of the kids and myself by leaving her then. But I didn't. I figured that economic pressures were eroding her and that I could ease the stress by finding a good job. I put my job-hunting program into high gear and in a few weeks signed on with Players as an accountant.

The hot shower felt cleansing after the abusive string of cusswords from Kathy. I dried off, dressed myself in my charcoal Armani, and once again looked at myself in the mirror.

At the same time, I wondered how I could get Kathy enthusiastic about moving to the Lake Charles area. A plan began to suggest itself. Next morning, I would find a real estate office and launch a house hunt. If I could call her back with something as tangible as a home to move into, perhaps I could reverse the trend in our relationship. Though I had no way of knowing it, damage control was soon to become a way of life with me in both my marriage and my job.

CHAPTER 3

PIGGIES

*

The phone rang as I was stepping out the door. I recognized David Fishman's voice. "John, are you ready?" he asked. "We're all downstairs."

"I've been waiting, David," I said, giving my voice a slight edge. Then I hung up. Tonight, I didn't want to put up with David's routine arrogance. I felt I held the cards, at least for now. We were in my backyard, and I had completed the Metropolis project impressively. No one in Players could deny that. Sure, David's brother had money and connections. And David was pretty good at connecting his wagon to Ed's star. But maybe I could show them they were out of their element here. I'll give it my best, I thought, looking at my mirror image again. The look and the feel of the charcoal Armani charged me.

The hotel lobby was empty except for two men who were sitting behind the front desk. As I approached them to ask if they had seen my associates, the older man introduced himself as Bill Woodward and asked me something I was used to hearing by now: "You're with Players, right?"

I thought he had a sly look about him. Later, I'd hear that he had once been involved with an insurance company that had been under federal investigation and that he had done what he had to stay out of harm's way.

"This is Tim, my manager," Woodward said as the younger man reached out and shook my hand, without speaking.

When I asked him how he was doing, he gave a polite nod by way of reply but remained silent. He looked to me like the sort of cowering dog that would snap at your heals as soon as you turned to walk away. I asked if they had seen Ed and David Fishman, and Bill pointed out that they were in his office, waiting for me.

David was seated at a long table in the middle of the room, with Ed, Marshal Geller (another member of the Players' board), and three men whom I didn't recognize. I figured they were the Jebaco reps.

One of the reps stood up and introduced himself as Wayne Ducote. I recognized his thick New Orleans dialect, the type that's often mistaken for a Boston accent. He was handsome, in his forties, I guessed. His black hair was combed back, with a slight crop hanging over his forehead. His sideburns were short, with a touch of gray—probably tinted in. He wore expensive tortoiseshell glasses, the style that John Lennon made famous. His suit was impeccable—Italian designer no doubt. It matched his silk tie perfectly. I wasn't surprised to see a nine hundred-dollar pair of Italian shoes.

"I've heard good things about you," Wayne said.

At this point, frankly, I was wishing I was back in the smoke- filled bar with either Harlan Duhon or Ken Schexnider. I liked people of a plainer cut who let you know up front where you stood.

Wayne introduced the young man to his right as his son, David. The son shared his father's striking looks and was also a study in Italian designer. His face was tanned, and his sandy hair was combed over in a sporty style.

Wayne then introduced me to Steve Rittvo, the third man on his side of the table. Steve was a little older than Wayne and somewhat stocky, though he carried it well. His full beard went with his salt- and-pepper hair. His suit was appropriate, but it wasn't in the order of an Armani. It showed that he had a sense of propriety and that he'd rely on more than superficial looks to make his impression.

I guessed that he was the Jewish component of this Jebaco trinity. I knew that he owned a company called Urban Systems that offered several types of analysis—business feasibility, marketing, demographics, economic impact, and the like. I had been impressed with the materials his firm had prepared for Players' initial presentation to the Gaming Commission.

I held our handshake a moment and said, "I've been looking forward to meeting you, Steve. The up-front work you did for us was a great help."

"All right, now where were we?" David asked. I could see that my forward statement to Rittvo had unnerved him.

I let the discussion proceed and listened, taking mental notes. The Ducotes showed the aggressiveness that had enabled them to scratch out a good living in the cutthroat business of downtown development in New Orleans. From what I understood, they owned and operated several parking garages in the city and showed no reluctance to do what it took to hold the high ground against competition. The Fishmans, on the other hand, especially David, indulged their Malibu mannerisms. By comparison with the Ducotes, they looked almost ladylike, sitting with their legs crossed high, almost up to their laps, like you'd expect a long legged, willowy figured female model to do. The Ducotes looked like a pair of predatory wolves sizing up a pair of sacrificial lambs. The way they'd see it, the Fishmans would have some utility, with their knowledge of how to operate a casino; also, Players had already been licensed in Illinois; its stock was at a record high; and it had millions in the bank.

The meeting continued on for about a half-hour. Then I could see that the Ducotes were anxious to leave. I decided to unnerve David a little more by again putting my best foot forward. I stood and suggested, "We're all a bit worn out, and it's getting late. Why don't we call it quits for now?" To the Jebacos I said, "I'll look forward to seeing each of you again soon."

Steve Rittvo stood and reached out to shake with me. "You haven't met all of us Jebaco folks yet, John."

I had already carefully looked over Jebaco's application for a gaming license and knew who the two locals partners were. "You're right," I said. "Frank Pryce and Rick Shetler. I expect to drop in on them right away." Out of the corner of my eye, I saw David's brow darken.

I woke the next morning at seven, feeling hyper-energized, gloating over having outpaced David last evening. I flung the covers away, hit the floor, and snapped off my routine push-ups and sit-ups. I had the feeling of an easy day ahead, house shopping and maybe exploring my way around Lake Charles, seeing how it had changed over the years since I had last been here.

On Lake Street, I noticed a Century-21 office. I went in and found that an agent, a young lady, was available for me. Among her listings, I saw one that I liked right off, located in the small town of Sulphur, just west of Lake Charles. We visited the property and I videotaped it, explaining to the agent that I'd need to consult with my wife before I could make an offer.

Returning to the Downtowner, I found David Fishman talking with Bill Woodward by the reception desk.

"We got it!" David announced as I walked up to him. "The gaming board met today and gave us the preliminary approval."

"How many of the *other* fourteen proposals got approved?" I asked. I wanted to remind him that the board had more on its plate than our project. He answered that only two applications had been reviewed today.

Only two out of fifteen—thirteen more to go, I thought. Listening to David's tone, you'd have thought we had reached the end of the process. Actually, we had negotiated only the first hurdle.

I grabbed the opportunity to again spring an initiative. I told him I'd schedule a press conference for tomorrow and that I'd also see to getting decent office space. "Best to get a leg up while we can," I told him.

"Yeah," he answered flatly.

I held the press conference the next morning at the Downtowner. In my address to the media representatives, I emphasized that the project would create new jobs and contracts that would boost the local economy. That done, I looked to the matter of office space. I chose the most prestigious location in Lake Charles, the Calcasieu Marine Bank Building, an aqua-colored glass structure located on the lakeshore. The agent showed me a space on the twenty-first floor that consisted of two offices. I signed the lease and moved in immediately. Knowing David, I was sure he'd be pleased with the larger office. I had no preference; I could work in a broom closet if I had to.

A week after we had set up shop, David and I met to discuss the contract for construction of the riverboat. I recommended the same shipyard, LeeVac, that had built our Metropolis vessel. LeeVac was conveniently located in Jennings, a small town about thirty minutes east of Lake Charles; they had done a good job on the first riverboat; and they had been easy to deal with. Also, their price would be hard to beat. As I spoke, David sat nodding, happy to let me do the thinking. He even approved when I suggested that we call the Lake Charles riverboat Players II, as a follow up to the Metropolis vessel, which we had named Players I.

Then David surprised me, displaying his ability to appropriate ideas that had been mine to begin with. "You should make at least some effort to meet the two local Jebaco partners, Frank Pryce and Ricky Shetler."

"I remember saying that myself," I reminded him. "I'll get on it tomorrow," I added.

"The sooner the better," he said.

The next morning, I consulted my copy of Jebaco's license application and looked over the credentials of the two Jebaco partners who lived in Lake Charles. Frank Pryce, a local businessman in his late sixties, owned a pharmacy in the central part of the city's black neighborhood, referred to as *North Lake Charles*. Rick Shetler was from a distinguished local family that owned several new car dealerships in the Lake Charles area. He personally owned a Mr. Gatti's Pizza franchise just south of downtown, on Ryan Street. I decided I'd look up Frank Pryce first.

I drove slightly northeast of downtown and had no trouble telling when I had found North Lake Charles. The streets were in disrepair; the parks were run-down; and the schools were dilapidated. When I walked into the Pryce Pharmacy, the looks I received told me very few white men came in here. I noted that the young woman behind the counter was addressing an older man as "Mr. Pryce." I approached him, offered my hand, told him who I was, and explained that I was just stopping by for a quick visit.

Straight out, he asked me if I'd tell him more about myself and the Players project. I briefed him on both counts. He then explained that his family's roots were in North Lake Charles and that he wanted to see this project benefit his people. I recommended that we form a committee to give Players the names of local minority businesses, so that we could spread the money from the project to his neighborhood. He was impressed with my suggestion and thought it would be a good idea to let the local state senator and the black city council members make the appointments.

We traded pleasant small talk until I could see by my watch that the afternoon was getting on. I still had to find my way to Gatti's Pizza, to meet with Rick Shetler. "Let's see more of each other," he said, after I thanked him for his time. As I walked back out into the neglected, black neighborhood, I felt that my day was on a positive track.

To find Mr. Gatti's Pizza, I had to follow Ryan Street south of Lake Charles to Interstate 210, a four-lane bypass that leaves Interstate 10 just west of Lake Charles and continues south before rejoining I-10 east of town. I crossed under 210 and found Gatti's two blocks farther on.

The young man at the cash register explained that Mr. Shetler was on the phone. He handed me a plate, invited me to help myself to pizza, and said he'd tell Rick I was waiting to see him.

I'm not much for big lunches; so I took only a thin slice of pizza, filled my glass with Coke, and looked around. The shop had the look of a family Mecca: a large room with several tables and a big-screen TV at one end playing television sitcoms. Just past the TV was a room full of kids playing the arcade games. I wondered about the surveillance cameras—there were so many of them. I didn't think organized pizza thieves were common in these parts.

A man I took to be Rick Shetler opened a door adjacent to the restrooms and walked toward me, in a hurry and looking serious. He had thin, light brown hair, dryly combed back. His eyes were intense, with his brow pulled down in a frown. He was about five-nine or -ten and appeared to be in his late thirties. He was dressed in a new polo shirt and pressed Dockers. He walked briskly over to me, apologized for keeping me waiting, and introduced himself.

As we shook hands, his frown lifted and he smiled openly, warmly. "C'mon to my office, John," he said. "You've got a few minutes I hope."

I followed him back through the main kitchen and the make-ready and storage areas to his office, which was paneled in wood all around. Beside the desk I noticed a wall of monitors that were attached to the surveillance cameras I had seen outside. Several of the pictures on the wall showed him with Governor Edwin Edwards.

"I see you're on terms with Edwin," I said.

He sat back in his chair, propped his feet on his desk, and in an easy voice explained, "I grew up with his oldest son, Stephen. We're best friends, Stephen and me. I even lived in the governor's mansion for a while. It'd be fair to say that we're pretty tight."

He asked me about my background and was pleased to hear that I had been raised in Houston and that I was familiar with Louisiana. Then he began a long account of his association with the governor and his son.

Both Rick's and Edwin's families were from a small town near Interstate-10, about an hour east of Lake Charles. He and Stephen buddied-up around the time they were eight years old. They went to school together, up through the grades. In the early 70's, when Edwin was serving in Congress, Stephen took him along on visits to Washington, DC. They were, Rick said, chauffeured around the town by a young man named John Breaux—now a distinguished United States Senator. After Edwin was elected Governor of Louisiana, he moved his family to Baton Rouge. Rick added with emphasis that he often stayed in the governor's mansion for extended periods.

Rick was also careful to point out that Stephen trusted him as a friend. After Edwin was indicted the last time, a lot of people shunned Stephen. Rick stood by him, however; he gave Stephen his ear if he needed to talk; he took him to Vegas; and he even gave him some money to gamble with.

After about a half-hour, one of Shetler's employees interrupted on the telephone intercom. Shetler lifted the receiver and winked at me.

"How are you, Stephen, buddy!" he bellowed. "He's in my office now. It's going good. Yep, yep. I got it. Okay. 'Bye."

"That was Stephen, Stephen Edwards," Rick said as he hung up and turned back to me.

I took note that Stephen knew I was visiting.

Shetler settled back into his story and explained how he hated the two Ducotes and Steve Rittvo, the three Jebaco partners from New Orleans. They had, he said, screwed him into taking a smaller part of the partnership than he deserved. Nor did they want to pay for what they were getting. Also, they had brought into the picture a character who called himself the Mallard. He went silent for a moment and then told me to forget I had heard that name.

He continued to explain that no one in Players was from Louisiana and that strange things could happen in these parts if you weren't properly connected. Players, he cautioned, had obtained only preliminary approval, not a license. The license needed Edwin's blessing; otherwise, there'd be no license. Very importantly, if he, Rick, wasn't happy with the arrangements surrounding the project, there'd be no blessing. Edwin himself, he emphasized, had made the appointments to the gaming commission. He then added that Edwin had divided the state into sections and that he relied on a trusted friend to conduct business in his interests within each of these sections.

"You see," he concluded, raising his hands palm up, "Lake Charles, is mine—I mean Edwin's, lock, stock, and barrel."

Then he got solicitous toward me. "I like dealing with you, John," he said, "you being from Houston and all."

I thanked him and told him I hoped we'd get along well.

"We will, if you can keep us happy," he answered. "I want you to go back and tell your bosses I'm going to need a percentage of the casino take or a healthy salary. Don't disappoint me here, John. I'm going to have to work hard to see your casino through. I lost a lot around here backing you guys. The church people don't even come in here anymore. My pizza sales are down. I need you to convince your people. You're a smart guy. I'm sure you know what I'm saying."

He began to rise from his chair, to signal that our meeting was finished. But then he sat himself back down. "Forgot to mention—you don't have a lot of time. Stephen wants to know something soon—real soon. You understand?"

"I do," I said bluntly.

He took a business card off his desk, scribbled his pager number on the back, and handed the card to me. "Get back to me no later than tomorrow," he said.

I left Mr. Gatti's Pizza with a bad taste of local patronage in my mouth. Now I'd have to report my talk with Shetler to David. How am I going to explain these expectations of his? I wondered. Is he really being serious, or is he bluffing, trying to grab easy money? I concluded that I had to take what Shetler had said at face value, that I couldn't afford not to—not with his connections.

I got up early the next morning and pushed myself through my push-ups and sit-ups, but without the enthusiasm that had driven me the previous morning. Then I showered, dressed, and went downstairs for breakfast.

As the lift doors opened, I saw that Tim, Bill Woodward's silent shadow, was talking to an older man across the front desk. The man was neatly dressed in jeans and a button-down, short-sleeved shirt. He was about five-six, portly, and somewhere in his sixties. He was clean-shaven, wore a straw-brimmed hat, and held a cane. On his wrist I noticed a gold Rolex with a diamond bezel. Dangling from a large gold chain around his neck was a large pendant.

As I walked into the lobby, Tim surprised me. He said something. "John?" he asked. "I would like you to meet Roland Manuel."

I politely introduced myself as I approached the two of them. As I shook hands with Manuel, I noticed that his pendant was a huge gold image of a duck.

"It's a mallard," he said.

"Looks like one," I said and asked, "Have you had breakfast?" Then I walked down the hall, toward the restaurant, with Manuel following.

"In the back is fine," he said as we passed the waitress, to whom he nodded, smiling.

Once we were seated, he wasted no time. He had always been an Edwards supporter and had worked in each election as a fund-raiser. Each time he pronounced the governor's name, he lingered over it as if savoring a liqueur. With special pride, he pointed out that his daughter was married to Edwin's youngest son, David.

Then he asked something that startled me.

"Where are you going to put my concession stand?"

I had no trouble saying I was in the dark. I was, utterly.

"Jebaco promised me an area where I can sell souvenirs and run a food concession. Didn't they tell you that? I need to know the best place to put it."

I'm talking to the "Coon-Ass" of Jebaco, the Mallard himself, I thought. I told him I had no idea of what he was talking about.

He gasped, as if the air had been knocked out of him. His eyes bulged to the size of silver dollars. "What do you mean? You telling me this ain't gonna fly?"

"Hold on!" I demanded. "I'm in no position right now to tell you whether it'll fly or nose-dive. I just don't know. I'm just meeting everyone and getting to know the project. Is there anything I can say to make myself clearer, sir?"

"I hear you," he replied and then started to say, "Look, you got to understand—"

"Look, sir," I said, "in a few days I'll have this project nailed down. I'll contact you then. That's all I can say right now."

He looked at ease for the moment. "All right, but you'd better be shooting straight." He wrote his number on a napkin, handed it to me, and said, "Get back with me soon. Now I'm going to drive over to Baton Rouge and see Edwin."

"Give Edwin my regards," I told him as I stood to leave. I had lost my appetite for breakfast and wanted to get the Mallard out of my face.

Back at my office, I called David Fishman and went over my meetings with Rick Shetler and Roland Manuel. He hadn't heard anything about an agreement to let Manuel run a concession in the Players casino. And I could tell he wasn't happy with what I was telling him about Shetler. He told me that he'd be calling me back soon.

About an hour later, I received a call from Howard Goldberg, a member of Players' board of directors who also owned the firm that was handling our legal work. He wanted all the detail I could give him on the meetings with Shetler and Manuel.

David called back later in the day to tell me that Howard and he would be in Lake Charles in a few days. He wanted me to arrange for him to meet with Shetler. Although he said nothing about Manuel, I called Shetler and the Mallard separately to let them know that my boss would be here to meet with them personally. I didn't mention that David would show up well heeled legally.

I turned my cell phone off and tried to concentrate on paperwork, to put the dregs of the afternoon behind me. Within an hour, however, I got a page. It was the main number to Mr. Gatti's Pizza. Then came a second, third, and fourth page—all from Gatti's.

I turned my cell phone on; it rang the second it powered up. It was Rick Shetler.

"You know what happened?" he yelled.

I told him I had no idea of what had happened and that he should try to calm down before telling me. But he was in no mood for advice.

"John, that little fuck needs to go back where he came from. You need to get over here right now, before I call Stephen. I mean right fucking now!"

I told him I needed a few minutes to get there and that I didn't want to talk about this on the phone. But he wasn't listening.

"Your son of a bitch boss offered me twenty five thousand a year! You hear that? And I have to come to work everyday!"

"Rick, not on the phone!" I shouted.

"Get over here right now! I'm waiting, and I'm not fucking happy!" he shouted back.

Shetler opened the back door to his office before I could knock on it. At the same time, he was talking on his cell phone. As I walked in, he said good-bye and sat at his desk. I took one of the guest chairs.

For a moment, we both sat in silence. Then I said, "So David offered you twenty five and you're not happy with that."

He started in on an extended monologue. First, clearly, he was disappointed in me for not convincing Players that he was the key to their prospects in Louisiana. David, he said, was numbnuts enough to think he could get something for nothing. Around here the best you'd get for nothing is a lot less than nothing. He didn't know what he was going to tell Stephen. He was worried about that because Stephen was expecting a call right away.

I mostly listened. My job, I felt, was to protect the company's interests and my own position. Rick ended by asking me to leave so he could make his phone call. He said he'd call me either later tonight or in the morning.

I said goodnight to him and walked out the back door, leaving him at his desk.

When I walked into my room, I could see the red message light blinking on my phone. It was Shetler, wanting me to call him back as soon as possible.

He had wasted no time in playing the "governor's son" card. "Stephen's coming to Lake Charles the day after tomorrow," he told me. "Arrange another meeting with David."

"Yeah," I answered. I could hear the fatigue in my voice. "I'll arrange it and call you back."

"You do that," he snapped. "By the way, I want you to meet Stephen before he meets David."

"I can arrange that," I shot back. "Tell me when he'll be here."

"When I know, you'll be the second to know. You just make sure that the Jew is ready."

With that, he hung up without saying good-bye.

I placed the phone on the hook and lay back on my bed. I'd go down for dinner, probably just a quick bite, in a while. Right now I wanted to think about getting a good night's sleep after what had been a roller coaster of a day. I wanted to put Shetler, the Mallard, and the governor's son—Shetler's golden goose—out of mind. But I knew that would be difficult. I also knew I'd be doing extra push-ups and sit-ups right off the next morning. Shetler and the Mallard were getting on my nerves in a way I didn't like.

CHAPTER 4

STEPHEN

＊

I reached the Players office well before Roland Manuel, the Mallard, was scheduled to meet with Howard and David, who were both already in, behind closed doors in David's office. I could hear that they had a conference call in progress.

When it ended, David opened the door that joined our offices and motioned for me to come in.

I greeted Howard and then asked David, "What's up?"

"There's something we need to tell you, John," he said and paused a moment, no doubt to let me wonder. Then he explained that Howard had just accepted an appointment as president of Players. "From now on, you report to him on anything political," he said.

I felt relieved. On my list of things I didn't like doing, working with David was ranked nearly even with talking to Kathy. "Congratulations, sir," I said to Howard. "I'm looking forward to working for you." I then looked at David, but I couldn't tell whether my point had registered.

Howard thanked me and asked, "When can we expect the honorable Mr. Manuel?"

"You mean the Mallard, don't you? We're expecting him here pretty soon. How do you plan to handle him?"

Howard explained that he had talked to the Jebaco partners, that they had promised Manuel a concession, and that he wanted to hear him out on the matter.

Just then our receptionist interrupted to tell us that Mr. Manuel had arrived and was waiting in the reception area. I did the introductions; then David and I left Howard and Manuel alone. I sat down at my own desk, and David explained that he was leaving for a meeting but that he'd be back soon.

Within five minutes, Manuel burst out of David's office in a red-faced frenzy. He stopped in front of the door to the hallway, turned, looked at us, and yelled, "I can't believe this!" Then he left.

"What happened?" I asked Howard as I went into David's office. Howard was sitting in a relaxed posture at David's desk, looking amused.

"Ridiculous show, if you ask me," he said. "When I asked him how he planned to operate the concession, he jumped up, glared at me a minute, and yelled, 'What do you mean operate?' He really thinks we're supposed to operate it for him and just hand over the profits. He says he put so much effort into getting the approval for us that we owe that to him. I told him we can't run things like that. We have a board and a body of investors to answer to. But that was obviously another language to him. You make any sense of this guy?"

"No," I answered. "What you said to him is clear enough to me. But you realize I'm the front man around here. I'll be getting some nasty phone calls, at the very least. And we'll probably find that this jerk'll stir up a lot of grief for us."

Howard agreed. "But we simply can't cut a deal like that. We can't, John, and we won't. The sooner this Manuel realizes that the sooner he can let his blood pressure get back to normal. I want you to relax for now; just see where this leads. Have your meeting with Stephen and let me know how it goes."

The next morning, David and I drove Howard to the airport so that he could catch his flight back to Atlantic City. Then we went into the office. Within half an hour, Shetler called.

"Stephen will be here in two hours. I want *you* over here. Right?" he dictated to me.

"Not entirely, if you mean right this minute," I replied. " I've got about thirty minutes of work to finish here. Then I'll be over." I couldn't resist adding, "Hope you said hello to Edwin for me."

Shetler ignored my comment. "I'll expect you soon," he said and hung up.

My mood dipped toward a negative peak as I walked back to Rick's office. I had gauged Shetler's rhetorical blustering as an indication that Stephen didn't have a warm and fuzzy bonding session in mind. Here, in Louisiana, I knew, having the governor's son pissed off at you was a good reason to schedule a vacation somewhere in the Arctic tundra.

Shetler was waiting for me, sitting behind his desk. As soon as I sat down, he started in on his pet theme that Players, if we were smart, would be sure to keep Stephen happy. For at least fifteen minutes he ran on, harping about Stephen this and Stephen that, all the time glancing at his watch. Then he stood and said we'd be meeting with Stephen at a small restaurant south of the Lake Charles downtown area.

In the restaurant, Rick took me to a table as far away from the other customers as possible. We ordered Cokes and waited quietly for a few minutes. Then Rick stood and called, "Here, Stephen!" to a tall man who had just walked in the front door.

Stephen Edwards looked to be in his late thirties. His face was delicate, with very light skin and a thin, pointed nose. A shiny crown with a half-moon patch of dark brown hair showed just above each ear. As would an object swept into a sphere of influence, Shetler gravitated toward him, meeting him halfway toward our table.

I stood to meet the governor's son. He shook my hand briefly and sat down at the table, beside Shetler. For a few minutes they talked between themselves, ignoring me. Then they paused, as if on cue. Stephen turned to me and said, point blank, "This stupid motherfucker David Fishman doesn't have a fucking clue, does he?"

Normally, such a display of vulgarity from a grown man in a business setting would have provoked me. But I didn't think Stephen was green to psych ops, and I figured he was trying to unsettle me. Also, I had become acclimated to the term *motherfucker*—Kathy's favorite word for me these days.

I looked at Stephen calmly and said, "I want you to understand that I'm here to get this casino project moving. That includes trying to get all the involved parties in the same happy bed." I paused and glanced over at Shetler, who had the look of a well-fed, contented puppy. Then I looked back at Stephen. "I realize we have some raw spots right now. I know we need to work on them. The way I see it, we need to avoid getting each other pissed off. I'm willing to do my part."

Stephen held our eye contact. "The way I see it," he said, "Players is pretty irrational in not moving on hiring Rick." He went on to explain that he was no babe in the woods regarding what it took to get a casino off the ground. He ran a law practice in Baton Rouge, and several of his clients were casino applicants. Players, he felt, should have enough common sense to know that it needed Rick. "To tell you the truth," he said, "it worries the hell out of me that I had to come all the way over here just to discuss something as obvious as this. What I'm saying, John, is your group has me really worried. I want to have confidence in Players. But you and your boss are going to have to help me on that."

I had to credit him for his directness and his ability to intimidate. He had the self-reliance and easy confidence to grab the high ground without relying on his father's name, and he was a master gamesman. Though I wasn't cowed, I was off balance, also at a disadvantage; and I knew he sensed his edge. The best I could say was, "Stephen, I appreciate what you're saying. We need to talk with David. He should be at our office now. So why don't we head over, sit down with him, and see if we can work this out?"

"Sounds like a plan. Lets go!" he said, rising from the table. As we walked toward the door, I could see that Stephen moved in deliberate strides and that his eyes held the intensity of a big cat locking onto its prey. Shetler, on the other hand, followed along, looking every bit the lapdog.

When we arrived at the Players office, David was stationed at the head of the conference room table that he liked to use as a desk. He waved us in. Stephen took a chair to his right; Rick sat to his left; and I sat beside Rick, on the side of him away from David. I introduced Stephen to David and said, "David, we seem to be stalled on a few points that Stephen's—"

"I'm not going to beat around the bush with Players," Stephen said, interrupting me and glaring at David. "You need to hire Rick. You need to hire him because he can do you a lot of good. You pay him $300,000 and Players won't have any competition in Lake Charles for two years. Pay him $600,000 and Players won't have any competition forever."

Rick didn't talk or move. He looked directly at Stephen sheepishly and avoided any eye contact with David or me.

Unshaken, David returned Stephen's glare. For a moment he didn't speak. Then he replied in an even tone, "I don't have the authority to cut a contract that big without board approval. I need some time to discuss this with my associates."

I had to credit David for his shadowboxing. By not even addressing what Stephen had proposed, he had forced Stephen to swing wide. In effect, he had bought time—in which Players could further strategize and in which Stephen and Shetler could stew in the matter.

"You do that," Stephen said, with slow and heavy emphasis, showing a crafty smile.

Now I had to tip my hat to Stephen. He could slip a counterpunch and swing back as if he hadn't been knocked off the offensive for even a second.

After a few moments spent in silent détente, the tension eased as the three of us—Stephen, David, and I—exchanged small talk for about ten minutes, with no references made to Stephen's demand or to its silver lining for Players. Shetler remained silent. Then Stephen stood, looked at his watch and then at Shetler, and excused himself.

In all fairness, I had to commend David. He watched until Stephen and Shetler were out of the door and then laughed, walked over to the wall, and pretended he was talking to it. "Speak into the microphone," he directed.

"Thanks all the same," I said. We decided to put Stephen's condition that we retain Shetler in the back of our minds and head for the Downtowner's bar. It would be one of the few good times that David and I would enjoy together.

Just after lunch the next afternoon, I called Howard at his Atlantic City office. Apparently, David had fully briefed him on the particulars of Stephen's demand. Howard said he'd be calling Shetler to set up a meeting with Pat Madamba, a New Jersey-based lawyer who worked in Howard's law firm and who had been charged with the responsibility of handling most of Players' work. For now, Howard had in mind a largely scaled-down offer. But we didn't want to disclose the particulars. He'd simply tell Shetler that we'd be coming forward with something but that we weren't right now in a position to specify exact figures. If Shetler called me, I was to say that the issue was out of my hands.

Shetler did call later in the afternoon. He seemed content, feeling that the whole matter would be ironed out in a few weeks, when Pat Madamba would arrive to make the arrangement official. I could tell that he was feeling me up, trying to get his hands on a firm indication of where Players stood. Any arrangement between Players and him was out of my domain for now, I told him.

"I hear you," he said and hung up.

I spent the next two weeks getting the construction of the riverboat underway. I had to get this phase started as soon as possible because of the total timeline that we needed—eight to nine months. I enjoyed this aspect of my job—working with people who had something real to do, something that could be measured against project management standards. Also, driving over to the shipyard in Jennings got me away from my office and out of the range of my cell phone. The more time I spent in the nuts and bolts shipyard environment, the easier I found it to cast off any dregs that had rubbed off from the likes of the Mallard and Rick Shetler.

During this period, Pat Madamba initiated his negotiations with

Shetler over the phone. I wasn't surprised that this tactic unnerved Shetler so thoroughly that he had to call me every day—at my office, on my cell phone, at the shipyard, or in my room late at night. He couldn't bear not knowing how his deal with Players was going to shape up. I insisted, repeatedly, that the matter was not my responsibility and that I was busy looking after a demanding construction schedule. That, of course, put him into a state of even higher anxiety. I understood how Howard was directing Pat Madamba: he was to wear Shetler down, hoping he'd come to their meeting with lower expectations.

I was waiting for Pat Madamba in the arrivals area of the Lake Charles Regional Airport the morning he arrived from New Jersey. He was carrying a small bag on one shoulder and his cased laptop on the other. He always traveled light; he didn't trust anyone, especially airline employees. He was dressed in a dark suit, and he was wearing prescription sunglasses, shaded to the darkest possible tint. He was advertising himself, I thought, as a condescending northerner. It wouldn't be long, actually, before I'd start thinking of him as an overt northern supremacist, a notion he went out of his way to encourage, often speaking ill of the entire south and sometimes, even, referring to it as being still under the boot of the Union Army. I had to laugh as I watched him approach the receiving doors. He looked so out of place here, in a state where it was routine for the hometown players to thoroughly carpetbag a naïve and arrogant northern opportunist.

But I understood what Howard was up to, sending Madamba. It was an informed move tactically: in negotiations, Madamba relied on what he regarded as his ability to intimidate.

"Hey, Brotherton," he said as he approached me, without offering to shake hands. "Nice to be in the land of cotton," he added with a smirk.

"Nice you coming down to see us poor folk an' all," I replied.

He looked at me, surprised. He had probably assumed that everybody shared his dislike of the south. "You've been hanging around these locals a little too much, John, I think."

I could see that he was in a hurry to get out of the airport. I placed myself in his way and replied, "Pat, you need to learn to pay attention. If you took a close look around you, you'd notice that *I am* one of these locals." "That worries me, John," he said almost sympathetically, as if I had just told him I had come down with a terminal illness.

He pushed his wrist out and glanced at his watch. "C'mon, John. I've got a busy schedule."

But I stayed in his way. "Pat," I said, "I'll take being a Texan any day, if that's okay with you. But if it isn't, I'll take being a Texan anyway. We're the only state that was an independent country. You're from New Jersey, if I remember right."

"And proud of it," he shot at me. "You wouldn't appreciate a place like New Jersey. None of the shit that goes on down here would fly up there."

I smiled and closed on him. "That's why the last four mayors of Atlantic City are serving time, right?"

"Fuck you!" he erupted. "Let's go. I want to get this over."

"Right," I said. "Let's go. You're going to love the Downtowner. The best of southern hospitality."

On our way into town, I briefed him on what I saw as the priorities in the dispute between Players, Stephen Edwards, and Rick Shetler. As we came to a stop in the hotel parking lot, he made a comment that took me by surprise.

"You know, you're a good fit for this project," he said.

This project? I wondered, repeating his emphasis on *this*. "I wasn't for Metropolis?" I asked him. Then, giving him no chance to reply, I said, "I know you don't care for these people, but I do. I can build this project faster than anyone. I can put this together and you know it."

His reply was a deliberate ambush. "What you can do isn't important right now. You need to be ready for the changing of the guard. Howard's taking over—the Fishmans are out. You need to pay attention to Howard's way of doing things—otherwise, you're out."

In your favorite wet dream, if you ever have them anymore, I thought.

He must have read my mind. "You'll see, John," he said, looking up at the sky.

His negotiations with Shetler started the next day and continued into the middle of the week. I avoided the issue and concentrated on construction of the riverboat. In the end, as Rick explained to me, Players offered him a base salary in the range of $100,000. In addition, he would carry the license for the video poker machines that would be located around the motel's first floor. For this, he'd receive an additional fee. He also told me that he'd be getting some hefty bonuses associated with the opening of the operation to the public. In all, according to what Shetler explained to me, the contract totaled between $200,000 and $300,000. (The FBI would later conclude that the new contract was a direct result of Stephen's request. Later also, Players would amend the contract with a provision that its terms would be terminated if another riverboat casino were to be located in the Lake Charles area.) To me, two to three hundred thousand a year sounded like a king's ransom—especially for someone who was not a Players employee. It was certainly a lot more than I was making.

Shetler, for his part, accepted the terms with enthusiasm. But he needed Stephen's approval. For that, he'd drive down to Baton Rouge and see Stephen in his law office. I was invited to go along.

When we arrived, the receptionist made it plain that Stephen was waiting to meet with Rick alone. I was to wait in the reception area.

As I was looking for the coffeepots, the door to the office across the hall from Stephen's opened; and a strikingly lovely lady stepped out. She had profoundly dark brown eyes, and her black hair cascaded in long, tightly spiraling curls. She wore an expensive though tasteful suit. She was only about five feet in height, but she moved with easy grace and efficiency.

The receptionist introduced her to me as Julie Fusilier. She offered her right hand and said, "I'm waiting for a call. Why don't you come in and chat with me for a moment?"

I accepted and followed her into her office, grateful to have something to do other than sitting in the reception area trying to look busy. As Julie and I talked, she explained that she wore two hats: she was both a lobbyist and lawyer. I pointed out that Players could use a seasoned lobbyist.

"To help is what we're here for," she said with a brilliant smile.

To help is what you're here for, I thought, wondering how Stephen, in the next office, was digesting the contract Shetler had agreed to.

I told Julie that I'd get together with my partners and size up our requirements for her capabilities and that I'd then let her know.

"I'll look forward to hearing from you," she said, again with her stunning smile. I could see how she'd be effective as a lobbyist: she could charm the venom out of any snake I knew.

After about fifteen minutes, Shetler stuck his head in the door and said, "Let's go."

As I stood to leave, Julie said, "It was a pleasure to meet you, John." Her smile shocked me by improving on what I had already thought was perfection. I looked forward to working with her. At the time, of course, I had no idea that she would later become the sort of friend I'd never want to be without.

Back on I-10, going west toward Lake Charles, Shetler explained that Stephen would allow him to sign the contract despite reservations about the wording. Though Stephen wasn't overly excited about the terms, Rick was in his best mood, pushing the needle over the one hundred mile per hour mark, trying to cover the distance back to Lake Charles in record time. I remembered the wrecked white car and the dead body I had seen along the exit on my first night in Lake Charles and could almost feel an omniscient open palm hovering over my head.

CHAPTER 5

EDWIN

＊

It wasn't long after I met Stephen's associate, Julie Fusilier, that I saw a use for her backgrounds. Despite the new jobs and business that the casino would bring to Lake Charles, not all residents felt positive about the project. Several interest groups and church representatives formed a coalition and launched a campaign for an election to give the Lake Charles population a chance to accept or reject the casino. Vic Stelly, Randy Roach, and Tim Stine, each a state representative, had overlooked to inform their constituencies that existing law provided a mechanism for a parish-wide election within a specific time frame and that this period had already lapsed. To cover their politician's butts for having been asleep at the switch, Stelly, Roach, and Stine drafted a new bill calling for another vote on the Lake Charles casino. They promised to bring the new bill before the legislative session that would be commencing in a few weeks.

Players felt that it had already met regulatory requirements, that it had invested more money than it could afford to lose, and that the bill was therefore unfair. I was charged with finding a way to stop it in its tracks.

I contacted Julie and she agreed over the phone to help us. Right off, she explained that we'd have a chance to kill the bill if we represented ourselves before the House Criminal Justice Committee, which had to give the bill a majority endorsement before it could go to the house floor. Julie offered to put together profiles of the committee members and to assess their leanings. We'd meet in Baton Rouge for a very early breakfast on the day the bill would be heard, and she'd run me through a briefing. Then, we'd address the committee and do our best to prevent the bill from moving on.

On the day of the bill's hearing, the media (including the Lake Charles television stations) and the concerned public (including prominent church representatives) were out in force, and the tension in the legislature building was palpable. The state representatives were first up. As Stelly, Roach, and Stine urged the committee to let the bill move on to the house, Julie kept a close eye on how the committee members were reacting. By the time the state representatives had finished, she sensed that the committee was hung.

As Julie and I approached the table, we passed Vic Stelly, who muttered a smart comment, no doubt to throw her off stride. He needn't have bothered; Julie was brilliant, as she argued the unfairness of the bill. I added that Players had been scrupulous about keeping project benefits local. Then Julie closed, emphasizing the bill was redundant in view of existing legislation. As Julie had predicted, the committee was deadlocked, lacking the majority it needed to move on to the house. By the closest possible margin, we had won.

On the front steps of the legislature, I was telling Julie that Players couldn't have managed this hurdle without her, when Shetler approached us, beaming. Julie greeted him, then excused herself, saying she still had a busy day ahead. As if he had brought on an apocalypse single handed, Shetler said, "I've arranged for you to have dinner at the governor's mansion."

When?" I asked.

"Right now," he replied. "I think you should come with *me*. There'll be no questions that way."

Though his arrogance was, as always, hard to bear, I knew that it would be politically incorrect for me not to go with him. Besides, I was anxious to meet the governor, the legendary "King of Louisiana."

As Shetler drove around the back of the mansion, down a concrete ramp that descended one level, I noted the state troopers stationed around the back entrance, watching the surveillance monitors.

Immediately inside the back entrance was a small lift, next to a stairway, across from a desk manned by another state trooper. Shetler pressed the button for the first floor, then looked at me, to show he knew the layout of the mansion. We stepped out and took an immediate right, down a long corridor. Off to my right, I saw a small but ornate family dining room. Its French doors with sheers looked out over a scrupulously landscaped yard. About forty feet down the hall, a man was sitting behind a desk.

"Where are we headed?" I asked.

"The governor's office," Shetler replied. "That's Sid Moreland at the desk. His office is across the hall."

Shetler turned to his left and opened a door to a small, informally arranged dining or breakfast area. In its center was a small wooden table topped with mounds of different types of cookies. To the right of us was a wooden door that I figured led to another room. Rick took a cookie from one of the piles and invited me to do the same. Just then an attractive young lady stepped into the room through the other door. With a cultivated southern drawl, she said, "Hello, Rick."

Shetler left me and walked up to her, without bothering to introduce us. They chatted briefly, ignoring me. From what I could hear, I could tell that she was well mannered, educated, and sharp of wit. After a few minutes, she led Rick to the door through which she had entered. He motioned for me to follow.

We entered a large kitchen, trimmed in white and stainless steel. At least ten servers and cooks, all black and dressed in white, were hurrying about the room. Later, Shetler explained that the kitchen staff were state prison inmates. As I understood it, each had been convicted of murder in the form of a crime of passion or under some other unusual circumstances.

The understanding was that Governor Edwards would pardon them at the end of his term if they served well here, in his mansion.

We followed the lady into the main dining room, which was trimmed in rich burgundy and hunter green, with a long table in the middle of the floor. Around the ceiling were large wooden trim pieces, surrounding an ornate coffer. The walls were hung with large oil paintings. Looking down, I noticed that the thick wooden floors were immaculately polished.

The lady led us through a set of double doors into the mansion's entrance foyer. To my left, I could see the double set of front doors. To the left of them, another state trooper was watching a monitor. He and Rick waved to each other. In front of me was a large entertaining and sitting room—also trimmed in burgundy and hunter green, in all a mirror image of the dining room we had just left. A set of French doors opened to a landscaped courtyard. Adjacent to the room's entrance, off to the right, was a spiral staircase that went up one flight. The lady left us and mounted the staircase.

"Who's that?" I asked, then added, "Nice of you to introduce us."

"Anna Edwards," Shetler answered, in a tone of reverence. "She's one of Edwin's daughters."

Overhead, I noticed a chandelier fashioned from thousands of tiny pieces of illuminated crystal. I turned to my right again and confronted a huge stuffed bear standing upright. I figured it to be about seven and a half feet tall. In places, its pelage was tipped by silver; so I guessed it was a grizzly. Its arms were outstretched, and its mouth was open, with teeth showing, and with its long tongue hanging out. Shetler reached into the bear's mouth, grabbed its tongue, pulled it out, and handed it to me. It was plastic. I handed it back to him and asked him to put it where it belonged. He then inflated his chest and led the way to Sid Moreland's desk.

"Is he in?" Shetler asked.

"He's with somebody right now, Rick," Moreland pointed out. "Want me to tell him you're here?"

"Nah. But thanks. I'll see him later," Shetler replied, casually.

On the wall next to the door to Governor Edwards' office, I saw a large, framed poster. The caption at the top read "Louisiana House of Representatives Final Vote Tally." The number of the bill was printed under the caption. The last names of the house members were listed, with a "Yes" or "No" linked by a black line to each of what looked to me to be about fifty names. Many "Yes's" and "No's" were crossed over and overwritten by new "Yes's" and "No's." Shetler noticed that I was puzzled and explained that the poster tallied the final vote that had squeaked the recently passed, controversial, New Orleans-based land-based casino law through the Louisiana house. He then told me how the bill had managed to make its passage and why it was such a signal moment in Edwin Edwards' administration.

The Speaker of the House, John Alario—from Westwego, a small town near New Orleans—wanted the bill to pass but was unable to marshal enough votes. So he let the session run almost to its end. He saw his chance late one evening, when most of the opposing representatives had left, thinking that no new items were to be introduced, and when the remaining representatives were all tired. Quickly, he submitted the bill for a vote—which amused the thinned out body. They took Alario's measure as a great lark and in jest kept voting one way, then another, going round about in this manner as Alario kept close watch on the board. He waited until just enough votes were tallied, acted to lock the voting mechanism, and announced that the bill had passed.

At this point, the total count was cast in stone. It was, however, possible for the representatives to trade their "Yes's" and "No's." During the bartering that followed, members who had voted "Yes" but who at heart opposed the bill scurried to find members who had voted "No" and could change their vote to a "yes" and live with it. Thus the numerous cross outs and rewrites on the poster outside the governor's office.

I followed Rick back down the hallway and into the small family dining room I had first noticed when we had gotten off the lift. An older man walked by the room's entrance. The suit he was wearing reminded me of the way a mortician would dress in Charles Dickens' time. He was small, with a thin frame. What hair he had on his nearly bald head was wiry and almost all white. His smile when he saw Rick was kindly, almost grandfatherly. "Hey, Rickeeee," he said and he walked up to us, extending his hand for Rick to shake.

I could hear Stephen out in the hall, talking to someone. Then he walked into the room, greeted Rick, and asked me how I was doing. Rick introduced the older man to me as Marion Edwards, Stephen's uncle.

As we were small talking, I heard a door open out in the hall and some loud voices. Then I saw Edwin Edwards standing at the entrance to the family dining room. The room fell silent. Immediately, I noticed that Edwin was neither as tall nor as imposing as he looked on TV but that he had an eerie quietude about him. He was trim and handsome, with a deeply tanned face. He appeared to be in his fifties—though I knew that he was, in fact, approaching seventy. His whitish-gray hair was perfectly combed to one side. His eyes were an extreme dark brown, almost black, and piercing.

Edwin looked at Stephen, said "We'll be having dinner in a moment," and went into the "cookie room," probably to wash his hands. When he returned, he looked at us and then proceeded to the head of the table and took his place. He then invited his guests to join him. But no one moved to the table until the he had taken his seat.

Then the room buzzed with conversation. Rick and I were seated side-by-side. He looked at me with a sly wink, and I knew he was about to introduce me to the governor.

"Excuse me, Governor?" he asked, and, waving his hand ceremoniously in my direction, announced, "I'm pleased to introduce John Brotherton."

I felt that Edwin's brown eyes were looking straight into my brain. For a second, I didn't dare to even think. The governor took his napkin from his lap, touched it to the corner of his mouth, then stood upright and extended his hand. Saying nothing, I stood, took his hand and shook it firmly. He returned the shake in kind and smiled briefly in acknowledgement.

"John is with Players International, in Lake Charles," Shetler chimed in.

"Good for you, John," Edwin said and then sat down and began eating.

I was relieved that I didn't have to speak. For some reason, I found the governor to be far more intimidating than his son.

Just as I was settling into my chair, the Mallard stepped into the dining room. He stood in the entrance and held his hand up in a gesture of hello. For a moment, he glared at me. I hadn't contacted him since his humiliating meeting with Howard at the Players office, and I had no doubt that he was plenty pissed. But I figured that he wouldn't get confrontational here, in this setting. The Mallard approached Edwins' chair and, leaning over slightly, muttered something in Cajun French. Tilting his head to the side, the governor replied briefly, then continued with his meal. The Mallard left the way he had come in.

Within seconds, the hallway was ringing with the sound of a lady laughing, not in genuine amusement, but more as an affected prologue. With pomp in her stride, she entered the dining room. In her own way, she was attractive—petite, and pretty, with spiraling curls.

"Hello to y'all," she said, sweetly, as she stopped and surveyed the table.

"Who's that?" I whispered to Shetler.

"Vicki Edwards, another one of the governor's daughters," he answered.

With the gait of a fine thoroughbred, she circled the table and approached Shetler. "Hello, Rickeeee!" she gushed, extending her hand, palm down, obviously expecting him to kiss it, which he did. "And who do we have *here*?" she asked, beaming her eyes at me, at the same time lifting her hand, in a fluttering motion, from Shetler's lips to her chest. If there had been a fan in sight, I would have handed it to her.

Rick stood to present me to *la belle*. "This is John Brotherton. He's with the riverboat casino in Lake Charles."

I stood also, offered my best smile, and said, "I'm delighted to meet you, Vicki."

"That's Victoria!" she demanded and repeated her name slowly, for proper emphasis.

"I stand corrected. Victoria it is," I quickly said.

"Whom are you going to have to entertain there?" she asked, now gushing once more.

I paused for a second, confused over what she meant.

Shetler piped in, "Victoria has a lot of friends in the entertainment business."

"Oh!" I replied, now understanding her question. I thought it best to play ignorant. "Victoria, I'm not really familiar with that end of the business. But I'd be pleased to put you in contact with the right people at Players."

"Maybe we could arrange to bring them over sometime, when we know you'll be here," Shetler inserted again. I could see that he didn't want to feel left out of this tête à tête.

As if blessing Shetler's attentions to her, she answered, "*That* would be *very* nice, Ricky."

Stephen stood and asked her if she'd be joining us for dinner. "Oh, no thank you," she gushed. "I must be on my way." She then sashayed out the door and down the hallway.

I saw that Stephen was rolling his eyes. I looked at Rick, who said, "I'll tell you later." I looked back at Stephen. He was smiling at me, looking hugely amused.

Holding a tray full of delicacies, a black, white-suited server stepped into the room and announced, "Anyone care for dessert?"

As I enjoyed some of the Savoy Truffle, a thin, short man with close cut brown hair and a large mustache walked into the room and approached the governor. He was wearing a brown leather jacket and dark slacks. He had a hardened look about him. His face carried the sort of wrinkled, leather-skinned tan that comes from staying in the sun too long. His eyes squinted nervously as he looked down the table at the governor's guests. He bent down and whispered to the governor. Edwin Edwards' face went grave as he stood. The two of them left the room and stood outside, talking in the hallway.

"That's Cecil Brown," Shetler explained, again whispering. "I don't know him very well. He's been a close friend of the governor for several years."

"Where's he from?" I asked.

"Eunice," Rick replied.

The name was familiar. I had heard that Brown was involved with another group that was trying to get licensing to operate a riverboat casino on the Westlake side of Lake Charles.

I mentioned this item to Shetler. "He's fighting a losing battle," he hissed. "Didn't I tell you who you have to go through in Lake Charles? You didn't hear me say anything about this Cecil Brown, did you? You need to remember to listen to *me*."

When everyone had finished with dinner, Stephen got up, placed his napkin down in front of him, and said, "Well gentlemen, I'm going to be on my way. I still have some things I have to see to this evening." He looked at Rick and added, "Be sure to call me later." Edwin rose and walked out with Stephen, toward the governor's office. Dinner at the mansion had been concluded.

Out in the rear parking lot, as Shetler and I were about to get into his car, I noticed a man in a dark suit approaching us. Though it was night by now, I could see that he had a tired out way of walking and that his hair was combed straight back with a slight pompadour, covered with too much hairspray or dried gel. He could have been wearing a toupee.

"That's Andrew Martin, the governor's aide," Shetler explained, as the man came closer.

"Hey Ricky, how's things with you?" Martin asked. "Who's your new friend?"

"John Brotherton, with Players in Lake Charles," Shetler answered.

Martin then turned to me and asked, "You remember talking to someone about operating your riverboat, some time ago?" I had forgotten the conversation, but I remembered it now. Back when I first arrived in Lake Charles, I had received a call from the representative of a marine operations company out of Morgan City. I explained that we managed our marine operations internally. The rep replied, "Things are different down here. Think about whether you really want to do that." A bit angry, I told him that I had built several million-dollar plus oilfield projects in Louisiana and off the coast of Mexico and that I had also worked on construction projects in Angola, during the Communist revolution. I added that I had seen fourteen rebels executed on my first night in country. I then closed the conversation with what I hoped he'd accept as an obviously rhetorical question. "Things are *really* different there, wouldn't you agree?" I said.

My aggressive tone had put him off balance. He asked if I'd consider a proposal, and I told him to send it to the Players office. When it arrived, I was shocked to see a bid to handle marine operations for over three million dollars a year, a cost that Players could cut in half easily by handling the work ourselves. I threw the document in the trash and didn't bother to reply even by phone.

I looked directly at Martin. "I remember the call. I said that we staff and operate our own boats." He stiffened and started to take a step toward me. Shetler grabbed his arm, however, and pulled him a good ten feet away. The two of them talked in hisses and whispers, but I was able to hear Martin complain, "Rick, I'm not getting anything off of this so far! Everyone else is getting fat off the riverboats."

With that, he broke from Shetler and walked toward his car. He didn't even look at me as he passed.

"What the hell?" I asked, as Shetler walked back toward me. "That turkey should know I can't even begin to do a deal like that."

"Fuck him!" Shetler said. "I never liked that shithead. Look, John, I already told you—you're covered. Listen to *me*. Will you learn to do that, please?"

Then he changed the topic. "You want to stay at the mansion? You and Kathy?"

"What... what do you mean?" I replied. I was dumbfounded, shocked—as if I had just seen him yank a huge rabbit out of a tiny hat. "You and I have to come back and forth a lot to Baton Rouge for this project," he explained. " I thought it might be nice for you to bring Kathy over and stay upstairs in one of the extra bedrooms."

"Up... upstairs?" I muttered.

"Yeah, they got a presidential suite. Your wife'd probably be thrilled."

For once, I found myself agreeing with him. I thought maybe he had hit on a cure for Kathy's perennial black study. I bought into the suggestion with enthusiasm, having no idea how wrong I could be.

CHAPTER 6

DONE DEAL

*

Kathy was sullen and quiet as we drove from the Baton Rouge airport to the governor's mansion, after our charter flight from Houston. I thought that she was perhaps worried about leaving the kids with her mother until we established a home here. Or maybe the idea of moving into the presidential suite intimidated her. I didn't know. Since we had boarded our flight, she had said little more than "Might as well get this show on the road."

Rick Shetler was waiting for us when we arrived at the mansion. Since I had agreed to his offer, we seemed to be headed into a friendship phase. Until recently, I had only seen the side of him that enjoyed receiving favors; now, with Kathy's arrival, I could see that he liked doing favors as well. He was thoroughly gracious toward Kathy and showed a genuine concern for our welfare. I have to say that I was touched by his sympathetic nature. His own marriage had run itself on the rocks, and he was in the process of a bitter divorce. I don't think he wanted to see another married couple in the grip of the same sort of misery.

Rick greeted Kathy and insisted on taking her single suitcase. Inside, we were met by a black man dressed in a white uniform. It occurred to me to be sure not to tell Kathy the backgrounds of Edwin's house staff.

Rick handed him Kathy's bag and asked him to bring it upstairs, to our suite. Then Rick offered to show Kathy about the grounds. She declined, however, saying flatly, and without thanking him, "I think John and I should get ourselves settled in." I was both embarrassed and relieved— relieved because it was becoming rare for Kathy to say much of anything without getting vulgar. But I also had a sinking feeling that she would compensate for her restraint as soon as we were alone.

Nonplussed by my wife's rudeness, Rick steered us toward the kitchen where he said we could catch a quick bite. I had to credit him for his instincts. He seemed to smell the tension between Kathy and me and was able to sense that we shouldn't be left to ourselves just yet. On the way to the kitchen, he explained to Kathy how she could call downstairs from the suite if she felt she needed anything. For a moment, Kathy seemed to warm to his easy hospitality

We were served an assortment of light snacks and ate quickly, with little conversation. Then Rick took us up to the suite. On the stairs, he whispered to me quickly, "I need to talk to you ." I nodded and figured I would get Kathy installed and then meet Rick downstairs.

It was a sound decision, as I found as soon as Rick left Kathy and me by ourselves. All she had to say was, "I'm sure *you'll* enjoy this place." With that, she took her suitcase and walked into the bedroom, closing the door behind her with eloquent force.

Rick was waiting for me by the upright, stuffed bear. "What do you think of us getting together with Roach and Stelly tomorrow morning?" he asked me. He seemed to be excited about the prospect.

"Thought we were done with that," I said. "Why dig up what's dead?"

Apparently, however, the bill to allow a public vote on the casino was not yet under the bridge. Roach and Stelly were trying to gather enough support to get their bill through the next meeting of the Criminal Justice Committee and before the house for consideration. Rick was worried that they might succeed. "But Stephen has an idea I think you'll like, once you hear it. I know you'd like to see the bill dead. And I'm pretty sure we could keep it down indefinitely. But Stephen thinks he has a better way."

I explained that I most definitely did not want the bill to come back into the light of day.

"Hear me out, now, okay?" Rick asked. "Here's what Stephen has in mind. What if we told the state reps that we'll support their bill, but only if they changed it so that it would grandfather Players? What if we told them we'd support it if *our* casino is not forced to a referendum?" I had to admit that Stephen's thinking was brilliant. On the face of it, we'd be permitting Roach and Stelly to save face among their constituents. In fact, however, we'd be puppet mastering them into serving the public interest in a way that would further Players'. By riding a wave of public dissent, they'd be helping to exclude our competition from the Lake Charles area.

"You think they'll let Players slide to get their bill through?" I asked. "They'll have a choice tomorrow," Rick explained. "They can have a dead bill or a bill with some changes. Understand, John, my family is old Lake Charles. These men will listen to *me*. This'll be their only chance. I'm going to pick you up early tomorrow, about eight. We'll get some breakfast and then we'll see these two assholes."

I agreed to be ready and said goodnight. As I was passing through the foyer, I saw the governor walking out of his office. He was alone, dressed in a fuzzy robe, and wearing slippers. In one hand, he held a small, empty plate. Obviously, he had been snacking. He looked up to me as I walked toward him.

I enjoyed coming across him in a moment in which he was so undeniably human, a mere mortal like the rest of us. Although I didn't like a lot of things about Governor Edwin Edwards, I had to admit that he was a juggernaut to be reckoned with, that he had, for at least three decades, laid the tracks for politics in the state of Louisiana.

To appreciate the legend of Edwin Edwards, you had to understand the fate that befell Louisiana's most infamous Governor, Huey Pierce Long.

Long was born into a farming family, as the eighth of nine children,

in 1893. He was reared in populist-socialist traditions and worked hard
to put himself through law school. In 1918, he was elected to the Louisiana Railroad Commission, which quickly gained sufficient power to become the Public Service Commission. Long took the title "Kingfish," a
name that still attached to him when he was elected Governor in 1928,
largely on the basis of his promises of better roads and free books for all
school children. Once in office, he became extremely popular among the
poor. To maintain their support, he built bridges, roads, and hospitals
and improved the school system.

At the same time, he managed to build a ruthless political machine
and made enemies as well as friends. The balance of the two became clear
when his foes gathered enough momentum to impeach him but his allies
countered in the Senate, preventing the number of votes needed to see
him removed from office. Eventually, though, his enemies would
penetrate his perimeter of friends in a way that would bring him to his
end of days.

In 1930, in the middle of his term, Governor Long was elected to
the US Senate. He would have to vacate his governorship. By normal
procedure, Lieutenant Governor Paul Cyr would succeed. Long, however, did not want to see the governorship devolve onto Cyr. When Cyr
took the oath of office, Long responded by calling out the National Guard,
the State Police, and the Highway Patrol. Troops circled the mansion to
prevent Cyr from occupying it. Long then accused Cyr of vacating his
office of lieutenant governor. In accord with proper succession, Alvin O.
King, the president of the Senate and a supporter of Long's, took the
office of lieutenant governor. Cyr was officially ousted.

On Sunday, September 8, 1935, in the state capitol building in Baton Rouge, Long was gunned down while walking down the first floor
corridor. Whether the killing was an assassination, carried out by the son-
in-law of one of Long's political enemies, is still unresolved. Some reports
have it that his own bodyguards incidentally shot him as they riddled his
assailant. Huey Long died of gunshot wounds on September 10th. He
was memorialized as a martyr. In 1948 and again in 1956, Huey's brother
Earl was elected governor of Louisiana. Earl's second term was tainted by

repeated allegations of corruption.

During Earl Long's first term in office, Edwin Edwards graduated from law school and settled in the small town of Crowley. He was elected to City Council in 1954. Later, in 1964, he was elected to the Louisiana Senate and then, in 1965, to the post of US Congressman from the Louisiana 7th District— an office he was to hold until 1972, the year he won his first term as governor of Louisiana, with wide support among Cajuns and minorities. During this term, he oversaw the creation of a new state constitution that protected civil rights and that streamlined government bureaucracy. He increased state revenues and made several appointments from minorities to top-level positions. As did Huey Long before him, he formed a ruthless political machine. He was re-elected in 1976 and again in 1984. During his third term, he was indicted for mail fraud, obstruction of justice, and public bribery. But attempts to convict him fell short. In 1992, he won his fourth term.

I had to admit that there was something in Edwin Edwards that I almost admired—perhaps because I was brought up to respect men who had balls enough to make and live by their own rules. It also amused me that Edwin so easily defied categorization, an ability that frustrated many people to the point of exasperation. As an example, a prominent New Orleans businessman once said of him, "He's the strongest son of a bitching governor we ever had. He fuck with women and he plays dice games, but he won't drink. How you like that?"

Though I always told people I was from Houston, I was born in a little town in southeast Oklahoma that was notable as a hiding place for bank robbers on the run from US Marshals, Pinkerton agents, posses, and pissed off boyfriends. I was a descendant of both the Dalton Gang and the Younger Brothers. At family reunions, my relatives would pass around photos of these old outlaws. We took a sort of stubborn pride in our heritage. Accordingly, it didn't bother me overly that Governor Edwin Edwards was an outlaw in his own right and on his own scale.

"Hello, Governor, sir," I said to Edwin. Standing there in his night robe and his slippers, he didn't look to be officially imposing. Nor did he look intimidating.

"Evening, John," he returned, with a cordial smile and then continued on his way toward the kitchen, to return the plate he had used. Is the institution of the late night snack also the great leveler? I wondered.

As I entered the presidential suite, Kathy welcomed me with, "It's about fucking time!"

I braced myself and asked, "What's wrong, honey?"

"I don't know how to use this idiot phone. When I pick it up, someone answers before I can dial. What the fuck is this?"

"That's the mansion's switchboard operator," I explained.

"Well, I want to call my mother. Think I can get a call out of this damned place?"

I saw no point in explaining the house's phone system to her. "Just use this; it'll be easier," I said, handing her my cell phone. She grabbed it from my hand without thanking me and walked into the bathroom, closing the door with emphasis. I prepared myself for bed, thinking, Ain't love grand?

Rick and I entered the state capitol building through the back door and walked down the hall toward the front, where we would be meeting Roach and Stelly. I asked Rick if he knew the spot where Huey Long had been mowed down back in 1935.

"Don't want to make you nervous," he said with a laugh, "but we're just about standing on it. Look at the walls. You can still see the bullet holes."

Looking at the polished, butterscotch-colored stone, I was able to count six bullet holes. As I continued down the corridor, I counted several more, close to fifty in all.

"One hell of a shoot out," I said.

He laughed again and answered, "Hope you're heeled for what could be another one."

Roach and Stelly were standing together, waiting for us, at the bank of glass doors near the front entrance. We shook hands and followed them to a small conference room off the bullet-perforated corridor. Rick took the lead and wasted no time in leveling the main points of our proposal. Calmly, in fact politely, he explained that we would, very simply, fight their bill as hard as we could unless they were willing to compromise on one point—that the Players casino would go ahead without an election. At first, Roach and Stelly held to the intent of their bill. Adeptly, Rick pointed out that we had already shown we could stall the bill and that it would be best for them to agree to something that would make them look heroic among their constituents. To come up empty handed, after all the chest beating they had done in public, would be political suicide, Rick explained.

As he had told me he could, Rick was talking the talk. After a lot of gut wrenching, Roach and Stelly suggested a concession that would allow them to save face. Players would go ahead without a vote, at first. But a vote would be called after three years, by which time Players would have recouped their project costs.

I liked this solution. Within the first three years, Players would have ample time to show their commitment to the community. Having made good on our promises to keep benefits local, we'd certainly come out on the smiling side of a referendum. At the same time, our PR machine would do its best to put nails in the coffin of any casino proposed for the Lake Charles area. The remainder of the available fifteen licenses would, then, be most likely granted for other areas in the state.

I had to admit that Stephen and Rick both knew how to deploy a politician's ego as the proverbial wool. As we cemented our understanding with hand shakes, it impressed me that the two state representatives weren't in the least aware that they had helped lay the foundation for a monopoly.

My upbeat mood was short lived. Out in the parking lot, as Rick and I were walking toward his car, my cell phone sounded. It was Kathy. She had mastered the out calling procedure.

"You and Rick better come over here *right now*. I want out of this place—*now!*" she yelled, loud enough for Rick to overhear. He opened the passenger side door and motioned for me to take my seat. He then walked off into the parking lot, to give me privacy.

"Calm down, will you, Kathy?" I asked. "Just tell me what's wrong. But keep it calm, please?" I was hoping that she'd be able to enjoy a relaxing morning at the mansion. The staff would serve her breakfast and she'd be able to relax by the pool, in the warm sun. I would have suggested this to her last evening or this morning, before I left; but she was in no mood for conversation. Slamming my head through a ten-foot thick, concrete wall would have been easier than getting through to her.

Her voice rose to an almost hysterical shriek. "They think this governor buddy of yours is fucking me!"

"What?" I gasped. I was utterly amazed. "Why would anyone think something so ridiculous as that?"

"I went down to the kitchen, and everybody, all the staff, kept looking at me. They think that's why *you* brought me here, to be his whore! Get me out of here, now!"

I was dumbfounded again, but by now my ass was beginning to pucker. In less than a day, she had no doubt made a goat show out of our stay at the governor's mansion.

Trying not to sound pissed off, I said, "Kathy, I need to wrap up a few things here and I'll be right there. It shouldn't take me too—"

"Ridiculous you said? You think it's ridiculous that someone wants to get in my pants? "

She was quick, even in a rage. I had to give her that. "That's not what I meant, Kathy. I meant no one there thinks Edwards is doing that— what you said."

"I *told* you to come get me, *right fucking now*, you asshole! I mean it! If you're not here in five minutes, you'll find me walking down Interstate 10! I'm not kidding, motherfucker!" She slammed the phone onto the receiver.

"Shit!" I gasped, as Rick opened the driver's door, to get in his car.

"What the hell was that?" he asked.

I filled Rick in on my talk with Kathy and asked him if he'd mind driving straight back to the mansion instead of Stephen's office, where we had planned to brief Julie and Stephen on the outcome of our meeting with Roach and Stelly.

"What kind of watch does Kathy wear?" Rick asked.

"A Gucci. I bought it for her birthday. Why?"

"You're sure it's not a Rolex?"

"I'm sure. What's with the Rolex?"

"If she had a Rolex, the staff *would* assume Edwin was banging her. After he was divorced, before he married Candy, he used to give each of his girlfriends a Rolex. It was safe to assume that any lady you saw staying overnight at the mansion and wearing a Rolex had earned it on her back."

As we turned into the driveway of the mansion, I had to laugh. I was wondering how many catfights the mansion had witnessed over duplicate Rolexes. Then I stopped laughing. Kathy was standing on the front porch, crossing her arms and shaking her leg back and forth—with her, signals that she was marking time.

I got out of the car to face her. "Okay, we're here," was the best I could think of to say.

"About fucking time!" she screamed at me, also shooting a deadly look at Rick. Sitting at the wheel of his car, he glanced out over the mansion grounds.

I said nothing in reply as I took Kathy's bag, put it in the back seat of the car, and then stood aside, gesturing for her to get in. I was willing to do anything it took to defuse a scene on the front steps of the governor's mansion, on our first day here. In fact, I decided to abort our stay, to get Kathy on a plane.

An Arctic chill hung in the car as Rick sped us toward the airport. Miraculously, I managed to get Kathy on a plane with no more out of her than a threatening "You'll be hearing from me." I turned, left the terminal, and found Rick waiting in his car, which he had pulled up to the curb.

"Didn't think you'd be long," he said.

In the days that followed, I put Kathy in the back of my mind and poured my energy into getting the version of the bill that Rick, Roach,

Stelly, and I had agreed upon passed into law. Julie saw to it that the revised bill made it through the next session of the House Criminal Justice Committee. Then Stephen initiated an influence peddling campaign that was crafty beyond all expectation. I had to tip my hat as I listened to him phone this and that legislator. He never stated outright that his father wanted to see the bill carried. By instinct, he seemed to know which button to push. To a legislator he knew to be strong on unions, he highlighted the jobs that the casino would create. If a legislator was pro-business, he argued that it was unfair to treat a casino as anything more than a routine business enterprise. And he'd close each conversation with the statement (not the question), "Then we can count on your support."

As a first step toward reaching the floor of the Senate, the bill would have to be voted through the Judiciary B Committee, chaired by Senator Larry Bankston, whom I'd come to know well within a few years. So too would the FBI, which would make him the subject of an investigation that would lead to his being convicted of participating in bribery schemes involving casinos.

To do my part in getting the bill through the judiciary committee, I called Bankston and asked for his supporting vote. He explained that he already knew about the bill and was planning to recommend it to the committee. As it happened, the bill sailed through.

It was now ready to be called to the Senate, a final step that we were anxious to see completed. Back in Lake Charles, potential competition was already rearing its head and causing us high anxiety. Hollywood Casinos of Dallas was wooing support to locate a casino behind the Holiday Inn Hotel, right next to the Downtowner. If this proposal were to get preliminary approval before our bill were passed into law, it too would be exempt from a local referendum. In that case, so much for Players' monopoly.

Our opportunity to take preventive action came the morning that the senate would be regarding our bill. This same morning, by coincidence, Hollywood was scheduled to make their presentation before the Gaming Commission. Julie and I were there early, looking over the bills that would be before the Senate. One bill, by Senator Don Kelly, looked sure to pass. This bill would exempt the casino boats in the Shreveport area from having to cruise during operation. We determined that Kelly had already solicited enough votes to pass this bill. We also recognized an opportunity to ensure our bill would pass by amending it onto his.

Julie and I found Kelly's office and knocked on the door. He opened and invited us in. Sitting in front of his desk we saw local lobbyist Randy Haynie. We stepped in and listened, as Kelly gave the lobbyist a verbal dressing down.

"You lied to me, dammit!" Kelly accused in a classic display of Irish temper.

"But Senator—" Randy tried to explain.

"You lied!" Kelly roared. "You know you lied. Are you going to try to tell me you didn't lie to me?"

I listened, amused, as Kelly tore strips off Randy, who kept trying to work in a few words of explanation. When he had finished venting, Kelly stood and excused Randy. Passing us as he left the office, he looked shame-faced. (Later, I'd become good friends with him and would appreciate, from watching him in action, that he was a force to be reckoned within the legislature.)

As soon as the door was closed, Julie said, in her straightforward manner, "Senator, I need your help." She then explained the main points of the bill we were trying to see voted into law. When she had finished, I summarized the bill also, making sure that I stuck to the points that Julie had covered. I then asked, "Can we attach it to your dockside bill?"

"Yeah. Why not? Go ahead," he said.

We thanked him and got up to leave. As we opened the door, we could hear over the intercom the announcement to muster the senators to session. I told Julie to go on ahead. I knew that the gaming commission was to hold session in a room in the basement and wanted to see how the Hollywood proposal was doing. Looking in the sidelight window of the meeting room, I could see that the session had not yet gotten under way. Sitting in the audience, I saw the Pratt brothers of Hollywood Casinos. I smirked and walked back upstairs.

As I entered the Senate floor, looking for where Julie had taken a seat, I noticed Senator Jim Cox, who represented Lake Charles. I admired Senator Cox. He gave you the impression that he ran on the pure guts you'd expect from a battled-seasoned general. His district included North Lake Charles, a minority neighborhood. I remembered a picture I had seen of him, taken before civil rights had become a popular issue, showing a street march. Walking on each side of the Senator was a black man. The three of them were locked arm in arm.

Senator Cox, I remembered, had always supported the common worker. He was one of the few legislators who voted from his heart with no reckoning of consequences. His presence today would determine whether our bill would pass. By the honor system that prevailed on the Senate floor, none of the legislators would vote for a bill carrying an amendment affecting Lake Charles unless they saw that he supported it. I resolved to approach him and to feel my way into the matter.

I walked over to the rail that separated the observers from the senators and looked toward Senator Cox. He noticed me, got up from his desk, and walked over.

"The local option bill should be up soon, don't you think?" I asked.

"I know," he said, looking down and shaking his head. "Well, I suppose you want me to vote for it, huh?" he asked.

"I would, Senator," I managed to say.

He looked down at the floor again, placed a hand on top of mine, and stood silent for a second. Then he looked me in the eye. Patting my hand, he said, "All right, John, all right." He then turned and walked slowly to his desk.

I felt chastened. I could have told him that he needed to vote for the bill because it was what the people of Lake Charles wanted. I could have told him that he should vote for the bill because Players was a great bunch of guys. I could have offered several reasons, each of them bullshit. But Senator Cox, sensing my situation, had made it unnecessary for me to explain anything. I felt, actually, that I had let him down. This bill would be passing for reasons that went against what he stood for. It had been put together to cover the asses of politicians who didn't seem to know or care what was right and who had probably never fought for a decent cause in their lives. Moreover, the outcome of this bill would be a monopoly for a casino company whose membership didn't give a shit about Lake Charles, Senator Cox, or anyone other than themselves.

Yet the Honorable Senator Jim Cox would be voting for the bill because I had asked him to, because he knew it would help my career. It was that simple, that human, in a domain where genuine human concerns were rare indeed—as rare as men like the senator.

When our bill came to the floor, it was debated for no more than fifteen minutes before it was called. As the voting opened, I saw the Hollywood Casinos representatives entering the Senate. Immediately, they looked up at the tally board, in horror. Then they walked over to the rail, near Senator Cox, and tried to get his attention. He sat in silence, ignoring them. A few seconds later, he slowly reached up and put his finger on the green "Yes" button. He paused for a brief moment, and then pressed the button. When the other liberal senators saw that he was supporting the measure, they also voted "Yes." As quickly as that, a *quietus* had been made of the Hollywood Casinos project, and we at Players had obtained our darling monopoly.

CHAPTER 7

ENTER HORATIO

＊

It was time for me to roll up my sleeves and get down to the actual business of getting the casino built. First, I needed an architect. I knew that a firm run by Joe Champeaux had done impressive work in the Lake Charles area. Also, I understood that Joe had won the respect of the city's leaders. I called him into my office for a screening interview and liked him from the start, both professionally and personally. He had more than enough experience for the project, and I was impressed with his soft-spoken, careful way of explaining himself. He was also an Edwards supporter, as I could see by the Edwards campaign sticker on his rear bumper, while I was walking him toward his car following our meeting.

Within days, we had completed the design and budget for the first floor of the Downtowner and its parking lots. I felt that we were now ready to put construction of the landside portion of the casino complex out to competitive bidding; the docking facility would be tendered later.

By this stage, I had also closed on the house in Sulphur and was ready to have Kathy get underway with moving in. It was a modest home, with considerable potential for upgrading. For starters, the green shag carpet throughout the main rooms would have to go. To my eye, it matched the décor of the Downtowner. Also, the work that the previous owner had started to convert the garage to an apartment would need to be com-

pleted. I had promised Kathy that I would hire a contractor to look after
both the carpet and the garage.

One evening, after a long day of meetings at the office, I was sitting
at a table in the bar in the Downtowner. While I was trying to decide
what to order, the waitress brought a drink to my table.

"Thanks," I said, "but I didn't order yet. I was waiting for you so I
could."

"This is on him," she replied, pointing to a very large man with
thick rectangular glasses, who was sitting alone at another table.

"His name's Ken Hagan," she added.

With a nod of his head, Ken got up from his table and came over to
join me. As he took the seat across from me, he reached out to shake
hands. His hand was so massive that it dwarfed mine. It was also cal-
loused—from, I assumed, hands-on work without gloves. His mostly red
hair, combed to the side, was beginning to turn gray, and his thick lenses
magnified his eyes. He was wearing a short-sleeve polyester shirt and
what looked like brand new blue jeans. I noted that his upper arms were
solid, with a vein prominent down each bicep.

"I'm Ken," he said.

"I'm John," I replied. This evening, I didn't feel like reciting from
my routine script. So I didn't add that I was with Players.

Ken explained that he was a construction contractor, that he had
once been in the US Army, and that he had made it through Ranger
training. The black beret, but still a brother, I thought. But when he
added that he was "personal friends" with Rick Shetler and Governor
Edwards, I began to get skeptical. I had developed a healthy allergy to
this sort of name-dropping, and I decided to keep closed mouthed about
my personal details. To keep our discussion going, I told him about the
work I needed done at my house and asked him if he knew anyone who'd
be able to help me out. He replied that he'd be happy to take a look at it
himself.

The next morning, Rick Shetler was waiting in the reception area of the Players office. As I came in, he stood up, walked toward me, and asked, "So you met Ken Hagan last night?"

"Word travels," I answered, walking toward my office. "It was nothing scandalous, so how'd you know?"

"Ken's a friend and he's a good local businessman," Rick explained. "He's well respected. You'd be smart to work with him. Remember, I know this area. I know who's good or bad to do business with. Hagan'd be good for the project—if you know what I mean."

Rick then pointed out that Players didn't yet have a license. "There's no guarantee that they'll get it either, unless you listen to me, John. You need to listen to me closely. Every time I tell you to do business with someone, you should listen. You know that if you all fuck up your company won't get licensed here in Louisiana. It just won't happen—period, simple as that. All your dandy Yankee lawyers don't make a bit of fucking difference around here."

Thinking of Pat Madamba, I couldn't blame Rick for his attitude. "Then I'll see what I can do," I said.

"You take care of Ken," he said on his way out the door.

I knew Rick well enough by now to realize that we'd be in dark waters with his friends if we did anything to piss him off at this stage, with the license issue hanging over our heads. I had to be sure to keep in his good books, at least until after the license was officially in our hands.

To initiate the bidding process, I drew up a preliminary list of local contractors and then short-listed those who used union labor. Then I short-listed again after an assessment of each company's overall backgrounds. In the end, I had narrowed down to three companies, not including Hagan's, which was referred to as Lake Charles Construction. It was my initial assessment that Hagan's company wasn't qualified to be on our bidding list.

Next, I called the three eligible companies to solicit their interest. One wasn't interested because it didn't approve of casinos. I was uncomfortable with only two contenders, so I thought I'd talk to Rick to find out more about Hagan's company.

I met with him in his office at Gatti's and pointed out the size of our project and how I had thoroughly assessed the capabilities of every local contractor. I then explained that I really didn't think Hagan's company could manage such a large scope of work.

Rick was upset. "Let me tell you a story," he said. By his tone, I was expecting to hear how some slick out-of-state opportunist wound up adding to the pollutant concentrations in the bottom sediment of Lake Charles. What he had to say was grim enough. A group of businessmen had come to Louisiana years ago, from California, to put together an oil and gas deal. After having spent millions up front, they found it difficult to get final approvals. When they were told the right people to hire to move the approval process along, they thumbed their noses. They wound up losing everything they had invested. "They got their asses reamed out so hard they had to be resleeved," Rick concluded. I got the point and decided to put Hagan's company on the bidding list. We were now back to three eligible bidders.

When the bid packages arrived on my desk, I carefully reviewed their details. The lowest bid was from Charles Miller Construction. My research had shown that Miller ran a tight ship and that his company had earned a sterling reputation. Hagan's total bid was the highest. And it was also strange in places. For one part of the project, he was asking in the order of $400,000—a figure I saw as disproportionate in relation to the project's total budget of one and a half million dollars. Looking at Hagan's overall document, I got the impressions that he had not previously gone after a project of this size and that his relatively small shop, with its hands on style of client communications, wasn't accustomed to the requirements of elaborately formatted proposals. When I showed the bid packages to David, he told me that we'd go with Miller's company. As for Hagan's submittal, he dismissed it summarily.

I knew I'd have to account to Rick for Players' rejection of Hagan. Back in his office, I carefully went through the document, pointing out the items that had given me concern. Rick was, as I expected, agitated. Though he could see that the bid package was short of documentation standard, he felt himself between a rock and a hard place, To my relief, he was more upset with Hagan. We decided to give him a fair chance to bid on the second phase of construction, the docking facility that would house the business offices and the passenger boarding areas. I also told Rick that I'd hire Hagan for the upgrades to my home. Though I knew this would be a small measure of compensation, I was sure the costs to me would be inordinately high.

Hagan, however, wasn't content with compensation. He wanted phase two, the docking barge, and he moved quickly to position himself to his advantage. Knowing that the Players casino would face a public referendum in three years, he put up his own money to rent a small piece of land in Westlake, another population center of the parish. Because the land was directly on the Calcasieu River, which fed Lake Charles, and because it was only a short distance from the berthing location for the docking barge, it was an ideal construction site. Also, we knew that the residents of Westlake would be voting in the referendum and that they'd be mainly concerned with economic benefits. Hagan had located himself so that he could easily subcontract locally.

In effect, he had us by the crotch. He'd get the contract to build the docking barge; that was axiomatic. The silver lining for Players at this point was that the agreement settled Rick's blood pressure. Putting a smile back on Rick's face, though, was small consolation for me; I had to terminate Hagan's work on my home to avoid a conflict of interests. To the extent that Rick was happy, Kathy was miserable. I began putting in longer hours at the office and less time at home to keep myself out of the caustic stream that routinely rolled off her tongue.

Not that the office was a harmonious surrogate home. To speed up construction, David decided that phases one and two should be built in parallel and that the ground was to be broken for both phases while design was in progress. Hagan's company was, therefore, released to begin its work; and thus began a round of maddening interactions—one that would over time fester into a conflict in which the Players' New Jersey team would be run off the court.

Not seasoned in project management, David had no appreciation of the difficulties he imposed by continually requesting design changes after work had been completed. It seemed, for instance, that he either couldn't or refused to understand that it was a huge waste of time, money, and materials to tear out and rebuild this wall and to move and rebuild that wall.

Out of the confusion that David caused almost every day, Ken Hagan emerged as the sort of grunt-level worker with whom I preferred to rub elbows. Together, we put in long hours on site to keep construction moving at a respectable schedule. I found that Ken and I worked well as a team, and I especially liked his pragmatic sense of humor. For example, he found that we could keep David out of our faces by posting a sentry at the construction site. Our lookout would warn us when he saw David's car approaching; Ken and I would make a quick escape; and David would be told we were out for the day. He'd then have to go back to the Players office, with his latest ad hoc design changes still in his hand.

During our drinking sessions at the Downtowner, Ken and I started developing a friendship that would become a mainstay in my life. I began seeing him as an older, more seasoned version of myself. It wasn't just our military backgrounds that drew us together. Ken was a down to earth, guy's sort of guy who preferred work boots to wingtips. Now, looking back on this early stage in my relationship with him, I appreciate the opportunity we had to get to know each other. Soon, I'd find myself in a war zone, with Ken as my best friend on the one side and Players as my employer on the other.

CHAPTER 8

THE WHIRLWIND OF CASH

✳

"We need to talk, tonight, at my place," Rick was saying, over my cell phone. Though I was tired from a long day at my desk, I half welcomed this opportunity to put off going home. There, whether I arrived around five, after working a normal day, or whether I came in late, after putting in extra hours, Kathy either ignored me or laid into me with verbal abuse from the moment I walked in the door. Later, I'd realize that Kathy's performance at Edwin's mansion had been a turning point in our relationship. Now, I only knew that being at home with her was causing me chronic depression.

I walked into Rick's office and saw that his face was as serious as his tone had been over the phone. "John, it's about the Mallard," he said. "We've got to settle this matter now, before he drives my blood pressure through the ceiling."

So the big duck's finally raised his head and is quacking! I thought. "He's getting on your nerves? I've found that's something he's good at doing."

Rick smiled slightly. "The worst of it is he's making Stephen miserable too. Every time Stephen goes out to the mansion, he finds Manuel there, bellyaching and pestering anyone he can get to listen to him. You've only got one solution to this. And I think you know what that is."

I answered that I'd have to discuss the matter with my boss, Howard.

"I understand," he said. "Get back to me soon. I need this off my back."

I called Howard the next day. He explained that he'd need to talk to Wayne Ducote and then get back to me. When he called back a few hours later, he said that he had told Wayne to take care of the problem. Jebaco had made the commitment to the Mallard; they would have to look to the details. For my part, I should just pass Players' position on to Rick and then assume a holding pattern.

It wasn't long before the Mallard got impatient. The morning after Howard had briefed me, I was walking into the lobby of the Downtowner. I felt like an early breakfast before heading out to the shipyard, to check on construction of the vessel. As I turned into the corridor, I saw Manuel standing at the restaurant door, obviously waiting for me.

"Good morning, Mr. Manuel. How are you today?" I said, extending my hand.

"Been better," he grunted. He declined to shake hands as he looked me up and down with one eye, at the same time keeping the other lazily half closed. He then removed his flat-brimmed straw hat and combed his fingers through his thinning gray hair. As he put his hat back on his head, he let out a long slow sigh. Putting his cane in front of his belly, he placed both hands on top of it and leaned slightly forward. Then he opened both eyes and stared directly at me. Seconds passed, and neither of us said a thing.

Finally, he asked, "You planning on having breakfast?"

"No, not this morning," I quickly lied. "I was looking for Mr. Woodward. I'm running late for a appointment, but I needed to talk to him before I left."

With a slight back and forth swagger of his legs, he said, "Young fellow, your appointment can wait. By the way, Bill is sitting in the restaurant. I saw him go in a few minutes ago."

Shit! Busted! I thought to myself, as I held down the impulse to tell him where I thought he should lodge his nose. Instead, I asked, "Would you care to join me for breakfast then?"

"Yes, that'd suit me just fine," he replied, grinning.

I could see that he was feeling full of himself as he asked the waitress, "We'd like to sit in back, away from the rest, so we can have a talk, if that's all right?"

As we sat down, the Mallard told the waitress, "Nothing for me today, dear. But perhaps Mr. Brotherton here would like something." His bush league attempts at being gracious, on the one hand, and menacing, on the other, were getting under my skin, aggravating instincts that I prefer to keep in check in civilized settings. After the waitress had filled my coffee cup and left, I asked, in an even tone, "What can I do for you, Manuel?"

"You know, John," he answered, "I've been pretty patient. But I think that you and Players been taking advantage of me. I think it's time you all did something. I'm getting tired of waiting. Edwin ain't happy either. He don't like the way you're treating his people. I was just over at the ranch in Texas and I'm headed to Baton Rouge to see him this morning. And I don't have no good news for him. I can tell you he won't be happy. He knows I put in a lot of hard work in getting things to where they're at now. You all don't seem to appreciate it. You still got a long way to go, young man, to get this thing off of the ground. You need to realize that. Time for you to shit or get off the pot. My... Edwin's patience is getting thin."

Satisfied that he had put the fear of God into me, he started to stand up to leave. I reached out my hand and grasped his wrist politely. "Look, sir, I need to tell you something." Surprised by the contact and by the tone of my voice, he sat back down. For a moment he looked frightened.

Had he been younger and more my size, the thought of him with a broken nose would have given me a warm and fuzzy feeling. I had to force myself to be patient. "You probably think it's my decision, you know, how this matter with you is to be taken care of. That's not the case. I *do* understand that Jebaco made a commitment to you. Even they don't deny that. But what you've done for them was before I ever got here. You need to understand that you're putting the wrong person on the grill."

Now I had a better grip on my anger. "I know Players is benefiting from all of the good work that was done before we arrived on the scene. It's very much appreciated. But there are three problems."

"Oh yeah? What problems would those be?" he asked, curious.

I decided to introduce an element of surprise, to put him off balance. Players had recently bought Jebaco out of the original operating partnership, something that I was pretty sure the Mallard didn't yet know. So I told him.

"Out! Out of what?" he asked, now alarmed.

I pressed my advantage. "They don't own any part of the casino company any more. They sold out—made out handsomely. And they didn't say anything about you before they ran with their money. Couldn't have been of much importance to them. Anyway, they got a couple of truckloads of Players stock, and it's jumping in value even while we're sitting here talking. You beginning to smell the coffee?"

"Right. I know how they are," he answered, quietly.

I didn't want to give him any time to think. "Now look. And listen. I'm not going to say this twice. Players doesn't like having concessions from third parties. They usually like to operate everything themselves. That clear?"

"I can understand that—"

"I told you to listen. It's my job to pass on information to Howard. But I'm also supposed to be running this project in the interests of Players' shareholders. Players is a large company. Investors all over the map. In the end, it's going to be Howard's decision, not mine. I'm doing everything *I* can. I'm also telling you that *I* can't do anything more that what I'm doing."

For a moment, the Mallard sat quiet, obviously prodding the mass between his ears. He then said, "Maybe I should have Edwin call Merv Griffin. You know, he knows Merv pretty well. Merv and him talked when he came to New Orleans."

I wasn't going to let him think he could intimidate me by name-dropping. "Don't do that, Roland. Think about this for a second. Jebaco made a commitment to you, then they sold out."

"But if they don't do something, somebody will," he replied, almost pleading.

"Look, I'll work my end, but think about what I just said. By the way, do you really want to spend your days standing in some little food concession? Come on, Roland!"

I could see that I had him where I wanted him, feeling as though his feet had been swept from under him. His pompous attitude was gone. In its place was a quiet desperation.

"Well, I have this company. I used to have the concession at the Lake Charles Civic Center. It's called Duralde. Maybe you could pay my company for something else, for consulting, or something like that."

Now, I wanted to nail him. "I just finished telling you, Roland, it's not *my* decision; it's Howard's. All I can do is pass this along to him. For now, that'll have to be good enough."

"You do that," he snapped, in a bratty manner. "Meanwhile, I think there's still a phone call or two that needs to be made."

"That's up to you," I said. "I'll let you know anything that Howard passes on to me. Fair enough?"

"Fair enough," he answered, rising to his feet to leave. I kept my seat, to let him know that I wouldn't be walking out with him.

The prospect of not getting a license obviously lit a fire under Howard. A few days after my breakfast with the Mallard at the Downtowner, Howard called me at the office to explain that he would be having an evening meeting with Stephen in New Orleans in a few days. That afternoon, he wanted to meet with the Jebaco partners, Rick, and me. He had already talked with Rick, who had offered to let us use his boathouse, located at the West End Marina on Lake Pontchartrain. Rick, he added, had already chartered a flight for the two of us, to a small, private airstrip located on the lake nearby.

Rick and I arrived first at the boathouse. He gave me a quick tour and then left, to take care of business, he said. Feeling pressed for time, Howard got the meeting under way immediately. He made it clear right off that the Jebaco representatives and he would be the main players and that I was to take notes.

It took less than thirty minutes for Howard to resolve the problem with the commitment Jebaco had made to Manuel. The Mallard would be bought out through his company, with Players and Jebaco sharing the cost—which, according to what the FBI would later tell me, was well over one hundred thousand dollars.

Howard then left to meet Stephen in New Orleans. He had little to say to me, and I took special note that I wasn't invited along. I was left with the uneasy feeling that I had been demoted to being a spectator. Nor did I expect the orgy of patronage that followed. Obviously acting on Stephen's cue, Players invited into its bed every business concern that was connected with the immediate Edwards family and that had anything to do with casinos.

First there was Riverboat Merchandising. With Stephen as one of its directors, it was to sell hats, shirts, and other trinkets in gift shops to be attached to the Players Lake Charles casino. Next came Juice Systems, controlled by Anna and David Edwards, and listed under the mansion's phone number—a detail that didn't escape the media. In a half-assed attempt to hold off rumors of touchy-feely associations, David explained to the press that Players had thoroughly considered all qualified vendors, even Pepsi-Cola, and had, by fair process, settled on Juice Systems as being supposedly the best company.

On the heels of Juice Systems came Punchline Promotions. Started up by the effervescent Victoria Edwards, and also listing the mansion's phone as its contact number, Punchline was being courted to manage stage variety shows for the Players' Lake Charles operation.

And so it went, one upstart company after another, each connected in some manner with an Edwards, adsorbing to our casino like pilot fish attaching to a whale. The analogy was, I thought, more than just cute. The little fish need only to suck onto the whale; the whale does all the swimming; and the fish feed off its carcass.

My own life, both on the professional and domestic fronts, settled into a continuum. The project was moving along ahead of schedule, and I had no real reason to stay after hours at the office. As my natural daughter, Macie, grew into a little girl, I looked forward to going home. To the manner of daddy's little girl born and bred, she deftly wrapped me around her little finger. Also, I had acted on my long outstanding intention to adopt Kathy's son, Derek. Though my home front wasn't wholly a bed of roses—an Arctic chill prevailed between Kathy and me—I did find fulfillment in being a father.

By the beginning of November, we hoped that we were no more than a month from starting up operation of the Lake Charles casino. Ed Fishman flew in specifically to update me on developments within Players. One concerned me directly. I had been promoted to senior vice president. I was offered a three-year contract with a raise and stock option package that so astounded me that I had no impulse to negotiate. It bothered me, however, that Ed forget to mention one detail—what I was to be vice president of.

Ed also explained that Scott Cooper, the general manager we had hired for the Metropolis facility, would be added to the Players executive line up, as a corporate executive vice president. His area would be operations.

To my mind, a more appropriate domain for Cooper would have been internal intimacies. Since he had come aboard with Players, I had watched him studiously hanging by David's side and constantly whispering in his ear during meetings. Cooper certainly knew how to work David to his advantage—and to my disadvantage. He'd simply dilute what David wanted to hear with tidbits of technical jargon. Increasingly, David came to lean on Cooper. Flattered by his studied solicitations, David was apparently blind to his agendas. As the basis of their relationship became more and more clear within Players, our executives adopted a mum's the word attitude out of fear of losing their jobs. For my part, I preferred to tell the truth, especially when the truth had to be told in the company's best interests.

As Ed continued, summarizing other recent developments, it occurred to me that Cooper's star was obviously rising and that mine was perhaps going in the opposite direction.

By mid November, Ken Hagan completed the docking facility, well ahead of schedule, in spite of David's continual changes. As a grand PR gesture, Ken arranged to have it towed around Lake Charles and then attached to the back of the Downtowner in broad daylight.

Charles Miller had transformed the Downtowner into a Vegas style accommodation. I had to credit him with a job thoroughly well done. The registration desk was now covered in black marble. Brass and mirrors abounded, and deep carpet was laid throughout. The restaurant was now a new buffet. And the bar had been transformed into Merv's Bar and Grill.

LeeVac completed the riverboat by early December. We installed the slot machines and the gaming tables at the shipyard. When the grand lady of riverboats was ready, I staged a press conference. I stood on shore, at the berthing site, and explained to the crowd—which included media representatives, local public officials, and a large turnout of the general public—that the riverboat would arrive any moment. In his Kamar express cruiser, Rick had met the boat just south of the city. The approach was signaled by the boat's horn. As I watched the riverboat coming toward the dock, navigated by Captain Ken Murphy, I felt a sense of accomplishment, of triumph.

On December 8th, the Louisiana State Police passed us on our live gaming test. We decided to start up immediately and to delay the grand opening gala until January. The specific date would depend on when Merv Griffin would be able to attend. It would be his role to launch the riverboat by shattering a bottle of champagne against its hull.

Our first night wildly exceeded our expectations. Though we hadn't advertised the event and were charging a fortune to get on the riverboat, the patrons came in mobs, for a straight twenty-four hours. Fattened lambs, I thought, as I watched them dispose of thousands at our slot machines, which were set as tightly as we could manage, and at the gaming tables, where the minimums were set incredibly high.

I was especially interested in watching the show at the "Whirlwind of Cash," a glass cage that we had placed next to the registration desk in the hotel lobby. The cage was stuffed with bills in various amounts, and a lottery was to be held. The winner would be locked in the cage for sixty seconds—while a fan spun the cash in a maelstrom—and would try to pluck as many of the windborne bills as possible.

I got to the cage just as the winner, a stocky, older man, was getting ready to enter. He was giddy with excitement. Once inside the cage, with the green bills whirling about, he flailed his arms crazily, reaching for the largest clusters. Each time he stabbed his hand into a packed cloud, the bills would explode like quail and disperse. Within seconds, however, he learned to aim at one bill at a time. I laughed and thought of duck hunting. Shoot at the whole flock and you won't hit anything is what I had always been taught. Then another analogy came to mind. I had to laugh again. We've actually put three of these whirlwinds into operation, I thought—one in Baton Rouge, one out on Lake Charles, and one right here in front of me.

I returned to the riverboat and wandered about, wondering what could be so compelling about throwing your money where you could be pretty sure you'd lose it. The game of chance? I wondered. I saw David and Scott Cooper leaning against the railing of the second floor lobby. As I approached them, I could hear Cooper saying, "We need a Vegas property to really put us on the map, David."

David just nodded as Cooper added, "Probably time we had another company jet too, so we don't have to bother with other people's schedules."

I continued on, thinking that Cooper could use several applications of toilet paper across his nose. I then noticed that Howard was smiling and coming toward me.

"John, you've done a good job here," he said, placing his arm across my shoulder. "Now it's time for you to move on and up—new horizons. I want you to move someplace that has an international airport. I'm not particular where. But there's got to be the airport. I need you to do this as soon as you can."

Having overheard David and Cooper only moments ago, I didn't need an explanation from Howard. I answered, "I'll be out of here before the New Year begins. You want another casino site? I'll find you one. How's Vegas sound to you?"

Howard's eyes widened. "What makes you think we'd go to Vegas?"

"Ask David," I said. "A little birdie told him so."

NEW DIRECTIONS

✳

I was excited about the grand opening gala, not only because Merv Griffin would be acting as master of ceremonies, but also because he'd be assisted in the launching by Earl Campbell, the legendary running back of the Houston Oilers.

I had always respected Merv Griffin as the sort of self-made man who had earned his prominence on pure industriousness, not luck. In his early years, he had gained a reputation as an engaging showman by playing to any audience he could find, no matter the size or location. Through sheer persistence, he established his talk show and produced such popular game shows as *Wheel of Fortune* and *Jeopardy.* He had also shown himself to be a smart prospector and asset manager. With his purchase of Donald Trump's Resorts casino, he entered the gaming industry and quickly converted Trump's financial black hole into a gold mine.

I also admired Merv for his talents. In addition to being a second-to-none talk show host, he was also a fine actor. I had seen his cameo appearance, in which he played himself, in *The Man with Two Brains,* which had starred Steve Martin. The movie was a comic mystery in which a series of murders are committed in elevators. Toward the end, Steve Martin steps onto an elevator and confronts Merv, who is standing there with a syringe filled with Drano. After some antic give and take between the two, Merv confesses that he is the serial killer. From then on, I always thought of Merv Griffin as the "elevator killer."

Earl Campbell had given me a basis for my lifelong fidelity to the Houston Oilers. Until they acquired Campbell in '77, the Oilers had been a sorry show with only two saving graces: their quarterback, Dan Pastorini, possessed the most magical passing arm that the Astrodome had ever seen; and wide receiver Billy "White Shoes" Johnson had the most reliable set of hands in the NFL. Without a running attack, however, the Oilers were unable to get themselves into the playoffs.

It was number 34, from Tyler, Texas, who gave the Oiler offense the balance it needed. With his short, 235-pound frame, powered by his 34-inch thighs, Campbell was a menace to defensive backs who vastly outweighed him. To me, Earl Campbell was an idol among professional athletes; and I felt privileged that I'd have the opportunity to meet him.

I was also looking forward to seeing Julie Fusilier and her husband, Robert Wooley, a couple with whom I had developed a solid friendship since Players had retained Julie to help us prevent a public referendum on the Lake Charles casino. Also an attorney and a lobbyist, Robert was tall, lean, and athletic, the sort of guy I took to naturally. Julie and he were both sailing aficionados, and we had spent several enjoyable days aboard their 41-foot Gulfstar ketch. Soon, we would experience a deepening of the bond between us in the course of a cruise that was anything but enjoyable.

I was especially thrilled that my parents would be on hand for the gala. I was proud of the work I had done in bringing this project to its operational phase and wanted them to see what I had accomplished. Kathy would be attending also. After her antics at the governor's mansion, I was girded up for anything from her.

By 6:00 P.M., it was time to launch the riverboat. The guests all moved to the deck that ran along the docking area and watched as Merv and Earl took their stations in front of the helm. Tied by a string to an overhead girder, the champagne bottle hung motionless in the air. Merv was to push the bottle out, away from the helm; it would then, on its return, hit and christen the hull. What no one noticed was that the bottle was hung very low, close to the level of Merv's waist.

Merv smiled to the crowd, to the press photographers, and to the TV station camera crews, then set the bottle on its outward swing with an underhand toss. As it began its return, he and Earl turned to face the hull. The bottle smashed, spraying champagne all over Merv's and Earl's crotches. By protective instinct, Earl crossed his hands and placed them over his groin. By showman's instinct, Merv laughed, raised his hands, and did a turn about, displaying the huge wet patch between his legs.

Above the roar of the laughing crowd, I heard behind me a voice that sent a bolt of nausea through me. One show had just completed itself; another, I knew, had just begun.

It was Kathy, shrieking, dressing down one of our security staff. "You don't know who you're talking to! You wouldn't have a job if it weren't for my husband! My husband is John Brotherton, Senior Vice President! He built this fucking place!"

I forced my way through the crowd, trying to swallow my panic, apologized to the security guard, and told Kathy to cool it. Walking her toward the front door of the VIP room, I asked, "What's the problem?" A voice in my mind said, Cover your ears!

Irate, Kathy howled, "These motherfuckers should be kissing your ass right now! This place wouldn't be here if it wasn't for you. You shit-for-brains dipstick, you let them take advantage of you. Especially that Fishman cocksucker. Everybody knows David Fishman is a bent over faggot!"

Appalled, I could see David standing about twenty feet away, looking right at us. I couldn't tell if he was just watching the commotion or if he had heard what Kathy had said. It didn't matter. David's lackey, Scott Cooper, was standing only a few feet from Kathy and me. Cooper looked at me, smirked in a self-satisfied way, then walked toward David. What David hadn't heard, Cooper would, I was sure, be reporting.

I was thinking of throwing Kathy into Lake Charles, if only to quench her tongue, when I heard my mother's voice behind me.

"John, Kathy," she said, "everything looks wonderful. We're having such a good time. Are you and Kathy going to go on the boat? I think I'd like to try playing the slot machines."

For a moment our eyes met and I could read her mind. "Later," I said to her. "I have to stay around here and play the PR man awhile."

"*Kathy*," she said, "why don't *you* show me around the riverboat?"

Shooting an eyeload of contempt at me, Kathy replied, "Sure, Fairel, just let me get another margarita."

As Kathy walked toward the bar in the VIP room, she passed David and Cooper, who turned their backs to her. I thanked my mother for her rescue attempt and told her I'd be along shortly.

Sadly, she said, "I've seen her act before. After all you've given her and done for her son, you'd think she'd have thought you hung the moon. But I doubt she'll get any better tonight."

"I'm afraid you're right, mom. But I can't say anything to her. That'd only make it worse. The best I can do is get her on the boat before it cruises, get her away from the people who could fire me right now, if they felt like it."

My mother had no chance to comment further. Kathy had returned with her drink refreshed.

"I can't wait to see the casino. Let's go get in line," my mother said, reaching to take Kathy by the arm.

But Kathy was on to my mother's tactics. Pulling her arm away, and looking directly at me, she said, in a spitting tone, "I ain't getting in no fucking line. Show them you got stroke around here. Take us over and get us right on."

My mother smiled faintly. "All right. I'll go with you, Kathy. I'll take you to the VIP entrance. They're letting all the VIP's on first. You'll have no trouble getting on there."

On the riverboat's entrance ramp, in front of the VIP entrance, I could see that some of the Lake Charles city officials and their wives were approaching the entry turnstiles. They had no doubt been waiting in line for at least fifteen minutes. Kathy, my mother, and I were about tenth in line.

"Go to the front of the line!" Kathy demanded.

I could feel the pressure of my mother's hand tightening on my arm, as she sensed my anger rising. It helped calm me a bit. To Kathy, I said, "We'll take our turn. The people in front of us have been waiting a long time. It wouldn't be right for us to—"

"Fuck you!" With that, she stepped out of the line and walked straight to the front. Confronting the security guard, she announced, "I'm John Brotherton's wife! He built this boat. Let me on, now!"

The guard looked at me, and I waved my hand to let her proceed. I then looked at my mother. "Sorry, mom. I don't know what to say."

"No need to apologize for her, son. And I can wait. I'll catch up with her on board and do what I can. You go do what you have to do."

I thanked her and walked back toward the crowd that had gathered around Merv Griffin and Earl Campbell. Maybe, I thought, saying hello to Merv, whom I had met before, and introducing myself to Earl would be a small measure of consolation. It also occurred to me that I was dumber than the nitwit who couldn't find a coffee bean in Brazil. How could I have hoped for a good time this evening, with Kathy along?

I noticed Howard coming toward me, with the look he usually wore when he had something he wanted to explain. What he had gave me a smell of the coffee.

"The little bird was wrong about Vegas," he said, with a specious smile. There were two things he wanted to talk to me about. First, with the Lake Charles casino now up and going well, Players was looking to Indiana, which had passed a law that would allow ten new riverboat casinos to operate on its waterways. Howard explained that five licenses were to be awarded to qualified operators in the northern part of the state, on Lake Michigan, and five additional licenses were to be granted for locations on the Ohio River, in the southern part of the state. After considering cities such as Gary, Michigan City, and East Chicago, Players had settled on Evansville, a small town on the Ohio River and just a few hours from our existing casino in Metropolis.

I was to ramrod the new Players project through the review process. As Howard talked, I thought of Kathy somewhere on the riverboat, no doubt forcing my mother to set new limits to her patience and tolerance, which had always seemed boundless to me. Then I thought of breaking the news that I'd be spending a lot of my time away from home, working in Evansville, traveling back and forth. I could hear her heaping damnation on everyone in Players, including me.

Next Howard explained that Players would be making a new appointment to its executive lineup. Steve Perskie was being brought aboard as a new director and vice president. I knew of Perskie and was aware that he and Howard went back as far as 1976, when Steve, then a New Jersey state representative, had put together a gaming referendum and had obtained statewide acceptance of it.

Perskie then drafted a bill that was passed into law as the Casino Control Act. By this statute, casinos would be permitted to operate in Atlantic City beginning in 1978. After he had completed two terms in the state Senate, Perskie became a Superior Court judge.

In 1988, both Perskie and Howard threw their support behind Jim Florio in his successful run for the governorship of New Jersey. Perskie then took on the role of transition director for the new administration. Shortly after, he was named Florio's chief of staff. Later, he was appointed chairman of the New Jersey Gaming Control Commission. According to what I had read in David Johnston's *Temples of Chance: How America Inc. Bought out Murder Inc. to Win Control of the Casino Business* (Doubleday & Company, Incorporated, New York, 1992), Merv Griffin was, by virtue of the close relationship between Howard and Perskie, able to obtain a New Jersey casino license for his Resorts International property—despite the several rumors of his associations with organized crime.

Perskie found himself out of a job in 1993, when Florio failed to win re-election, losing narrowly to Christine Todd Whitman, a raptor-minded lady who lost no time in demonstrating her capabilities. Florio's loss, Howard explained to me, had been Players' gain. Perskie was highly literate in gaming industry issues and a veteran politician; he'd stand Players in good stead, Howard maintained.

I sensed that I was being circled about by a pack of wolves and that my campfire was dying fast. To survive in this organization, I needed an ally. I needed one desperately. I knew whom I wanted, and I thought I knew how to get Howard's consent. I'd use the petard he himself had hoisted earlier.

"So Evansville is where it'll be for your favorite shock trooper," I said to Howard, to set him up.

"That's the spirit, John," he replied. "That's what I like about you. You're a good soldier. Not yours to reason why."

"Not mine to do and die either," I felt like saying. Instead, I asked, "I hope you trust me, on the basis of what I did here in Lake Charles. The other night, you seemed to think I had handled this project impressively."

"Absolutely," Howard said.

"I'm going to need help in Evansville. I've learned from what happened here to be proactive. I want Julie's husband, Robert Wooley, with me. I'd like Players to hire him. I'm confident he can help us clear the roadblocks that gave us a lot of trouble here." I almost said, "At least he can pull his own weight in real work done, not in asses kissed."

Howard fell silent for a moment, then said, "I need to think about that, John. I like what you're suggesting. Give me a day or so."

As it happened, he took less than a day. Before he left Lake Charles the next day, he stopped into my office and gave his blessing to enlist Robert. It would turn out to be one of Howard's best decisions. In the course of time, Robert and I would become known as "the wrecking crew" for our ability to derail our competitors.

Almost as soon as he started with Players, Perskie was promoted to executive vice president. At first, Howard was ambiguous about Perskie's responsibilities. One day, Perskie would be designated as company counsel; next he was billed as chief of public affairs; then his responsibility package seemed to change by the week. This rapid exchange of one hat for another would have amused me were it not for my feeling that Perskie was on the loose, looking for a domain into which he could settle. Then I heard that he was promoting himself at large as an expert in my area of responsibility. I began consoling myself by recalling a *Playboy* interview with Robert Blake, when he was starring as Beretta. "These days," Blake said, "anyone who ain't paranoid is sick."

In fact, I began feeling totally wholesome in my paranoia as I watched how Scott Cooper would, in one meeting after another, go out of his way to endorse whatever Perskie came up with. For his part, Perskie swallowed Cooper's attentions whole. I was glad I had Robert. We both felt contempt for Cooper and became severely frustrated with Perskie's attempts to intrude into our area, where his inexperience could only frustrate our strategies.

With his sense of diplomacy, however, Robert thought it best to play low profile, not to do anything that would ignite a war in the Players organization. He told me to remember the only intelligent thing he had ever heard Henry Kissinger say—"Don't precipitate."

I agreed. "Looks like we're screwed for now," I said to him, one night over a few evening drinks. "We've got to look over our shoulders for this Perskie, Howard's new darling. I can't for the life of me think of a job he could do on his own. And he's going to be calling the shots in this company? I drink in thanks to you, Howard."

"Sometimes," Robert commented, "you get the feeling we're trying to fix a hole in the ocean by making a dove-tail joint." He raised his glass to meet mine. "Here's to the great escape. What you and I deserve is a vacation."

"I'll drink to that!" I replied, as I raised my glass in a salute and then belted my drink down.

CHAPTER 10

TEMPEST

Though his bark cannot be lost,
Yet it shall be tempest tossed.

– William Shakespeare, *Macbeth*

※

Robert grabbed the first opportunity to get us an R&R leave. Sometime ago, he had sailed his yacht to Clearwater, Florida, and had left it docked there to have the single Perkins drive engine rebuilt and have the vessel outfitted with a new front furling sail. He was also having some other items repaired as a result of a collision with an offshore oilrig during his cruise to Clearwater from Louisiana. The work had been completed, and now Robert needed to sail his yacht back to its homeport. He and Julie would take a long weekend; and he invited Kathy and me along.

In Clearwater, in preparation for cast off, we split into teams, with what Robert and I felt was a fair division of responsibilities. Kathy and Julie would go into town and buy the food and liquor we needed. Meanwhile, Robert and I would walk around the pier looking for a bar that had the Weather Channel.

We settled into the third bar we found and watched the TV screen
for the forecast for Clearwater and the Gulf of Mexico. Just as we started
to enjoy our drinks, we heard that *Beryl,* a small tropical storm, was approaching the Atlantic side of the state and that it was expected to peter
out as it hit land. The report for the Gulf anticipated calm conditions
overall, with a slight chance of rough seas. Wave height was presently
about three feet. What shape conditions would take would depend on
how the tropical storm behaved as it passed over the upper portion of
Florida.

Robert was mildly concerned. "Could be rough out there, John. I
don't know. Do you or Kathy get seasick?"

"Never," I replied. " But there's no hurry. I'll order us another fifty
rounds and we can just wait and see."

As we tipped one glass after another, becoming definitively sloshed,
we laughed off the recent antics within Players. In the background we
heard Jimmy Buffet, one of Robert's favorites. Suddenly, Robert ham-
mered his glass down onto the table, in the manner of a judge calling a
session to order, and then stood up, wobbling slightly. "Enough, John!
The sirens call us to sea. Let's go!"

We staggered out of the bar and down the sandy street to where his
yacht was moored. The ladies had returned. Kathy was handing bottles of
wine and liquor to Julie on the ketch, so she could stow them away.

"Hey girls," I shouted, strutting arm in arm with Robert.

"Boys will be boys!" Julie shouted back. Kathy, for her part, was
laughing. Her spirits seemed to be high, and my hopes were up that this
long weekend would be a blast for all of us.

"What's with the weather?" Kathy asked as Robert and I staggered
our way on board. She pointed to the east. "It looks pretty bad over
there. What did the Weather Channel say?"

Robert answered, "It's supposed to be good, unless the mess from
the Atlantic makes it over here. Right now, we're just seeing a local thun-
derhead or a heat shower. Could be okay, but there are three-foot seas in
the Gulf."

Kathy did know a thing or two about sailing. "Three-foot waves, not too bad; but it's not going to be smooth."

Robert suggested that we wait a while before setting out, to give us a chance to check the Weather Channel again. I was puffed up in confidence from all the drinking I had done. "What are you worried about, Robert? I spent a winter on boats in the North Sea. It'd have to be pretty bad for me to want to abort, especially after coming all the way here. This boat can handle a three-foot chop. After all, it's a forty-one footer."

Robert became half serious. "That's not the point, John. The boat can handle the weather. But we can put away our bathing suits and the tanning oil. This is going to be a different kind of trip if the seas get any higher."

I laughed and looked at the ladies. "I ain't worried about getting wet. Any you folks fussy about getting wet? Any wimps here?"

"Not in the least," Robert answered. "But tell you what. To be on the safe side, let's go back to the bar and see what the Weather Channel has to say now."

The report was now forecasting winds up to 25 knots and waves up to five feet. Conditions could get worse if Beryl didn't die over the mainland.

Robert rapped his glass down on the table, in frustration. I reached over and slapped him on the shoulder. "It'll be okay, Robert. I'm game. You game?" I looked at Robert, then at Julie and Kathy. They turned their eyes on Robert.

"Fuck it!" Robert responded. " Look, I'll do whatever you want. I'm not looking forward to making another run in bad weather, but we're already here. It's not going to be a bowl of cherries, I promise you that. But I could be making too much of it. The weather is anybody's guess. Let's take a vote."

Julie, Kathy, and I raised our hands in favor of setting out. By this point, I was totally crocked. Julie and Kathy had downed a few, enough to cloud Julie's judgment. Kathy, for her part, seemed eager to take on an adventure.

A half hour later we were puttering out to sea under the power of the small Perkins, roughly mustering three to four knots. The sails were down. Sky of blue, sea of green. I settled back in my seat, listening to the stereo and watching Robert pilot. We continued to drink, trading a fifth of Jack Daniels back and forth. Julie and Kathy were below, having a great time. I could hear them laughing. I closed my eyes, tilted my head back, and let myself totally relax as, to the southwest of us, the sun lowered toward the Gulf.

Earlier, we had had assigned eight-hour shifts for piloting. Robert and I would take the first shift, which would run until four the next morning. As the evening wore on into night, Julie and Kathy turned in; and Robert and I continued to work the bottle.

About the time we reached its bottom, I noticed the sky: it was beginning to change to a dark green that I had never seen before. Just then, the wind blasted and whipped hard, causing the vessel to scoot sideways.

"Whoa!" Robert yelled as he immediately corrected the course.

The wind gusted a few more times and then became a blow, continually gathering velocity. Then, abruptly, the Perkins engine died. Robert made several attempts to restart, using the starter switch. But the engine failed to respond. After several attempts, he stopped. "Damn!" he hissed. "They were supposed to fix the engine!"

As suddenly as the engine had died, the rain came on, sideways, with pelting force. The wind-driven pellets stung our faces and arms.

From below, Julie screamed, "Robert! We're taking on water! Robert! Shit! We're taking on lots of water! Get down here!"

Robert motioned for me to take the wheel and then bolted below. In a moment, I heard him yelling, "Fuck! This ain't good! Julie, get me some wood plugs and the hammer. Fast! There's a ton of water down here. We're sinking!"

I heard Julie pulling out drawer after drawer. Then I heard Robert: "It's the bilge pipe! It's busted! Water's coming back in!"

Then I heard Julie again. "I found the hammer! I can't find the plugs! Where did you put them, Robert? Oh... I think I... here they are! I found them!"

I heard her run back to the engine room. Then I heard Robert hammering the plugs into place. "There. I've slowed it down enough for us to get a handle on things," he said.

As soon as Robert had spoken, a blast of wind came across the port bow with enough force to knock me off the wheel. In all the commotion below, I hadn't noticed that the weather had become much worse. Looking starboard, I saw that the waves were now at least ten feet. I looked out to the horizon, fully expecting to see a waterspout forming ahead of us.

"Robert!" I yelled. "It's going to hell fast up here!"

"What now?" he said with a sigh, as he came back to the helm.

"Look, Robert! Look over the bow!"

"Holy shit! John! Julie! Get the lifejackets out! Everyone, get in a lifejacket!"

"Where are they?" I heard Kathy shout. "I'll get them!"

Kathy was showing her plus side, instinctively kicking into action in the face of an emergency. She could be tacky, true, at the worst possible times; but a water ass she wasn't. If we got into a world of very serious shit, she could pull her weight better than most men I knew.

"This ain't right," I heard Robert say to himself as the bow shot straight up in the air. Then the entire hull rose, turned sideways, and leaned hard to starboard. It hung there a moment, then slammed back down, causing the aluminum mast, which was shaking like a rapier, to ring out with a *Clang! Ching! Clang!*

We were all knocked off our feet, except Kathy. "What do we need to do Robert?" she asked, poking her head up top.

As Robert picked himself up, the bow shot straight up again. Before it slammed back down, he told Kathy, "Find the radio so we can get the weather!"

We were slammed back down with such force I could hear the wooden hull creaking.

"Here it is!" Kathy yelled from below, as she turned the large boom box on and turned the AM dial until we heard, "All vessels are to be advised of the severe storm danger. Once again, tropical storm Beryl has reorganized in the Gulf, just off Clearwater, and is approaching hurricane strength."

"Shit!" Robert yelled, as he beat his fist down on the console. "We're fucked! We're dead in the water!"

"We're still breathing," Kathy said. "We're not fucked yet. What do we need to do now, Robert, John?"

"Get on the VHF," Robert said. "See if we can call the Coast Guard for a rescue helicopter. We're probably too far out to reach them though. I can't do it. I have to steer the boat out of these troughs so we don't roll over."

Kathy looked directly at me. "John, come down here and help me work the radio." Then she turned her back and went back below. She was ready to fight this storm with everything she had.

"Let's go," I said, following her. "I think the radio's on the wall under the stairs."

We found the radio, and Kathy turned the big white knob. She handed me the mike.

"United States Coast Guard, this is the sailing vessel *L'Envie*. United States Coast Guard, do you copy? Over," I called into the mike.

There was no reply. I repeated the distress message. Again, there was no reply. "We're too far out," I said. "They can't hear us."

Again, the hull slammed down into the bottom of a trough, this time knocking Kathy and me off our feet. Kathy got up and offered me her hand.

Julie, Kathy, and I struggled our way back up top, with Kathy behind Julie, supporting her. In the limited visibility, we could see the walls of what looked like twenty-foot waves. The wind had gathered into what felt like a gale. Robert was using all of his strength to hang on to the wheel.

"We could get rolled over!" he warned. "But I've been keeping her out of the trough with just the wheel. The wind's at our back. I'm keeping her moving. As long as I can do that, we'll stay afloat. The wind alone can't turn us over on this heavy of a keel—at least not permanently. Anything on the VHF, John?"

"Can't raise the Coast Guard, Robert. We must be out of range."

"I figured that."

"We can't be rescued by a helicopter in this, can we?"

"I don't know. If they can rescue us by air, I'll have to scuttle my boat. That's what I do know."

We slammed back down toward the bottom of another trough. It felt like we were on a huge roller coaster. As we rose to the top of the next wave, the bow inclined almost straight up. When we reached the peak, the bow held its upward point for just a moment and then plunged downward, as the hull crashed back down. I was concerned the hull couldn't hold up much longer without failing. Each time she fell I could hear her joints stretching.

"Julie, take the wheel. John, come aft with me," Robert said. "I'm going to try to raise the mizzen. Too much wind for the main."

Julie took the wheel as I followed Robert. Behind us, we heard Julie scream, " I can't hold her, Robert!"

We turned starboard as a wave caught us and as the hull started surfing down the wall sideways toward the trough. Robert turned, grabbed the wheel, and whipped it hard to port. We came back about and the bow dug into the wall. We stopped hard and the hull came backwards. In a moment, Robert had her under control, moving again on course.

"Try it again," Robert said to Julie.

Not much above five feet tall, and not weighing much over one hundred pounds, Julie dug in both her heels and wrapped her arms and body over the wheel.

"You got it, girl!" Kathy shouted.

Robert turned to me and shouted, "Let's go!"

We made our way aft and began raising the mizzen. When we got it halfway up, we stopped. It was useless. There was a large diagonal rip all the way from top to bottom.

"Hell with that!" Robert said, as he dropped the lanyard. "I'm going to try the front furling sail. They put a new one on in Clearwater."

The front furling was a small triangular shaped sail hung on a steel cable that ran down from the top of the main mast to the bow. It was spring loaded and rolled up into a round sheath like a pull-down window shade.

I followed Robert as he made his way slowly around the port deck on the way to the bow. From behind, I heard Kathy yell, "Damn it, Robert! Get back here and put a lifejacket on! You're not going to make a widow out of Julie!" Kathy had noticed that Robert was the only one of us who hadn't followed his own order to don lifejackets.

Robert ignored Kathy's advice. I could tell that the situation had him pissed off to an extreme. I followed him up to the bow. He put his hand on the end of the sail and pulled. But nothing happened. He repositioned himself so that he could get a grip using both hands. He pulled again. But again no response.

"Shit!" he yelled. "It's jammed. Brand new and it won't work."

In desperation, he started jumping up and down and pulling. While he was in the air, a wave smashed over the bow with amazing force, blinding us in a torrent of spray.

As I wiped the water from my eyes, Julie screamed, "He's gone!"

I looked ahead of me and couldn't see Robert.

"Oh God! Oh God! No!" Julie screamed, hysterically, as Kathy held her in a tight embrace.

I grabbed a life ring and looked out into the dark water, first port side, trying to sight Robert. As I looked out the starboard side, I saw a single hand holding on to the safety cable that ran around the perimeter of the boat. Somehow, Robert had been able to grab the cable while he was riding the wave. I reached out with both hands and grabbed his upper body to help him on board. Kathy was right there, helping me, as behind us Julie screamed, "Get him! Help him!"

Just then, the impact of another huge wave knocked me off my feet. But Kathy held her ground. I looked up, slightly dazed, and could see that she was still holding on to Robert, who had managed to get both hands on the cable.

Together, Kathy and I pulled Robert aboard. She hugged him, crying, "Thank God!"

"Good work, honey," I said. Behind us, Julie was dead quiet.

Robert had gathered his wits, if ever he had lost them. "Alright, John, we have to act now. I'm going to get out the satellite EPIRB and set it off. The Coast Guard'll send a rescue helicopter or boat once the beacon goes off. You get back on the VHF and find someone, anyone. Ask them to relay a distress call to the Coast Guard." He looked at his handheld Global Positioning Device. "Look, our coordinates. Try to get someone to relay our coordinates to the Coast Guard. Let's quit fucking around and scuttle her. If we don't, we're going to die out here."

"Aye, aye," I replied.

"That's the fucking spirit," I heard Kathy say. This time, there was nothing vulgar about the way she said *fucking*. It was a soldier's reply to the need to start returning fire.

Back on the VHF, I called, "This is the sailing vessel *L'Envie*. Mayday! Mayday! Mayday! Any vessel within range of this signal, please respond. We're in severe distress. We need assistance. Over." I waited a moment and then called again, "This is the sailing vessel *L'Envie*. Mayday! Mayday! Mayday! Over!"

Once again I waited. As I was about to repeat the call, I heard the response cracking over the speaker. "*L'Envie, L'Envie*, this is Kojak. I read you loud and clear. I thought I was the only one stupid enough to still be out here. I was just about to give up and head back. You all shouldn't be out in this stuff. Over."

"Roger that, Kojak," I replied. "We're in a forty-one foot ketch, dead in the water. We've got no engine or sails and we're going to roll if we can't get off her soon."

"Roger," came the response, interrupted by signal noise. Then I heard, "My best friend died out here just last year in a sailboat. No way I'll let that happen again. How can I help?"

I asked Kojak for his coordinates. He answered that his Loran positioning indicator was acting strange and gave me the best reading he could get. I looked at the chart and noted that he was about thirty miles away, on the land side of us. I gave him our own coordinates and asked, "Kojak, can your radio still reach shore? Over."

"I think so. I can hear jabbering from them boats that made it into port. Over."

"Good, Kojak. Please call the Coast Guard and tell them we need a rescue helicopter fast. We're not going to be able to stay dry side up for long. Over."

"Roger that *L'Envie*. Give me a few minutes and I'll be back. Over."

I listened, trying to hear what he relayed to the Coast Guard but couldn't make out the details. I did hear him say "Thank you" as he ended his call.

Then I heard, "*L'Envie, L'Envie*, this is Kojak. They've got a helicopter and a rescue ship headed out to you now. Won't be very long, can you hang on? Over."

"We're going to give it all we've got. Over."

"I'll stay out here until they got you. Over."

"I appreciate that Kojak. We've got some damage, but I think we'll hold up until the helicopter arrives. Over."

"I'm having my own problems too. Storm's blown out my windshield, my radio's been acting up, and my engine's throwing oil as fast as I can pour it in. Got to tend to that. Over."

When I returned to the deck, Robert was back at the wheel, fighting the waves. Julie was hanging on to him for dear life—his dear life.

"Oh shit!" Robert yelled. The boat came down hard on her starboard side, leaning until the mast was close to the water. Then, she came straight up again and did the same thing on her port. We were thrown violently back and forth.

"Damn! Crossing waves!" Robert shouted, as he tried using the rudder to regain stability.

Mercifully, that was the last of the crossing waves. We were left to contend with the mad roller coaster pattern. From below, I heard, "*L'Envie, L'Envie*, this is Kojak. Over."

I sprinted back down the stairs, halfway down misjudging the timing of the roller coaster. I was dashed to the floor, amid clusters of broken glass. I could feel the shards biting into my skin. Kathy had followed me and was there to pick me up.

"Kojak, this is *L'Envie*. What you got, buddy? Over!" I called into the mike.

"I got some bad news. The helicopter's turned back. Over."

I felt Kathy's grip on my arm tighten. "Why? Over!" I pleaded.

"Don't quite know. Maybe the wind's still too much for a safe transfer. I don't know. Over."

Shit! I said to myself and then asked, "What now, Kojak? Over."

"It ain't good, but you still got the rescue ship headed your way. Over."

"How long do you think she'll take? Over."

"Thirteen, fourteen hours, I guess. I know the vessel; her name is *Sudden Pressure*. She's a real bad girl. Nothing'll stop her—nothing. Over."

I could feel Kathy pressing against me. To Kojak, I explained, "We aren't going to make it, friend. It's 0400 now and that would put her to us around 1800 tomorrow. It's a fight to stay up now. I don't think we can hold up that long. We're in bad danger. We're rolling with every wave as it is. Over."

Kojak answered, "If I can catch up to you, I can hold you against the waves. I can't tow you and it won't be pleasant, but it'll save your lives. Over."

"Roger that, Kojak. But you've already taken some damage and sounds like you'll be lucky to make it in with your engine throwing lube oil. Over."

"Right, *L'Envie*. I reckon it don't look so good for the home team. But I ain't leaving you in this. Can't do it. I'm skinning back and coming on full. Over."

I could hear his engines rev over the speaker. Then he asked, "*L'Envie*, how fast you think you're moving right now? Over."

"I show about four knots. Over."

"Damn! With just the wind at your back? Over."

"Roger, Kojak. Over."

"*L'Envie*, get everything you can use for a sea anchor and tie it aft. Slow her down as much as you can without losing your steering. Over."

"Roger that. Over," I replied, with a sinking feeling. Kathy was no longer with me below. When she had heard Kojak's instructions, she had gone straight up to the deck. She knew there was no time to waste.

"Do me a favor *L'Envie*. Will you? Over," I heard Kojak ask.

"Roger that. Over."

"Make sure you relay your position about once every hour. My guess is that I'll see you some time late morning. Over."

"Roger that, my friend. *L'Envie* standing by. God bless."

As Robert and Julie struggled to control the hull's position, Kathy and I made sea anchors out of everything we could find, including blue jeans, bedspreads, and sheets. This measure slowed us to around three knots. I also made sure to go below every hour to relay our position to Kojack.

By morning, we were all miserably seasick, unable to hold down water or food. Kathy was holding up better than any of us. During the night, Julie had gone to the aft cabin and given herself a dose of Thorazine, which acts like a time portal that opens to tomorrow on the next side. Once you take it, you are completely out except for breathing. We wouldn't be seeing Julie again until later today.

At about 0800, the wind died down, posing a new menace. With no wind at our back, we weren't being pushed forward. As a result, we were losing our steering and going down sideways in the trough. Kathy and I quickly pulled up the sea anchors, as Robert began doing something that showed his remarkable presence of mind, even when he was near total exhaustion. As the bow came out of the top of the wave and started to slam down, he steered straight for the bottom of the trough, getting as much forward momentum as he could by surfing down the side of the wave wall. Just before he reached bottom, he turned the wheel to kick us diagonally, to keep the bow from digging into the wall of the next wave. As we rose to the top of the next wave, he would lose all steering. But when the crest broke under us, he again steered toward the bottom and then forced the hull diagonally again.

At 0900, I went below to update Kojak on the VHF, but there was no reply. I repeated the call over and over, with no answer.

I went back up to help Robert. At 1000, I tried relaying our coordinates to Kojak again. But, again, there was no reply. At 1100, I tried to relay to Kojak, once more with no luck. From the deck, I heard Kathy yell, "John! John!" By the time I got up the stairs, Robert was slumped limp over the wheel. The boat had turned completely sideways and was heading down into the trough.

Kathy and I both yelled at Robert, to snap him back to attention. He looked up at us, then quickly steered us straight. Looking over to me, he said, "John, I want you to try taking the wheel. Kathy, you listen too, in case you have to take over. I'll tell you what to do."

He explained how to surf the waves as he had been doing for hours. I tried my best, at least a dozen times, but felt I was losing control. For a moment, I felt my confidence slipping and panic taking hold. I had always thought I could do anything I set my mind to. But I could see that the task I had in hand now needed the touch that Robert had gotten from years of experience at the helm.

I looked over and saw that Robert had one eye shut; the other was drooping. He was on the edge of passing out. "Robert, you can't go to sleep!" I yelled. "I can't do this alone. I don't know how."

"No choice," Robert answered, in a voice that seemed to be coming from very far away. " I can't hold on the wheel. I can't feel my fingers—they're dead."

I looked down to see that he had released his grip on the wheel. He was only able to slap against the spokes with his hand. "How long can you hang on?" I asked.

"Maybe another thirty minutes, John. I don't know."

"Well that's it, then," I said, in near resignation.

"Looks… looks… that way. Goo goo g… joob," he stuttered. Then, for a moment, he regained his voice. "We need to get ready. Hope whatever happens, you end up somewhere good."

"I hope you do too, my friend," I said, as we shook hands the old warrior's way, with thumbs wrapped.

"I need to talk to Julie now," he said.

I hadn't noticed that Julie was present. Kathy had gone below to check her and found that she was awake.

I left them alone and crawled over to Kathy. "Come down with me for a minute?" I asked her. "They want to be alone and we need to talk."

Below, I asked her to sit down. I sat down next to her.

"Kathy, Robert's going to have to stop. He's got nothing left. I tried to copy him, but I just can't get it. No one on board can keep us up now."

She embraced me. "Then we're going to roll?"

"Yes, we'll roll," I whispered to her. "If we're on her when she rolls, we're likely to be killed or at least knocked out. The mast will probably break off too. It'll be a mess. We'll have to jump before that happens."

Kathy looked into my eyes, her own expression clear and focused. I knew I loved her at that moment. I knew I was seeing her at her best. Ever since we had realized we were in dire straits in this storm, she had been able to snap the grip of the demons. If these were to be our last moments, I'd be buying the farm filled with pride for her fighting spirit.

"John, I—" she began to say.

I put my fingers to her lips. "It's not important. We haven't been the best match. I know that. But I love you, Kathy."

"I know," she said, looking down. When she looked back up, I could see she was starting to cry. So was I. She reached over and held my hand.

"Listen, " I said. "No matter what, you have to come out of this alive. I want you to take the EPIRB beacon and attach it to your lifejacket. They'll be sure to find you with the beacon on. Now that the wind has died down, the helicopter may be already on the way. They may find all of us. Who knows? But they'll certainly find you."

"Why me?" Kathy asked, in a bare whisper.

"Think of the kids now. We can't risk them being orphans."

"What about you? Can't we tie ourselves together?"

"No, Kathy, we can't. That would be suicide. The rope could get caught on the boat and strangle us both. When we jump, we've got to put as much distance between us and the boat as possible."

Her head dropped as she started to sob.

I could hear my own voice breaking. "Kathy? Two more things, honey. Raise them well. Teach them who I was and what I stood for. Tell them every chance you get that I loved them. And, honey, I do love you. I should have—"

"*L'Envie, L'Envie*, this is Kojak! Got my radio working, do you copy?

L'Envie, L'Envie, I see your mast straight over my bow. I'm coming on full. Over."

With one arm around Kathy, who had gone inert, I reached over with my other hand and grabbed the mike.

"Roger that, Kojak!" I tried to yell. Instead, my voice came in sobs. Without realizing it, I was weeping like a slob. "You sure are one welcome sound, my friend. Over," I managed to say.

"Roger, *L'Envie.* Told you before that my radio was acting up. I think I found the problem, though. Spent the last few hours running some new wires. I could hear you, but I guess I wasn't transmitting. Over."

"Got you. Come on, my friend. We have the welcome mat out. Over."

I dropped the mike, ran up the stairs, with Kathy following close behind me, and slapped Robert hard on the back. He was near to being totally passed out, with Julie clinging to him, weeping silently.

"You'll want to stay up for this show, buddy. Kojak found us. We're getting the hell out of here."

With one hand still on the wheel, Robert placed his free arm around me and pulled me close to him and Julie. I hugged the both of them hard. He then reached out to Kathy and pulled her into us. None of us spoke.

It took half an hour for Kojak to secure our position so that we were pointing into the waves, not catching them broadside. Kathy and I did the work at our end. Robert was totally spent; and there was no way that Julie was going to let go of him. After *L'Envie* was secured, Kojak waved to us from his deck. We were at least eighty feet away, but it was easy to see how he had earned his nickname. He was as bald as a bowling ball. When he walked back inside his cabin, I hailed him on the VHF.

"Kojak, it's about time we knew your name, don't you think? And one other question. We got ourselves into this mess through our own stupidity. But what the hell were you doing out in this? Over."

"You can call me Carl Paige, buddy. What was I doing out here? Well, I was fishing. I need real bad to catch a big fish. I ain't had much luck lately and I got bills due. Thought I'd fish ahead of the front. Looks like I overstayed. Over."

"He won't have any bill problems once I get home," Kathy said.

"Amen," I added. I keyed the mike again and spoke. "Kojak. I mean Carl. Do you mind giving me your address? Over."

Carl, Kathy, and I talked back and forth for hours. *Under Pressure* arrived on schedule, attached us, and began towing us on our long journey back to the mainland. Within a few days, Kojak's picture was on the front page of newspapers all over northern Florida, with a feature article detailing his stubborn heroics. A week later, he received a Care Package in the mail that Kathy had assembled especially for him.

Once we were on land, Robert, Julie, Kathy, and I—calling ourselves "the survivors"—took sanctuary in the most sumptuous hotel we could find and ate and drank ourselves into oblivion. Our ordeal had drawn us into a closeness similar to the bond that establishes between infantrymen in combat. We felt like brothers and sisters—as though we would never allow anything to come between us. All too soon, however, the demons would renew their claim on my wife.

Back at the Players office in Lake Charles, I felt that my experience during my so-called vacation had rekindled the "keep on rucking" spirit that had been drilled into me at Fort Bragg.

The phone rang as I was reveling in my sense of invincibility. It was David, and what he had to say showed me that he and Scott Cooper were now acting entirely as a law unto themselves.

David wanted me to get myself to Las Vegas as soon as possible. Shortly after the Lake Charles casino had opened its doors, Cooper and David had nosed about Nevada for a good casino property. I had caught wind of their thinking, had done some assessment of my own, and had recommended that we continue to pursue a site adjacent to the Galleria Center, in Green Valley, a suburb of Las Vegas. Although they had condescended to have a look at my recommendation, they wound up championing Mesquite, a small sleepy town well away from Vegas. Cooper's concept, which impressed me as being more full of holes than a block of Swiss cheese, was that a casino in Mesquite would draw customers from casino employees in Vegas. Later, it consoled me that a casino did start up in Green Valley and that it developed into one of the flagship success stories of the gaming industry.

I read Cooper's and David's foolhardy adherence to Mesquite as a conspiracy to cut me out of the Players herd, and my suspicions were supported by the way they conducted themselves throughout the project. They went almost the whole nine yards without me—from negotiating the approvals to hiring contractors for design and construction. I sat back and let them stumble their way onward, knowing that sooner or later they'd lay a blood trail and need me to clean it up.

David's call made it plain that the time for mop up had come. The higher mysteries of budgeting, scheduling, and establishing lines of accountability for contractors had gone beyond his and Cooper's combined ability. David was now asking for Players's tried and proven shock trooper to do damage control.

"I'll book a flight and be in Vegas tomorrow," I told David, thinking Asshole! as I hung up the phone. I thought a moment of the pair of them, David and Cooper. I detested butt kissing and couldn't understand why my colleagues couldn't see it when it was so plainly hurting Players. I found it difficult to think of Cooper without wishing I was back at Fort Bragg. There, we had a way of dealing with guys like him.

I then dismissed Cooper and thought about the career dilemma I had on my hands. Players was now split into two camps. In one, there was Howard and his sidekick Perskie, who would be more than content to see me on the street. In the other, there was the David-Cooper symbiosis. They'd like to see my butt on the sidewalk too. Well, Brotherton, I said to myself, if they want to slip the dagger in your back, show 'em that you didn't get your medals and commendations for being a pushover.

I left my office, went to the local Radio Shack, and bought a tape recorder and a phone line splitter.

CHAPTER 11

ENTER THE REVEREND

*They know not the subtle ways I keep and
pass and turn again.*

– Ralph Waldo Emerson, "Brahmin"

＊

I soon learned that my job paranoia wasn't without a basis. Once I had the Mesquite project moving along nicely, Howard had me fly to Atlantic City for a meeting the purpose of which he kept vague until I got there. After a nominal period of small talk, he edged his way into a proposal that one of his Atlantic City sidekicks, Steve Labov, be brought aboard Players to assist me in construction management. From the way Howard talked, I could tell that he and Labov were close. They had, Howard explained, been friends since childhood and had partnered in business ventures. I took mental notes and let him continue. Once he got warmed up, he started pitching Labov as a construction management guru who'd turn out to be of great use to me.

I didn't, however, see that I needed any assistance—so far I had completed all my projects under budget and in record time—and felt I was being railroaded. But I could sense that for me to mount a protest would have amounted to an act of career sepuku. If I could have foreseen then the seismic contract crisis that Labov would eventually help precipitate, I would have walked out of Players' door, with no looking back.

From the outset, as it happened, I found little in the way of common ground with Labov. His arrogance made it difficult for me to get factual information across to him. Nor did he seem to have much use for it. Mainly, from what I could see, his primary goal was to ingratiate himself with David. In fact, he found his way to David's right-hand side so quickly that I felt any attempt to buck him would be an exercise in futility.

That, however, turned out to be a tactical mistake for me. First off, Labov grabbed the high ground politically by letting everyone in the company know how close he and Howard were. He also made capital of his ability to sense what David wanted to hear—an art form that was contrary to my own practice of highlighting what needed to be said. Next, he started overtly eroding my control of the Mesquite project, which soon became burdened with nebulous scopes, budget overruns, and lapses in timelines. No one in Players seemed to hold him accountable; nor did anyone challenge his high fees.

Feeling I had no choice but to accept Labov as an albatross factor, I decided to dedicate some of my time to scouting other projects around Baton Rouge and New Orleans. I made friends with Senator Francis Heitmeier's brother, Bobby, who had developed several contacts in the riverboat industry. One night, while we were sitting in the bar of the Royal Sonesta on Bourbon Street, Bobby asked me if I thought Players would be interested in participating in a casino project in Belize. A colleague of his, Duke Robin, had been working on a proposal to the government of Belize and felt that a partnership with an experienced casino operator would strengthen his hand.

I ran the suggestion by Howard, got his go ahead, and a week later was on a TACA flight to Belize City, with Duke. After he finished briefing me, he shifted to a new topic, one that opened the way to a relationship that I hold dear to this day. "A friend of mine will be taking us out to Ambergris Cay, where we'll be staying," he explained. "But I think I'd better tell you about this guy now. So brace yourself, John."

"Really?" I asked.

"He's a spook, or something like that, and a good one. I've heard people say he's the best. To me, he's a complete puzzle. I've never known what to make of him. Five minutes with him and I'm totally confused."

I was finding this interesting. I'd known more than a few intelligence operatives during my military career and had always found that the better ones were inscrutable, if not unfathomable—that they were that way effortlessly, by nature, rather than by any studied effort. But I wanted to know the basis for Duke's confusion. "What do you mean?" I asked.

"Well, sometimes you see him he's all business. You'd think he's a Ross Perot, efficient to the bone, obsessed with it. Next minute he's chasing his tail. Wait till you see him. And wait till you see his plane. At least that's what he calls it."

"What kind of plane is it?"

"It's what's left of a Cessna. You get in it with him and no telling where he'll take you. Could be Guatemala, Cuba, you never know."

I thought it was odd that Duke hadn't mentioned his friend's name and so I asked.

"I have no idea. For some reason, he wants you to call him the Reverend. Damned if I know why. And damned if he'll tell me. His real name is a mystery."

I thought I had a very good idea of what the Reverend's code name signified. "Sounds like an odd sort of bird. You think he's what the British would call daft?"

"No. He's not daft. He's brilliant, really. He loves anything esoteric. 'Esoterica' he calls it. He's always talking about ancient cults and rites—Egyptian stuff like Osiris and even Asian gods, deities he calls them, like this Shiva the Destroyer. And he reads around in the Kabala, the Koran, and some Tibetan book. He even likes James Joyce of all people. Also Arthur Conan Doyle. I don't know what to call it, but I wouldn't call it daft."

From my window seat, I looked at the Caribbean below us. "I guess you'd have to call it the Reverend," I said.

As we stepped off the ladder onto the tarmac, Duke pointed his finger to our right. "There he is, over there."

I turned to see the Reverend. He looked pretty old, in his seventies I guessed. He also looked like he had both seen and been through it all. He walked toward us with a pronounced limp and carried what looked like a cane in his right hand. But he didn't seem to really use it to help him walk. It looked to me like a sheath for some sort of blade, and I wondered whether his limp was put on.

In height, he was about five foot ten. He was completely bald, but I couldn't tell whether it was natural or whether he shaved his head. As we walked toward him, I noted that his eyes were kind, almost paternal; but I had the feeling that he could look through me, into the depth of me, without trying.

Behind the Reverend I could see a small, single-engine Cessna that looked like it had been painted red at one time.

"Good to see you, Mr. Duke," the Reverend said, reaching out to shake hands. Then he looked over to me. I could feel his eyes boring into me, like twin, high-speed drill bits.

"And you must be John. Pleased to make your acquaintance, young man," he said, in a formal tone that sounded natural to him.

"Pleased to meet you too, Mr. Reverend, sir," I replied.

He laughed. "No need for formalities. Just plain Reverend will do. I see you've already coached the young man some, Duke."

I saw a scar on the Reverend's upper lip and wondered how he got it. It looked like the sort of wound you get from hot shrapnel. Duke must have seen it too. "I never noticed that scar before," he said.

"This one?" the Reverend replied, running his index finger over his lip. "Got this in '64."

Wow! 1964! I said to myself. L.B.J. vintage! Probably earlier. Maybe even back to when the CIA was supposed to be staffed by Ivy League grads. No wonder Duke thinks he's brilliant. I looked at the Reverend closely and noted his intellectual bearing and how aged he was. I had no doubt that he traced back to at least the early fifties, when Truman appointed Lieutenant General Walter Bedell Smith as Director of Central

Intelligence. Under Smith, the CIA came into its own, realizing the earlier but frustrated vision of the immortal Major General "Wild Bill" Donovan. The Reverend, I saw, was looking back at me with a bemused expression. Don't think I'd want to piss this old owl off, I thought. No telling where he's been and what he's capable of.

"I'd like your passports," he said in an easy, matter of fact way. He took our documents, and we followed him around to the backside of the airport building. "Wait here," he said and went into the building through an unmarked door. In a few minutes he came out and handed us back our passports. "Here you go, all set. Get your bags and let's be on our way."

As we approached his Cessna, I saw small punctures in the rudder and all over the fuselage. I recognized them as bullet holes. The most alarming detail was the lube oil that was conspicuously leaking from the side of the engine.

"Hop in now," the Reverend said as he opened the side door for us. He took the copilot's seat and buckled himself in. I noticed that his seat rocked back and forth, that it wasn't even bolted down. I could also see that duct tape had been applied throughout the interior. I was looking to see if any had been used to repair the propeller, when the pilot started the engine.

Putt per putt, putt per putt, the engine went, missing its proper timing and sounding as if it would prefer to die outright. The pilot pumped the throttle and then revved the engine abruptly to a high rpm. I saw smoke surge from the exhaust.

"Where's our parachutes?" I asked the Reverend. "Can't expect me to be comfortable without a parachute," I added, trying to make a joke.

The Reverend snickered. "Not to worry, young man. Any problem and we'll ditch 'er in the water. Hope you swim well. I do."

"Great," I replied, looking at Duke, who turned his head away from me.

But I felt a little better once we got in the air—even though the engine kept me on full alert with its constant faltering. Then I dismissed any concerns I had when I saw that we were approaching the cay. Below us, the Caribbean was so perfectly clear that it looked to be nothing more than a denser phase of the air around us.

When we landed on the small airstrip and crawled out of the plane, its stubborn engine still coughing, two golf carts were waiting for our use on the island. Duke left me with the Reverend and drove to one of the beachfront hotels.

"None the worse for wear, I see," the Reverend said. "I'm taking you to the Belize Yacht Club. You check in; I'll tend to some business of mine; then we'll meet Duke downtown for dinner."

About an hour later, we were heading into San Pedro to meet Duke at a little restaurant called Elvi's. As we walked through the front door, I saw that the restaurant consisted of one room with no floor. There was just sand and one huge tree in the middle, supporting the thatched roof. Duke was waiting for us, seated at one of the tables. After we had eaten, Duke said he wanted to turn in for the night. "Sweet dreams," the Reverend said to him as he got up from the table. He then turned to me. "Tonight, young man, I'm showing you about. What do you say? You game?"

"Jolly good of you," I said. "You be my Virgil. You lead; I'll trust and follow."

When we got to the cart, the Reverend tossed me the keys. "Do some work, young man. Now you take a turn behind the wheel."

After a couple of blocks, I noticed that we had a problem. "Sir, I think the accelerator's stuck."

"Really? Try pumping it."

I pumped the pedal over and over. "No use. And another problem. The brakes—they slow us down, but they're no good for stopping. Sir, I think I prefer that plane of yours."

The Reverend laughed, again in a snicker. "Accelerator stuck, you say? And bad brakes? Not good. Here, use this." He reached down to the lever that switches from forward to reverse and moved it half way between the "F" and the "R". The cart lost power and rolled to a stop.

"There now, young man, you see? Use the lever to stop and go."

He looked away from me and straight ahead.

"Of course, sir, I should have known," I replied.

We continued on our way, stop and go, until we came to a small bar, called the Pier Lounge, on the beach.

"Stop here, young man," the Reverend said as he started to stand up in the cart while it was still moving.

"Aye, sir," I replied. "I know your thinking. Roger that."

"Good lad. What do you say to a few, on me?"

"Roger that again," I said. I turned the lever and we slowed to a stop right at the front doors.

Inside, over our ice-cold beers, he remarked, "So, I understand you were Special Forces, J.F.K. First Special Warfare Battalion, Fort Bragg. Then 82nd Airborne. Sergeant, I believe. I remember Urgent Fury well. Bad intelligence there. You All Americans did good work, though. I understand that you were awarded a commendation medal for your efforts on behalf of Urgent Fury."

The Reverend was referring to the US's military operation, under Navy command, against the junta that had ousted Grenada's government, headed by Maurice Bishop, who was executed during the coup. The Navy had assumed that there wasn't much of an enemy on the ground to fight. But at one of the major objectives, the newly expanded Port Salinas airfield, Cuban regulars were waiting, fully armed and in prepared positions. The 82nd Airborne Division, traditionally nicknamed the "All Americans," had advanced on the airfield and taken it in short order.

"I hate to think of how that would have gone, sir, if Metcalf hadn't decided to put General Schwarzkopf second in command," I commented. "He did it right on the deck of the *Guam*, the second day."

The Reverend laughed. "Right. Vice Admiral Joseph Metcalf, Atlantic Command. When Norm was first assigned to him as a liaison officer, Metcalf told him 'try to be of some help around here.' Norman said he was standing on the bridge thinking of the stranded American medical students at Grande Anse, trying to figure the fastest way to get to them. He could see the building where the students were and the beach in front of it. It was a perfect drop zone. And there were all these helicopters sitting unused on the deck. You know the rest, young man. Anyway, God bless the 82nd, I've always said. And there's no end to those who'd agree with me."

"Thank you, sir. I won't ask how you knew all that about me." He must have good sources, I thought: I hadn't mentioned my military background to Duke. And, as far as I knew, my DD-214s were still sealed.

The Reverend leaned close to me. "Ever work with anyone from the Company?"

"On occasion," I answered and left it at that. I was reluctant to offer my own opinion of the CIA personnel I had known.

"Well, what did you think of them?" he asked, as if he had been reading my thoughts.

"The ones I knew were usually pompous and always strange. They never seemed to have a boss. Or, if they did, they never seemed to know who it was. If you don't mind me saying, sir, they reminded me of the blind leading the blind."

"Hmmm," he replied, looking away, lost in his thoughts. After a few moments, he turned back to me. "Why don't we head back to the Yacht Club. Bar's pretty nice there. Right on the water. I think we should talk a little more."

"I'm with you, sir," I replied. "As I said, where you lead, I follow."

I took the driver's seat because I still had the keys. Not remembering that I had put the cart in gear earlier, I placed the key in the ignition and turned the switch. The engine started; the cart sat still for a moment; then it shot forward and crashed into the cart parked in front. The impact threw us both from our seats into the sandy road.

"Ha, ha! Ha, ha!" the Reverend laughed, lying on his back in the sand. "Ha, ha! Ha, ha! You forgot about the lever, didn't you? Ha, ha! Ha, ha!" He was obviously enjoying this mishap greatly. I was surprised that he could laugh so loud. He sounded like a mule braying; but I didn't want to tell him that.

"Help me up, if you would, young man. Or get my cane over there," he asked, still laughing, but in a snicker now.

"The least I can do," I said, as I crawled around in the sand, looking for the cane. I found it and handed it to him. "Your Dai Katana, sir, you old Ronin."

That started him belly laughing again. His "Ha, ha! Ha, ha!" echoed out into the night. I was sure that the whole island could hear him.

I looked at the cart and could see that its tires were spinning in the sand. Then I heard a humming noise. As I reached over to turn the key off, smoke started billowing from the battery compartment under the seat.

"Sir!" I yelled. "This fricking cart is smoking!"

The Reverend used his cane to get to his feet. He hobbled up to the cart and lifted the battery compartment cover. Flames shot up from one of the battery switches.

"Shit!" he yelled. Then he started scooping up handfuls of sand and throwing them on the flames. I was surprised that he could move so fast.

In a moment, the fire was snuffed. "Good work!" I said. "I see you guys can put fires out, too." Immediately, though, I regretted the remark. But the Reverend sat himself down in the sand and started laughing again. I sat down beside him and joined in.

After he had exhausted his fit, he stood and offered his hand to help me up. "Well, it looks like we're on foot," he said.

We began walking south, in the direction of the Yacht Club. But almost immediately a cart came by, and the driver offered us a ride. "The Yacht Club, if you'd be so good," the Reverend requested.

"My pleasure, Reverend, sir," the driver, a young man in his early thirties, answered.

In the Yacht Club bar, we sat where we could look out over the water and ordered another round.

"On me, this time," I insisted.

For a moment, we quietly sipped our beers. I wanted to know more about his occupation. But I had to work up the nerve. I braced myself, then asked, "So, tell me about your work, sir. What do you do?"

He looked at me for a long moment before replying, "I do the Lord's work."

Vengeance is mine, I thought. I knew that kind of work. All I could think of to say was "Oh?"

He knew he didn't need to explain further. After some small talk, he patted me lightly on the back. "You know, we get along pretty good. You're not a bad chap at all. In fact, I think I like you, young man."

"Thank you, sir," I answered. "We do make a pretty good team. And I had a great time tonight. I didn't know you covert types could be so much fun."

"The pleasure was all mine," he said. Then he took a pen and a piece of paper from the top of the bar and scribbled on it. "Here. I want you to have this. It's a phone number. Use it to get hold of me if you ever find yourself in really deep shit."

I looked at the number and noted the area code. How strange. "This isn't Belize. It's for—"

"I know. Doesn't matter. You call that number and they'll know how to get me on the spot. As I say, if you're ever in deep shit."

"Thank you. Thanks a lot," I said.

"Don't mention it, young man," the Reverend said as he stood up. "Now I think it's time I be on my way. I still have business to attend to tonight."

"All right, sir. What time do I need to be ready in the morning?" I asked.

As the Reverend extended his forearm to look at his watch, I noticed that he was wearing it on his right wrist.

"You're the only person I've ever seen who doesn't wear it on the left wrist," I said.

His face turned serious; then he smiled slowly. "I can wear it on either. Depends on my mood. Also depends on my mood whether I'm right-handed or left-handed. Some people say I'm one; some say I'm the other. I'll pick you up at 0600 then," he said and turned to leave.

"Wait a minute, sir," I said. "You don't have a cart."

"No matter. I'll be fine."

Again, he turned to leave. But I thought of something else I needed to ask him. "By the way, where are we going in the morning?"

"To see the prime minister. Wear something presentable. I'll see you in the morning. Now good night, young man."

"Good night, sir," I said as he walked away, carrying his cane. I noticed that his walk was more lively than it had been when I had seen him at the airport this morning. As he stepped out into the night, he shifted the cane from his right hand to his left hand and whipped it around in a striking motion. Then he turned, looked back at me, and smiled. Filipino stick fighting, Arnis, I thought. Should've known.

At exactly six the next morning, the Reverend knocked at my door. "Up betimes," he said, cheerily, as I opened the door to leave with him. When we arrived at his Cessna, Duke was there waiting for us. The *putt-sputter-putt* rhythm of the engine missing its timing was now familiar to me, as we made the crossing to the mainland. We landed at the small municipal airport on Belize City's north waterfront and were ushered into a private black sedan that the Reverend had arranged for the day. Downtown, we turned down a series of back streets and stopped in front of a large Victorian style government building. On top of the building, a large Belize National Flag was whipping in the westerly sea breeze that had kicked up since we had left the cay.

We followed the Reverend as he led us up an outside flight of stairs to the second floor and into a reception room. At least fifty people were lined up in front of a desk that was positioned in front of a large door. The Reverend didn't bother to get in line. He went directly to the young lady sitting at the desk and waved for us to follow him.

"Well, good morning, sir!" the lady said. "So good to see you again!"

The Reverend asked her if the prime minister was in.

"Yes, sir. He certainly is," she replied.

He walked to the wooden door and without knocking opened it about halfway. He mumbled something to whomever was inside and then closed the door and stood, waiting. Within a minute, the door opened and two men walked out. "Let's go," the Reverend said to us as he walked inside the room.

Prime Minister Manuel Esquivel was standing behind his desk. He was well over six feet and large in build, with no fat. His black hair was short and slightly curly; his skin was olive; and his eyes were a deep brown. He wore an elegant dark suit with a conservative tie. His shoes, I could see, were not extremely expensive; but they were perfectly polished.

Our meeting lasted about twenty minutes. He greeted us on behalf of the people of Belize and asked the Reverend how he thought the casino project would impact the political climate of his country. I listened closely; and, although I was in the dark about the people and issues they were discussing, I sensed that the prospects for Players were positive.

The Prime Minister asked me whether Players would consider building and staffing a new business school, to train residents to take advantage of jobs that the casino would create. I explained that it was always Players' policy to localize project benefits. He then requested that I have Players draw up a proposal that would include a conceptual design and financial details, including a tax rate that was standard in the casino industry and recommendations to dedicate revenues to diversify Belize's economic base.

I told him that we would need a week to prepare the proposal.

"Good," he said, standing up and extending his hand. "I look forward to hearing from you soon." Looking at the Reverend and back at us, he added, "Now you must excuse us for a moment."

Duke and I waited in the reception area for about ten minutes before the Reverend came out. He proceeded directly toward the stairs. Duke and I followed. No one said a word until we were all back in the sedan.

"Well, young man," the Reverend said to me, "looks like you've got some work ahead of you."

I answered that I would have to report the meeting to Players' President, Howard Goldberg, and that we'd need to assess the economic feasibility of participation before we submitted a proposal.

"Fine," he said. "I can get things together here quickly if Players is interested."

Because Duke was leaving on a later flight, he and the Reverend were to drop me off at the airport. As we approached the main terminal building, the Reverend grasped my hand firmly and said, "Young man, I'm glad we met. Have a safe trip back, and hope to see you again sometime."

"Likewise, sir," I said as I got out.

As soon as I arrived back, I met with Howard and briefed him on the prime minister's request. He had already decided that the economics of the project were weak. The casino would depend on tourists for its patronage, and most visitors to Belize were divers, sport fishermen, and ecotourists—all very low on the gamers profile list. Also, he explained, after some thought, it was probably not a good idea for Players to go international until the company had solved the deficit in management's capabilities at their existing US properties. I passed the word to Duke and was pleased that the Reverend took the trouble to call me, to let me know that no noses were out of joint. He repeated that he hoped we would run into each other again.

A week later, at my home in Houston, I was alone one evening while Kathy and the kids were out shopping. I poured myself a drink and sat down in the kitchen. I pulled my wallet out and found the slip of paper on which the Reverend had written his contact number. I repeated the number over and over in my mind until I was sure that it was committed to memory. Then I used a cigarette lighter to burn the paper. Much later, the number would prove to be the angel on my shoulder.

CHAPTER 12

The Tribe

＊

To deal with Rick Shetler, I had developed a way to tell which of his calls were friendly and which were emergency-driven. At the office and at home, I'd let the phone ring without answering. I'd then listen to the messages and prioritize them. If it was Rick calling, he'd either leave a message—if he was just being social—or he'd hang up and call back immediately on my cell phone—if he was in the grip of a crisis. This morning, he was doubling up: first my desk phone; then, within a few seconds, my cell phone. So I wasn't surprised that he was frantic.

He was calling to tell me that the arrangement Players had engineered to ward off competition in the Lake Charles area was under siege. Though we had created a wall at the state level, we had failed to recognize that businesses operated by federally recognized Native American tribes residing on reservations came, substantially, under federal regulation. Recently, a federal statute had been passed that allowed tribes to operate casinos in states that had already legalized gambling. The review process for such a casino involved staged state and federal approvals. First, before a tribal proponent could submit for federal review, it was required to negotiate a Compact at the state level. The Compact had to specify which games the casino would offer and how it was to be operated.

Located on a reservation near Kinder, approximately thirty miles northeast of Lake Charles, the Coushatta Tribe had not been blind to the success of the Players Lake Charles casino. They leaped on the opportunity that the federal legislation offered and purchased a large plot along Highway 165, close to the reservation boundary. Recognizing that a casino site would have to be contiguous to reservation property, the tribe then made several purchases to close the gap.

Rick's strategy was to get me alarmed over this threat to Players' monopoly and then to relieve my anxiety with the solution that "they"— meaning the Edwards clan, a tribe in its own right—had at the ready. "You've got to realize you're too far into it now to see it blown out of the water," he urged. "And we don't completely own the fed. That should be obvious."

I knew the road down which he was trying to lead me but thought I had leverage. "I hear you, Rick," I said. "But you need to realize that your agreement with Players is toast if the Coushatta Tribe gets a casino off the ground, so close to ours."

He got my point. "All right, let's us both calm down here."

"Fine. Sounds like you have something in mind, up your sleeve, rather."

"*They* do. It's simple. You pay them a million and a half, and they'll see to it that these injuns'll never be able to go federal."

His use of the term *injuns* bristled me because I was part Choctaw. My grandmother had been a full-blooded Native American. Before her, my great grandfather had been sent to the gallows for having raided white settlements. And relatives of mine even further back had died on the Trail of Tears.

I felt like telling Rick to watch his mouth, that my DNA gave me the knowledge of how to lift his scalp slowly. Instead, I asked, "How's that, Rick? How can they roadblock a project if it's legitimate?"

"Easy. They'll just make sure it's *not* legitimate at state."

"I'm all ears, Rick. Go on."

"Edwin'll kill it in the water by writing a letter to the feds. The letter'll say that he can't grant a Compact. He'll hang 'em on the way they took the land for the site into trust or ownership. Something like that. I don't understand the legal details."

Rick sounded to me as if he had already discussed this in detail with Stephen. "You sure about this, Rick? You're talking a lot of money here. You sure they can derail this thing on that basis?"

"They know what they're doing. Don't you worry about that. You worry about getting your ass in gear. You don't have much time."

I told him I'd have to run what he was suggesting up the flagpole to Howard, Ed, and David.

"You better get your heads together fast. They're worried about this. I said you don't have much time. They wanted me to make sure you understood that."

I explained that Howard, Ed, and David were in town, staying at the executive manor that Players had recently bought, and that I'd meet them this afternoon, at the latest.

"That's what they need to hear," he said, as he hung up.

Up until now, I hadn't been involved in the issues surrounding the Coushatta proposal. Howard had kept it under his own wing. But I had kept notes on any details that dribbled in my direction. I was therefore aware that the matter was more complicated than Rick had explained. It was more than just a foray on the part of the tribe into our market area. The Coushatta Tribe had been astute enough not to wing it on their own. They had enlisted participation from Grand Casinos, a recently formed, Minnesota-based gaming company that was experienced at stick handling reservation-based casinos through the review-approval process and into operation.

Ed, David, and Howard were, I knew, chewing their livers over Grand Casino. On their own, without consulting me, they had tried deploying preventive measures. Howard had directed his weapon of choice, Pat Madamba, to retain Akin, Gump, a well-heeled law firm based in Dallas and with and an office in Washington, DC, to help stop the project.

Howard had enlisted Gary Sawhill, a New Jersey-based environmental engineer, to try to unearth negative environmental impacts that would derail regulatory approval. In this, my peers showed they had no notion that they were producing and directing a major farce as well as starring in it. The best Sawhill's investigators could dig up was that the project might endanger an obscure species of woodpecker.

On the local level, Pat Madamba had contacted a tribal member, Mr. Bertney Langley, who felt that the Coushatta Tribe's administration had launched into the project without allowing the tribe to endorse or reject it by a vote. Bertney, Madamba claimed, was agitating for a referendum and could possibly be recruited to act covertly as a Players ally.

David greeted me at the door of the Players house and invited me in. Howard was sitting on the living room couch, looking over documents that were spread out on the coffee table. I could hear Ed milling about upstairs. It amused me that I was walking in, uninvited, to throw a spanner into their tight little proceedings.

"What's up, John?" David asked. "As you can see, we're busy here. Anything of importance?"

I looked at David first, then at Howard. "Depends on whether you think a million and a half dollars is important, David."

"A million and a half dollars? What for?" Howard asked.

"A million and a half is what Rick says Edwards and kin want to make sure this Coushatta project gets killed at state level. For that, they'll make sure it can't go to the fed. As I said, a million and a half."

"Rick said that!" David yelled at me. "What the hell. He's already on contract to make sure our asses are protected. Didn't you tell him that's what we're paying him for?"

"David," I said, slowly, with emphasis, "I'm only telling you what Rick said to me, just this morning. Keep your tone out of my face, will you? I've been told to keep out of this, remember?"

"That's right, David," Howard said, raising his hand. "Sit down, David. John, thank you for coming right over. You did the right thing, staying out of it for now. Did he say what the million and a half would get us?"

I talked to Howard and totally ignored David. "He says that's what it'll cost to get a letter from Edwin to the fed, invalidating the Compact. The basis will be irregularities in the way the Coushatta Tribe has annexed new land to the original reservation property. That's the way I understood it, Howard."

"What?" David interrupted again, his wits confounded.

"Okay, I see the thrust of this," Howard said. "Clever, if I don't say so myself."

"Far as I'm concerned now," I said, "I'm out of this. It's your baby. You wanted it. You got it. You take it from here, unless you want to change my standing orders." I could see David's pupils dilating. He never liked it when I grabbed the initiative like this.

"What do you think, Howard?" I asked. "Up to *you*."

"John, if he calls you again on this, tell him he'll have to talk with me. I'll tell the idiot to ram his demands where the sun doesn't shine. I'm tired of fucking around with Rick."

I excused myself and decided I'd drive over to the casino instead of going back to my office. I'd also turn off my cell phone. Tomorrow would be soon enough to let through the inevitable call I'd be getting from Rick.

At eight the next morning, the desk phone rang, then the cell phone.

"I know! I know!" Rick yelled in my ear. "You're telling me it's Howard this and Howard that. You can't say fuck all. You must think I go around with my head up my ass. I can smell what that Jew is up to. You'd better tell him that a million and a half is small change compared to what Players is going to lose if this injun' casino gets itself open."

I replied as Howard had instructed. "Rick, how can I make it any clearer? I'm not in the loop on this. I've got bosses to answer to, and I'm supposed to stay out of it. You need to talk to Howard. You've got to stop using me as a middleman. You know Howard's here. You know his number. I'm sorry. Nothing more I can say."

"Nothing!" he roared. "Shit! This ain't good. Nothing is what you guys'll be reduced to if you don't take care of this." With that he hung up.

Later in the afternoon, Rick called again, this time fooling me by dialing my cell phone directly.

"Okay," he began, "I've been on the phone all morning. You'll get your letter for a half million. A half million! For a half million they'll cover your butt. The way I see it, Howard's really taking us to the cleaners this time. Peanuts is what I call a half million. Peanuts!"

I couldn't resist replying, "Rick, sounds to me like you're getting a half million more to do what you were supposed to do in the first place. I really can't see what you're pissing and moaning about."

"It don't work that way, John," he shot back. "You tell that tight ass he's only got until the end of the week. After that, no deal. That clear? End of the week or no deal!"

"I can tell them, Rick. But that's all I can do. I keep telling you that I'm not part of this."

He went on as if he hadn't heard me. "You just tell the greedy Jew bastard. He'll smell the money, if he's smart."

I let Rick hang up without any further exchange, then called Howard in and briefed him on the reduced demand. For a few moments he was quiet, no doubt savoring Rick's ethnic slanders. "If he calls again, say *nothing*, nothing other than that he's to call *me*."

Rick did call again, sooner than I expected, once more directly to my cell phone.

"Well?" he asked.

"I mentioned our last conversation to Howard just a little while ago. Howard told me to tell you to call him."

"What else did he say?"

"Nothing. Absolutely nothing. You're to call him. Beginning of story. End of story. Want me to repeat it?"

"Call him? What the fuck does that mean?"

"It means, Rick, you call him to discuss this, not me. I've been trying to tell you that for a long time."

"Shit! All right," I heard him snap before the line went dead.

Within a week, the Players elite saw fit to call me into their sacred circle. I wasn't in the least surprised that they wanted me in a damage control capacity. In short, they had worked out an understanding with

Rick and wanted me to hound him until Edwin had produced the letter that would kill the Coushatta project.

As Rick explained to me one evening over dinner in Lake Charles, He had received his new contract. In addition to a hefty raise, Players would loan Rick $240,000. The amount of the raise was calculated to pay off the loan and its taxable impact over time and to line the appropriate pockets even more. As I added it up in my head, it seemed that the package came close enough to the half million to which Rick had conceded. (Later, the FBI would sum up the figures the same way.)

Once the ink had dried on his new arrangement with Players, however, Rick lapsed into day in, day out equivocation on the letter. At the same time, the law firm Players had hired to obstruct the Coushatta project was, from what I heard, getting nowhere in its efforts. Nor were Madamaba's hopes that his so-called mole, Mr. Langley, would alienate the tribe from the proposed casino bearing out.

Unless the letter was forthcoming, it looked like the Coushatta casino would erect itself as a force for Players to contend with. I started to apply the screws to Rick at every occasion, to the point where I was calling him at his office, at home, or on his cell phone. As often as I could manage it, I would tape the calls.

Rick finally assured me that the letter was, "even as we speak," being sent from the Governor's Council Office. It was water under the bridge, he insisted; I could tell Howard, Ed, David, and Madamba to relax, that the half million had been well spent. If we had any doubts, he'd fax a copy of the letter to Madamba.

I passed Rick's assurances on to Howard, who seemed to accept them at face value. I conducted as much of this matter as possible over the phone, making sure to record every conversation. Once I had recorded enough documentation, I labeled the tapes I had made and stored them in my safe at home. Then I told Howard that I thought I deserved a break, that I wanted to take Kathy to Rio de Janeiro for the world-famous annual Carnival.

The trip was remarkable only to the extent that Kathy and I managed to get through the festival without gnashing at each other verbally. Mostly, she remained in the hotel room, to keep out of the heat, which she found unbearable. At night, I'd let her fall asleep; then I'd go out on the town on my own.

I had lived in Rio on and off during the early eighties, when I was single and employed as a troubleshooter for oilfield service companies, and had participated with abandon in three previous festivals. Now I was content to walk the streets, watching the Bacchanalian madness that drove the five or so million visitors.

Being in Rio had always given me a "life is good" feeling. The people I had met here—both European expats and native Latin Americans—were open, friendly, and fun loving. And the city itself, its surroundings and its sights, were certainly exciting. There was Sugar Loaf Mountain, famous in its own right, even more famous as a result of the James Bond movie *Moonraker*. And there was Rio's best-known icon, Corcovado—the monolithic statue of Christ, presiding from the summit of another mountain, just east of the city, with arms protectively extended.

On my most interesting night during this, my fourth carnival in Rio, I wandered from nightclub to nightclub until I found one where the party atmosphere had amplified to an extreme. The odor of marijuana wafted out onto the sidewalk in dense clouds. Inside, dozens of stoned, crocked, shapely young women, both Latin and Caucasian, had fallen under the spell of the Samba and were undulating their sweat-sheened, naked bodies to the Bossa Nova beat. Several others were ripping their clothes off with abandon as they danced. Not to be outdone, several guys were also tossing their clothes overhead, pressing themselves through the living mass of the crowd out to the dance floor.

As I stood at the back of the crowd, watching and sipping the last of a Cubra Libra, I saw a young Caucasian man approaching me. I braced myself for what looked to be an odd encounter—his hair extended all the way down to the small of his back. He introduced himself to me—as I recall, his name was William McMillen—and straight out invited me to his house to "smoke some stuff." I tried to move away from him but was hemmed in by the crowd. Ignoring my unreceptive body language, he started explaining how, back in the early seventies, he had hitch hiked all the way down here from the states and had found construction work around a small town whose name translated to "region of the bean." He then asked me over to his house again. "I don't get a chance to party with real Americans very often down here."

"No thanks," I said and started forcing my way to the bar to order another drink. But right in front of me was a lovely Latin American girl, snaking her limbs as she tore at the buttons of her blouse. Quivering, looking into me with her warmly dark eyes, she asked me to dance. Knowing where this Lilith was trying to beckon, I declined and found a spot where I could stand, leaning against the bar, watching as she finished stripping. I'd be a liar if I said my thoughts weren't hot and steamy.

I returned to Lake Charles to learn that Governor Edwards hadn't produced the letter invalidating the Compact for the Coushatta casino. Worse from Players point of view, the Compact had been blessed at state level and was headed for certain federal approval. Rick was tight lipped. His new contract was in place and—given the nature of the agreement— there could be no going back on it. Obviously, the way I saw it, Players had been suckered into lunging at a bullshit carrot. Either we had been duped by an ingenious scam, or the Coushatta tribe had feathered Edwards' nest more abundantly. Whatever the case, Players was left utterly in the dark. Not a word of explanation. And we were plainly over a barrel. To raise any manner of fuss would be for us to bare our own culpability in patronage.

By an ironic twist, however, the Coushatta casino proved to be a golden goose for Players. When it came into operation, on the heals of a massive ad campaign, it generated a huge increase in customer traffic to the Lake Charles area. A substantial percentage of this traffic spilled over to the Players Lake Charles casino. In short order, the volume of patronage stressed the capacity of both casinos. As Players' bankroll bloated and its profits soared, we had every reason to be grateful to the Sovereign Coushatta Nation. Their up-front investment had dwarfed the half million we had dropped into Edwards' piggy bank. At the same time, our own returns at least matched theirs.

By an equally ironic twist, however, the coven within Players saw it as a failure on my part that the Coushatta casino had gotten off the ground. I had been given an assignment; I had fallen short on my performance; their protected market had been invaded; and to evade the stain I had fucked off to Rio. No matter that I had done everything—short of subjecting Rick to extended deep torture—to get the letter out of Edwin. No matter that Howard and his legal wizards should have known that competition could rear itself on the basis of federal regulations. No matter that we were actually reaping rather than starving.

As I grew accustomed to being ostracized from the executive circle, I started thinking of a saying about dogs: that it's the size of the fight in the dog that counts. So Howard, Ed, and David were thinking they could kick this dog with impunity? I thought. I'd tape as many conversations as I could. I'd then let my collection grow against the day I'd show them I was a dog out of their worst nightmare.

CHAPTER 13

BOTTOMLESS HOLE

*

In the two years since it had opened its first casino, in Metropolis, Illinois, Players had developed into a several hundred million dollar national company. In addition to Metropolis, there was the Lake Charles Casino, also under operation; in developmental stages were the Mesquite project (in its final phase of construction), the Evansville project (to which I was now assigned), and a casino project in Maryland Heights, Missouri, a western suburb of St. Louis, located on the Missouri River.

More conspicuous as indexes of corporate growth were the company's icons of self-importance and the self-indulgence of its upper management. Our executive brass, for example, no longer had to suffer the indignities of flying commercial. With two private jets, we were able to kick back in style as we shuttled back and forth, from coast to coast, aggravating dehydration by fueling up at the wet bars. And under the boot of the majority formed by the two Fishmans, Howard, and Perskie, our board voted quantum increases in top level executive salaries with each step Players took toward being a giant in the casino industry.

Not that I was short changed. I too was earning a fat paycheck. I was concerned, however, that Players was degenerating into a "too much chocolate" mentality and that it would be soon unable to support its bloated body of executives. Out of survival instinct, I began thinking about alternatives. If a suitable opportunity crossed my path, I would certainly consider jumping ship—taking my collection of tapes with me for good measure.

In fairness, I have to say that Howard was quick to pick up the trail laid by smart money. For a long time he had been trying to think of a way to get around the Louisiana law that restricted how long a riverboat casino is allowed to operate while it is dockside. Specifically, the law restricted gambling to short periods just before a riverboat embarked and just after it returned. Howard felt that this condition put a riverboat casino at a disadvantage in competition with a land-based casino, which could operate unburdened by the inconvenience of having the patrons disembark before they would be stranded on another cruise.

He called his strategic concept "near dockside." If he put another riverboat into operation at Lake Charles, one boat would be coming to dock just before the other boat was scheduled to leave. Patrons could get off the outgoing boat and board the incoming one, minimizing interruptions to their gambling.

What Howard needed to implement his "near dockside" scheme was, of course, another riverboat and another license. He was interested in looking into purchasing a riverboat casino that was close by, in New Orleans, and rumored to be on the auction block. Referred to as the Star Casino, this riverboat was operated by Showboat (which also owned a large casino in Atlantic City), with participation by a New Orleans business venturer, Louis Roussel. Well known for his success as an entrepreneur and for his ties with Edwin Edwards, Roussel had earned bad press by delivering campaign contributions to state senators through no less than the president of the Senate—who, in what proved to be a slapstick blunder, handed out some of the contributions right on the Senate floor.

According to the accounts that were going around, the management of the Star Casino tried to bypass the restrictions on dockside gambling by claiming that a mysterious submerged object endangered the riverboat on its cruises. Its constant presence at the dock roused the attention of the Orleans Parish District Attorney, Harry Connick, who started bearing down on the operation, to bring it into line with regulations.

Showboat and Roussel had ventures going elsewhere (in Australia, for example) and apparently didn't need the headaches that Connick was inflicting.

Howard saw these headaches as an opportunity for Players. I wasn't surprised that I was being summoned into this project to nurse along any arrangements that would be needed to ensure that Players would be able to obtain a second license for the riverboat to be added at Lake Charles. The way I saw it, these arrangements would probably include the blessing of Edwin and his family members and friends—attended, I didn't doubt, by hefty patronage costs.

When I received my new charge from Howard, I was staying at the Omni Hotel in Indianapolis, working on the Indiana license competition. Robert was with me and had flown Julie up for a relaxing weekend. The city had just received a foot of snow, with the forecast calling for more. After an enjoyable dinner and an even more enjoyable walk in the soft snowfall, we had come up to my room for a nightcap. It was approaching midnight when Howard called.

"Look, John, I've just struck a deal with Showboat to buy the Star Casino. I know you've got your hands full up there, but I really need you here. I'm sending the jet for you tomorrow morning. I want you to plant your ass in Baton Rouge and I want you to wring whatever you can out of Rick. Also, find out anything you can about how touchy-feely Edwin and his bunch are with Crown and Capri. Then see if you can baby-sit my deal with Star through Rick, Stephen, Edwin, or whoever else. I'm hearing a lot about this Crown and Capri project, and it's getting me nervous. Remember, we have some leverage with Rick. If Crown and Capri get going, his arrangement with us is history."

Crown and Capri (short for Isle of Capri) were two companies that had joined to propose a riverboat casino directly in our backyard—at a site in Westlake, just across the Calcasieu River channel from the Players Lake Charles operation. Crown and Capri were not, of course, aware of the arrangement between Rick and Players (by virtue of which Players had been assured of a protected market in Lake Charles). Rather, they were seizing on an opportunity offered by a recent decision by The Louisiana Supreme Court that the bill requiring a referendum for any new casino in Lake Charles was unconstitutional. That judgment, the way Crown and Capri saw it, amounted to an open door to newcomers into a blooming gaming market in Lake Charles.

Crown Casinos was, moreover, hardwired into the Edwards network in a way that looked impossible to beat. For one thing, Stephen's father in law had been a participant. As an additional assist, the owner of the San Francisco 49ers, Eddie Debartolo Jr., a close friend of Edwin's, had also joined Capri. Players didn't, I realized, have in-house friends of equal order. All we had is what Edwin's machine had been wringing out of us all along—money. Also, I knew that Howard thought our consulting arrangement with Rick gave us leverage. But I saw it differently. I saw two alternatives—either one of which would spell trouble for Players. Rick could jump ship if a better deal were dangled in front of him. (And I didn't think he'd bother to give us notice. We'd know of his attrition only when he'd start coming up short in helping us achieve our agendas.) Or Crown and Capri could outbid us for special favors. In either case, I saw myself in unfamiliar terrain, and I needed Players to define just what they expected of me.

"Might sound straightforward to you, Howard. But I need to know just what you want me to do. I mean, do you want me to negotiate arrangements, or do you want me to feel them up for what they want and report it back to you? Which do you want?"

"Find out what they'll take to make sure we get this second riverboat; keep them happy; but don't give them closure on anything. If they start demanding dollars, tell them to call me."

So that'll be it, I thought. I'm being slotted back into my traditional role of vice president of pandering. "I've got it," Howard," I said, looking at Robert and Julie with raised eyebrows.

Before he hung up, Howard asked, with a note of caution, "And *John*?"

"Yes, *sir*!" I replied, in the manner of a private answering to a hard-ass drill instructor. For Robert and Julie's amusement I snapped my heals together.

"John, I don't want anyone fucking up this deal. I want this one, John. I want my second boat in Lake Charles. Call me and put me in the loop as soon as possible."

"Sounds fascinating," Robert said after I had hung up.

"Howard's actually bought the Star Casino, before getting an imprimatur from the clan with the belly potent," I said.

"The appetite that doth grow with the eating," Julie added, expanding her hands out from her stomach.

Robert started whirling himself about the floor, singing, "Start up Whirlwind of Cash Two" and making toward Julie, with open arms, inviting her to dance.

But Julie wasn't inclined. She held up her hands to ward off Robert. "No way I want in on this. I'll sit it out, thank you. If they think they can get a second license out of the gaming commission, they're dreaming their wildest dream. The commission is on record as saying they won't grant a second one to any company—period."

Robert continued dancing, spinning himself about, singing, "Whirlwind of Cash. Oh, Whirlwind of Cash! With just one spin, the rules do crash."

As Julie sat herself on the bed and belted down her drink, a grimace crossing her face, I charged into Robert with a block that knocked him to the bed beside Julie. Slightly crocked from our evening out, the three of us lay there laughing, enjoying each other's company.

We were in the mood for fun. Noticing that the time was well past midnight, I thought it would be a great lark to prime the system by calling Rick.

"Hang around, you two," I said. "I'll give Rick about a half hour before he's calling me back with word from Stephen. You know the drill. 'This is bad. *They've* got serious problems with this. *You* guys at Players'll have to come with something fast.'"

It actually took less than thirty minutes. And there were problems—the series of alarms that I expected. Stephen was unhappy—for reasons Rick didn't see fit to explain. He'd be waiting for the Players jet at the Baton Rouge airport tomorrow morning, and he'd be taking me straight to a meeting over lunch with Stephen. It didn't sound like it would be a cordial get together. I did, however, sense a difference in Rick's tone. He didn't sound anxious enough. I figured he was fronting a take it or leave it attitude, to make us think that if we didn't ante up to satisfaction Crown and Capri would.

I told Robert and Julie to hit the sack, that I'd have to be up early. Robert pulled Julie up from the bed and spun her toward the door. She screamed, laughing, as he crooned, "Whirlwind of Cash, Whirlwind of Cash, funneling into the Edwards' stash."

On the flight down to Baton Rouge, I learned that Players was as shoddy in its attention to aircraft maintenance as it was in its management of casinos. Julie had taken advantage of available space—the private jet had been sent solely for me—and was sitting beside me. We were enjoying a drink, with the song "I'm so Tired" playing on the stereo. "Miss him, miss him," we heard over the speakers; then buzzers started sounding. Abruptly, the plane lost altitude; the oxygen masks dropped; and I felt my ears pop.

"What the hell!" Julie yelled, grabbing my arm first, then letting go and clasping her hands to her own ears.

"We've lost cabin pressure!" one of the pilots yelled back to us. As I felt the plane dropping like a rock, I saw that the speed indicator was showing 250 knots. The plane's normal cruising speed was over 400 knots.

"Shit! We're going down!" I yelled back at the pilot.

Eyes wide, Julie looked at me, too frightened to speak. Then the plane started to climb slowly.

"What's up?" I yelled up to the pilots.

"We're under control now," replied the same pilot who had just said we had lost pressure.

As I felt the cabin pressure up, I said to Julie, "I don't know about you, but I hate flying without a parachute. Makes me feel like I'm naked."

"Up yours," she replied, half laughing, obviously relieved. "I hate flying with you. You're crazy. Nuts."

The pilots explained that this incident had occurred three times in one week and that the autolight on one of the engines had also been malfunctioning. They had been yelling for corrective maintenance all week. With the faults not yet repaired, we were flying out of compliance with FAA regulations—that is, we were now in the air illegally.

As it happened, it was a short lunch. Rick drove me straight to the restaurant, saying very little along the way. We took our table and waited for Stephen, who arrived within minutes. Point blank, Stephen told me, "That fuckhead Goldberg's got it wrong. He won't be able to buy the Star. He doesn't have a deal."

I remembered Stephen's shock tactics from my first meeting with him and knew to go along with him. "I see," I replied. "I just got back from Indiana and have been involved in what we're doing up there. I'm going to need to talk to Howard to see what's going on with this deal. Last I heard he had it well in hand. But things may have changed. I'll have to ask him. Not much more I can say."

"You do that," Stephen said in an even tone. "Now let's eat. I'm hungry." As he looked at the menu, I noted the fire in his eyes, the same predatory look I had seen at the end of our first meeting. Maybe, I thought, he's seeing us a carcass that regenerates its flesh every time he gluts on us.

"Me too. Let's eat," I said, happy that this discussion was dead for now.

A few days later, my phone rang as I was getting out of the shower. Good ol' Rick, I thought.

"Look, John," he said, "I've been talking to Stephen some more. But I need to know what's up with Howard. You talked to him at all since yesterday?"

Actually, I had talked with Howard the previous evening. He had insisted that that he had a firm lock on a deal on the Star riverboat. More interesting, he had talked with Stephen and had offered him a hefty retainer, which he had accepted. But I didn't want to do the talking here. I figured that Stephen had filled Rick in, and I wanted Rick's voice recorded as much as possible. "No," I lied. "I couldn't get Howard, Rick. Any chance you can save me the trouble of the call? You know anything that I should know at this point?"

"A few things," Rick answered and then sang like a bird. He explained in full that Players had retained Stephen. He added that Howard had agreed not to cancel the arrangement with him if Crown and Capri got permission to move to Lake Charles. He then piped in an additional detail as the cassette tape turned.

"Howard was pretty reasonable. But Stephen still's not happy. You want the second riverboat; you want to expand Lake Charles; you want a second license out of the commission. You want, you want, you want. They need more out of this. They want you to give me seventy-five cents a passenger. Seventy-five cents from the get go. Stephen wants to know something soon. Not much time, John."

By now I knew my script cold. "Rick, you know I don't make these decisions. I'll talk to Howard and have him get back to you."

"He'd better get back fast—"

"I know, Rick. There's not much time."

I was hoping that I had kicked off what would become to be an extended flurry of calls, from me to Howard, from me to Rick, then from Rick back to me, after he had consulted Stephen. I wasn't disappointed. I even managed to set up a few conference calls between the three of us.

At times, the exchanges got superheated, with Howard and Rick trading profanities that would have had Kathy taking notes. In the end, Howard actually talked Rick into wringing thirty-seven and a half cents per passenger from Bill Woodward, to be paid from his portion of the head fees. The way Howard reasoned it, Stephen was already getting $180,000 from his new retainer. Through bonuses to be conveyed to Rick down the line, Players would bring the moneys paid to a rough equivalent of the seventy-five cents per head that "they" had originally asked for. As I expected, Rick had to call Stephen before he could give us his okay. And, as I also anticipated, Stephen agreed with extreme reluctance. He could, Rick said, live with the new arrangement.

Though Howard was happy with this new understanding—assured that it was good enough to buy off any hurdles that Edwin or Stephen could put in Players' way—I wasn't in the comfort zone. Whenever I heard

Rick qualify an agreement from Stephen with "He says he can live with it," I was sure that Stephen, through his medium Rick, would be coming back for more. Then Howard would, I knew, pull me off any real assignment I had in hand and put me back on point. Out of my need for a paycheck, I'd have to play along; but I'd also cover my butt as best I could against a possible day of reckoning.

With no further requests from Rick, we were able to present our proposal for the Lake Charles expansion to the Louisiana Riverboat Gaming Commission. Our total budget, we explained, would be in the order of eighty-two million dollars—mainly covering purchase of the second riverboat and design and construction of a new thirty-room hotel, of two five-hundred car parking garages, and of a forty thousand square foot entertainment docking barge. Merv Griffin lent his presence by proxy, through a slick videotape in which he gave a project overview. Whether due to our impressive dog and pony show or to Edwin's undercraft, the commission was pleased. Within a week (specifically on February 8, 1995), it gave us a precedent-setting second approval.

In short order, Players's management went into what we called "chickenshit" mode in the military: they lapsed into power grabbing, ego-satisfying tactics that had no application to winning the war, so to speak. As an inevitable consequence, the Lake Charles expansion rapidly degenerated toward clusterfuck status.

As the initial blunder, Howard and David handed control of the project to the self-styled construction management guru, Steve Labov. In time, his refusal to recognize that Napoleonic law (which saw oral contracts as binding) applied in Louisiana would hideously snarl our contracting arrangements. Moreover, it wasn't hard to see that Labov's fees were bloated and that he was loading the project with personnel from his Atlantic City office. From what I was able to determine, they didn't perform any genuinely billable functions other than running up expenses and drinking to excess each night at the casino.

Several of my recommendations for contracting did prevail, enough, anyway, to give the impression that we were distributing project benefits locally. Architectural work for the landside improvement, for the building to be positioned on the entertainment docking barge, and for marine aspects was awarded to small firms located in the Lake Charles area or in New Orleans. Construction would also be local, and it would be strictly union.

Having developed a best practice from a lesson learned, Ken Hagan did what he had to make sure he got the contract to build the entertainment barge. First, he told Labov that it would be suicidal to go outside the immediate area. If that were done, Ken said, the forty thousand square foot barge would need to be transported across the Gulf of Mexico, where it would break up in even moderate seas. A more commonsense alternative, he explained, was to build the barge close by, capitalizing also on the goodwill benefit of hiring local. Accordingly, he rented an extensive plot on the Calcasieu River, a few miles south of Lake Charles. It was a proposition that even Players recognized as irresistible.

As for David and his tendency toward redundant effort, he first retained the same Las Vegas architectural firm—headed by Ken Murphy (not to be confused with the Captain Ken Murphy who headed Player's Marine Operations Department)—he had used to burden the Mesquite project with his ego-driven enhancements. In this case, David charged Murphy's group with looking after what he called "the aesthetics." With devoted support from Scott Cooper, David then brandished this term about in its full-blown ambiguity. No one knew what the hell he meant; nor did anyone dare to ask. But at least he sensed the confusion and tried to clear it up. To make his notions tangible, he had Ken Murphy build a small scale-model of his aesthetically enhanced barge out of balsa wood. When a question arose about the design, he'd hold up the Lilliputian model and say, "Just make it look like that. Is that too much to ask?" We all knew that it was indeed too much to ask him to get it through his head that construction should proceed from competently drafted, detailed blueprints.

As the project went along, David seemed to fixate more and more on the entertainment barge, which had been contracted to a local architect, Bob Kleinschmidt. From our back row seats, Ken and I could see Bob wince and jolt every time David decreed another "enhancement." First, prompted by his Las Vegas designer and supported by a benignly smiling Cooper, David added a second story to the original single-story design. Next, it was a huge atrium and dome to be painted like the sky. Then came animatronic birds, a pirate, redwood-scale fake trees, and wood millwork and brass.

Ken and I had to sympathize with Bob as he watched the limb-by-limb mutilation of the design. As for budget, the total estimated cost had been conservative—based on a cost of $150 per square foot for a forty thousand square foot, single-story facility. That there was no margin for David's extravagance was evident to everyone in the room other than David and his cronies. Every time Bob appealed to budget reality, David stood, frowning furiously at him. As if on cue, David's minions would frown likewise. I remember Ken saying, "It's an in-house production of 'Village of the Damned.'"

But Ken was far from amused. The prospect of trying to keep to cost and schedule was enough to point him toward Merv's Bar and Grill, to run its inventory dry. As he put it, "You tell me. How in fucking hell am I supposed to build something when I don't know what I'm supposed to build?"

"At least you're the type of horse that has sense enough to drink," I replied.

My own frustrations with David and his crew came to a head one night when he, Labov, and I were having dinner. The two of them were so smug that I felt I had every right to beat the shit out of them, preferably both at once. I had no illusions about how they'd pass the blame when their excesses came out in the wash. I was pretty sure that I'd ultimately be held responsible for the cost effectiveness of the project work; and I had already gotten wind of comments suggesting that I'd be scapegoated if costs got wildly out of hand. I had to say something now, for the record. I had to hit David square between the eyes with a hard-core picture of reality.

I waited until Labov excused himself to go to the men's room. "David, I have some concerns," I began, politely. "I'd appreciate if you'd listen a moment."

David looked at me quizzically and then back to his plate. For a moment, he dabbled at his lips with his napkin. Then he carefully placed the napkin in his lap. "Concerns, John? What about? I don't like thinking that you're unhappy with us."

I did my best to lay it out cold for him, to make him see that moving walls around willy-nilly meant you had to re-engineer the structure. I tried to get him to see that his game of musical design changes would expand the scope of work and escalate costs. But he turned deaf ears.

As Labov approached the table, David looked toward him, back at me, and sealed my despair. "Look, John, I hear you. When you get more experience under your belt, like Steve here has, you'll have a better understanding of what you're talking about."

At one of the last design meetings, my frustrations escalated into raw anger as I overheard an explanation of a scheme that struck me as being beyond farce. David's enhancements had placed such a load on the barge that the draught would exceed the available depth at the docking site. Players had, from what I was hearing, agreed to a plan to dredge out the lake bottom at the docking site, to increase its depth. A dredging barge was to be built specifically for this purpose. A tugboat would be used to push the barge around the docking site while it scooped up a load of toxin-rich bottom sediment. Then the tug would move the barge out to the middle of the lake, where the load would be dumped into a huge hole that had been excavated years ago, to provide landfill for construction of the civic center. The load deposited, the tug would push the barge back to the docking site for another round of dredging.

Openly, Players was advocating an operation that would violate some of the most shark-toothed federal and state regulations. Stupidly, the company was inviting the glare of three of the most dreaded watchdog agencies: the Federal Environmental Protection Agency, the state Department of Environmental Quality, and the U.S. Coast Guard.

To dredge up the lake's bottom sediment would be to stir up deadly toxins (settled out long ago from effluents released from chemical plants) and suspend them in the brackish water flowing through the lake. The lower Calcasieu River would receive the polluted outflow and would carry it down to the estuary and into the Gulf. If Players were caught, implicated executives would face both civil and criminal charges. For starters, we could each expect a fine of one hundred thousand dollars and a one-year jail term.

Outside, in the parking lot, I cornered Ken. "We know each other, Ken. Tell me what the hell you guys think you're doing. You think that the bottom of this lake is ours to play with?"

For a moment he stood quietly; he knew my point was well taken. Then, in a subdued voice, he said, "Well, John, no one'll know what we're doing. We're going to do it at night. Once we sink it all in that hole, no one'll know any better."

"There are two people right here who know better—you and me, Ken," I said. "I don't know all the rules about this, but I'll tell you one thing—I'm not involved, not at all. You're on your own on this one, Ken." Then I turned and headed for Merv's, where I knew Ken Hagan was waiting for me.

On my way, I did a sit rep on how precarious my situation in Players had become. In its desperate enterprise to obtain its second gambling license, Players had nearly advertised its dubious connections with Edwards. It wouldn't surprise me if we soon found ourselves ringed by the eyes and ears of no less than the FBI.

And to what avail? Despite the arrangements with Rick, we'd be having competition, the Isle of Capri, on our own turf. What's more, from here on we'd find ourselves locked with the Isle of Capri in a bizarre contest that neither of us could win. Edwards would probably see to it that his delegates would work us—first one, then the other—to his own ever-abounding advantage. I could hear a great sucking sound draining the whirlwind of cash.

In Merv's, Ken pushed out a chair from his table. "John, Merv's been calling your name for a good half hour now."

"I can't hear it," I answered. "My brain is screaming too loud for a drink."

CHAPTER 14

DRY HOLE

✸

With Players offering the Lakes Charles project as an open target, I felt driven by a "get out of Dodge" impulse; but I had no place to go, no solid leads to pursue. In Louisiana, Players had already obtained two gambling licenses. Although the commission would soon be granting licenses for the Shreveport area, for Players to take on a new project anywhere in Louisiana would be to ask the commission to heap one precedent upon another. To facilitate a third license, Stephen and Edwin would, I was sure, lure Players even farther onto a limb that was almost ready to snap. It almost made me laugh to think of Players dropping into an FBI office, right through its roof, maybe onto opened files marked "Players Patronage."

I could think of only one possible way of getting away from Lake Charles, a dubious opportunity at best. In New Orleans, the River City Casino, which berthed two riverboats (each owned by a separate participant), had filed for bankruptcy, leaving both its employees and its vendors without paychecks. For an update, I called my friend Bobby Heitmeier, who had given me the tip that had led to my meeting the Reverend in Belize. As far as Bobby knew, the two riverboats were still up for grabs. He suggested that I drive over to "N'Awlins" and join him for a Saints game.

I cleared my mission with Howard and called Bobby back to accept his invitation. We'd be sitting, he told me, in his skybox, in "The Headliner's Club," which was reserved for members and guests who had earned notoriety by being defamed on the front page of the New Orleans *Times Picayune*. "I'm sure you all at Players know what I mean," he commented, laughing sarcastically. "From the hear tell that comes my way, it won't be long before you guys are shredding and burning." He had obviously caught wind of proceedings within Players, and I sure as hell knew what he meant. Lake Charles would turn into a media circus overnight if the regulatory agencies got wind of the dredging or if the FBI were alerted to Players' relations with Rick, Stephen, and Edwin. I could then expect management to hike the public relations function to me and head straight for the showers, leaving me exposed to the blitz.

After checking in at the Royal Sonesta on Bourbon Street, I met Bobby at the Superdome. I was happy to see him. We were both good sports and always enjoyed ribbing each other. In front of the door to the club, he stopped and said, "Don't know if I can get you in, John. You don't have a scandal sheet. You need the right credentials here."

Once we had settled into our seats, I looked out over the field. Then a commotion in one of the other skyboxes, about thirty yards to the left of us, caught my attention. I noticed that the box was appointed palatially and that several people were filing into it. The last to enter were Edwin and Stephen Edwards.

"That's the governor's box," Bobby pointed out.

"I gathered," I said, noticing that nearly the entire stadium was now focused on Edwin's party.

"He's really something, that Stephen," I said, more to myself than Bobby.

His head jerked in my direction. "You know Stephen?"

"I'm getting to," I answered, "pretty well, in fact."

When the Saints had fallen hopelessly behind before the end of the first quarter, Bobby began looking away from the field below and toward the walkway that ringed the Superdome.

"Getting restless?" I asked.

"Dull game, as usual. Warm beer, as usual," he answered. "Let's stretch our legs and meet some of the people who've made this club what it is today."

As soon as we got out on the walkway, we heard a voice from behind calling, "Hey, Bobby."

Bobby turned around and then turned back quickly. "Wayne Ray. Not exactly someone I want to rub elbows with even here. But no way out now."

We turned to meet Wayne. Tall and thin, dressed in jeans and cowboy boots, and with a scowl on his weathered face, he looked like the classic bad guy in a silent western.

"Wayne, this is John," Bobby said. "John's with Players in Lake Charles. He's here looking at the River City boats. Players might want to bring one of them up to Shreveport."

If I could have done it without making a scene, I would have kicked Bobby in the ass. I had mentioned Players' interest to him, but as a "keep it between us" tidbit.

"Just a cat we're kicking around," I said, extending my hand to Wayne and then looking at Bobby, hoping he'd get my drift. Whether he did or not, it was plain to me, by the way he was shuffling his feet, that he wanted to avoid this Wayne like a bad habit.

"Shreveport's where I'd be thinking, if I were you," Wayne said. He looked around a moment and then stepped closer to me. "I can help you up there. I know who Edwards is giving the next license to. I know him real good. You interested, John?"

"Sure," I replied.

Bobby tuned away from us and said, "I'm not hearing any of this."

Laughing as if he was taking too much enjoyment in a dirty joke, Wayne said, "Bobby here likes us to think he hears no evil. Anyway, John, the next license for Shreveport goes to Ed Powell. You know, the Superdome Commissioner? Bobby, you know Ed."

Bobby stepped farther away and ignored Wayne's statement.

"You can take that to the bank, man," Wayne continued. "I know it for a stone cold fact."

"You're that sure?" I asked.

Wayne leaned toward me. He smelled like stale alcohol and old cigarettes. "Sure as the bear shits in the woods. Look, I'm going to give you my number. You call me tomorrow, first thing. I'll set you up with Ed."

He then stepped back, allowing me a breath of fresher air. He wrote his number on a book of matches and handed it to me. "Got to get back to my friends. I'll be waiting for your call. Enjoy the game, Bobby."

Once Wayne was out of earshot, I asked Bobby, "Who was that?"

"Not anyone I was hoping to run into," he answered.

"Really? Anything more to his stink than booze and smokes?"

"Booze and smokes are the least of it, John. You want to deal with him, you be careful. You be real careful."

"You think he really knows about the license?"

"I wouldn't doubt it. I hear he's close to Edwards—that they have what you could call a relationship. I also heard that he took a fall for Edwards and wound up doing time. Word is that Edwin's been taking care of him ever since he got out. As I say, that's what I hear. It's more than I want to know."

The next morning, I sat over a cup of coffee on the balcony of my hotel room, looking down on Bourbon Street and mulling over whether I should call Wayne Ray. If he could connect me with Ed Powell, and if Powell was in fact in line for the next Shreveport license, it might be worth it to make the contact. Wayne's shady reputation aside, factors particular to Shreveport, on the one hand, and to River City, on the other, were linked in a way that offered me a chance to cut my association with Lake Charles.

Although Shreveport already hosted three casinos, I figured that there was margin for an additional casino to operate profitably and that the infusion of new jobs and contracts into the area would be welcome benefits. Back in New Orleans, moreover, one of the eyesore issues regarding the River City bankruptcy was the unpaid vendors. If Players were to buy at least one of the River City boats, the vendors could be paid at least partially.

The more I thought about it, the more calling Wayne recommended itself. But I thought it would be best to check with Howard first. Presently, he was in Atlantic City; and he wouldn't be coming into his office until a few hours. I'd call, leave a message for him to call back, and then relax, enjoying the view and reading this morning's *Times Picayune*. It would be interesting to see if anyone new had qualified for membership in "The Headliner's Club".

Howard returned my call in less than two hours. First, I told him about Wayne Ray and his connection with Ed Powell. At the outset, Howard wanted nothing to do with either. Wayne, he felt, would be another mallard in our flock. And Ed would no doubt want to come aboard the enterprise as a partner. Howard didn't think there would be enough money to go around.

Then I covered the points that I thought supported moving one of the River City boats to Shreveport. But I was concerned that the sticking point would be obtaining a third license. "That's where we need Ed," I explained. "The way I see it, we're in with a chance, especially if he's in line for a dose of grace from Edwin."

Howard agreed reluctantly. "If we're stuck with this Powell, we might have to string along with him, for now anyway. So all right. Call Wayne. But get by him fast. He's your door to Powell. Nothing more. And don't commit to anything with Powell. Leave that to me if we come to it."

I had, then, my standing orders spelled out clearly. For now, at least, I could dismiss Lake Charles as a bad dream.

I called Wayne and had no trouble keeping the conversation brief. He had been busy in his own camp. Ed Powell was interested in getting together with me. If I came up to Shreveport, Wayne explained, I'd find Ed at his dealership almost any day of the week. But I should let him know when I was coming. I told Wayne I'd be up early in the morning two days from now, asked him to pass on to Ed that I'd meet him at his dealership, and told him to let me know if that was inconvenient for Ed.

I arrived early, before Ed, and sat in his office, looking through the latest issue of *People*. I was relieved to see that no one from Players had made it into the magazine's widely read crime section.

As I was reading about upcoming movies, I heard a deep voiced "John" from the reception area and looked up to see Ed Powell. He had the appearance of a well-conditioned, aristocratic rancher. He was tall and lean, with short white hair, and was wearing jeans and western boots. He reminded me of George Jones—though he was better looking and in better health.

He also had an engaging openness about him. He sat on the front edge of his desk rather than behind it and straightforwardly asked, "Players is serious about buying one of the River City boats and moving it here?"

"We're looking at it," I answered. "But we have a few concerns. We thought talking to you might help shake out the license issue. It'd be our third from the commission and would mean that Players alone would hold twenty percent of the entire number of casino licenses in Louisiana. So getting the license might be a problem, even though we think our proposal would fix more problems than it would create."

He stood up from his desk and took one of the guest chairs next to me. "You might have a licensing problem on your own, but not if you were with me. The next license here is coming my way. I have Edwin's word on that. The first round I was in with a group called Golden Horseshoe. But we had too many preferables in front of us, if you know what I mean. Edwin told me he couldn't help me the first round, but he committed solid to me for the second. I trust Edwin when he says he's committed."

"How would you feel about working with Players?" I asked.

"What I want to do is set up a meeting at Edwin's, at the mansion," he said. "But I need to be clear about this. It'll be you, anyone you want from Players, Edwin, and me. No one else. I deal as directly as I can with Edwin. I need to know you understand that, John. It's important to me."

I thought of what Howard had said about not wanting any more mallards; I thought of the patronage load on the Lake Charles operation; and I assured Ed I understood him loud and clear.

"Pleasure to have you visit, John," Ed said, making it clear that he had to get back to his workday. "I'll let you know about the meeting soon as I clear it with Edwin."

That afternoon, back at the Royal Sonesta, I called Howard in At-lantic City and updated him. He was still dubious about getting into bed with Ed Powell but was excited about meeting Edwin. I reminded him again that we were going to be asking the commission for a double prece-dent if we proceeded and that Edwin's commitment to Ed offered us our best chance. He agreed that we should pursue it, though with reluctance. I was to let him know when the meeting would be on; and I was to tell Ed that he'd be bringing Steve Perskie along.

Before getting ready for dinner, I put myself through my daily physi-cal training drill. I had neglected my PT this morning and was feeling "fallen to pot." As a measure of self-punishment, I snapped off an extra ten reps in each set of push-ups and sit-ups. Then, feeling energized with the weight of Lake Charles lifting, I added ten more reps. I felt great as I headed for the shower.

But the phone rang as I was turning on the hot water. For a mo-ment, I considered not answering. I was sure it was Kathy, and I didn't want her deflating my mood. Since we had come together briefly during the near perfect storm we had survived with Robert and Julie, she had slipped steadily downhill, into chronic depression and fits of rage. That my home life had become a domestic version of near hell—relieved only by the relationships I had with Derek and Macie—was something I could also lay on Players' doorstep. As a stay-at-home housewife, Kathy had little insight into the internecine crap that had become SOP in the com-pany. And I found it nearly impossible to explain that I felt I had a family to support, that I couldn't simply bolt the Players fold in a heartbeat.

I had no doubt, moreover, that the strains on me—ranging from going jobless to going to jail—made me less than an ideal companion. Nor did it help that Howard was thinking of moving me to Atlantic City. The rationale behind the game of musical locations that large corpora-tions like to play with employees was unfathomable to Kathy. As the mother of a family, she harbored a protective instinct and saw Players as disruptive, diabolically so. I could see that she felt isolated from me and the world in which I moved.

I let the phone ring until it stopped and the message light began to blink. Then I lifted the receiver and dialed in the retrieval code. It wasn't Kathy. Rather, it was Ed Powell, letting me know that Edwin would be expecting us around mid morning, two days from now, and reminding me that attendance was to be strictly limited.

As I drove around behind the mansion and down the ramp to the door to the elevator, I sensed that this meeting would indeed involve conversations of influence. Outside, there was only one car. By its dealer tag, I recognized it as Ed's. Howard and Perskie, I knew, would be met at the airport by one of Player's local attorneys, Billy Broadhurst, who'd drive them here and wait outside.

I felt an eerie silence as I stepped out of the elevator onto the first floor. The last time I had been here, the mansion had been alive with members of the Edwards family, dinner guests, and staff. Now, from what I could see or hear, the place seemed deserted. Even Sid Moreland's post outside the office was unmanned. I felt lonely and so went to find the stuffed bear with the plastic tongue.

Within moments I heard a door open down the corridor to Edwin's office and then footsteps echoing. Ed Powell walked into the foyer. "Good to see you, John," he said, walking straight up to me and reaching out his hand. "Just been in with Edwin a moment. I thought I heard someone out here."

I told him that I had come out early, to re-acquaint myself with the feel of the place, and that I was expecting Howard and Perskie soon.

"Steve Perskie, I think it was," he commented, showing his salesman's memory for names.

Just then, the elevator door opened, and Howard approached us, with Perskie trailing behind, looking awed by the surroundings. Howard looked full of confidence and anticipation. I introduced Ed, and Howard turned on the charm I knew he could assume to disarm his adversary. We chatted for a few minutes; then Ed came to the point that was uppermost in his mind. Looking at Howard, Perskie, and me, he said, "I can't wait to get started here. I'm going to enjoy being a partner with you guys."

Howard's congenial exterior evaporated, and his face went serious. Ed looked at him for a moment before saying, "Let's go see the governor. He's waiting."

Howard stood aside to let Ed walk ahead and then turned to me, tilted his head down, and looked at me over his wire rim glasses. Here goes, I thought.

Edwin was sitting behind his desk. As we entered, he stood and extended his hand to welcome us. Ed Powell started toward Edwin, but Howard walked by him, straight up to the governor, and said, "Howard Goldberg, Governor. Pleased to make your acquaintance."

As he introduced Perskie, I watched Edwin's eyes shift for a moment toward Ed and then back to Howard.

"Gentlemen, have a seat," Edwin said.

Howard took a chair in front of the governor, to his left; Perskie sat down directly in front of him; I took the seat to the left of Perskie. Ed walked around behind Edwin's desk and sat in the corner of the office, to the right of Edwin.

With no prompt from the governor, Howard took the floor and summarized the essentials of the Players proposal, emphasizing that the project would create jobs and contracts in the Shreveport area and would help pay off the out-of-pocket vendors in New Orleans. The issue of a third license was sensitive, he realized, but he thought that the package offered needed advantages.

Edwin looked around the room, first at Howard, then at each of us in turn. His silence was maddening. I could hear the clock on the wall ticking and could see Perskie fidgeting all over his seat. Howard sat calmly, his eyes on Edwin. He had the tact to know that he had made his points and that the next turn to speak belonged to the governor.

"Gentlemen," Edwin announced, with an emphasis that sent a spasm through Perskie, "there are those who say that you have to be a friend or an associate of mine to get things done here. I tell you, gentlemen, that is *not* true. But I will tell you that it will not hurt your cause to have associations with the good and upstanding businessmen of this state."

Edwin hesitated a moment and then made a gesture that puzzled me momentarily. With his elbows resting on his desk, he drew his left hand into a fist and cupped his right hand over it. He twisted his fist and the palm of his hand against each other. Then he withdrew his fist and extended his left index finger against the palm of his right hand. With his index finger screened, he pointed it for a split second toward Ed Powell. Though Ed couldn't see the gesture, it was plainly visible to Howard, Perskie, and me.

Edwin rose and graciously thanked us for our time. Howard stood, offered his hand, and asked him to seriously weigh the proposal.

"I certainly will," Edwin replied. "You can count on it. Thank you again for coming all the way here, and have a safe flight home."

Once we were out in the hall, I asked Howard if he had seen Edwin's gesture. "See what?" he snapped back at me. "I didn't see anything— anything at all." Looking straight ahead, he stepped up his pace. A few seconds later, he peered at me over his wire framed glasses.

I returned to the Royal Sonesta, to wait for a follow up call from Rick, specifying the new arrangements that would be needed to facilitate our Shreveport proposal. This time, I was hoping to hear his script. It would mean that I could keep myself away from Lake Charles for the time being.

But several days passed with no call, and I felt the onset of a *something's gone wrong* intuition. It turned to panic with the realization that Lake Charles would be my only option if the Shreveport scheme went dry.

I called Howard, and what he had to say sounded like a sentence. He had made a cash offer on one of the River City boats, intending to move it to Shreveport, but he had excluded Ed Powell, who got openly upset in response. The Players offer, in turn, had been refused. Instead, River City sold to the Isle of Capri, which, of course, was associated with Eddie DeBartolo, a close friend of Edwin's.

That River City had chosen the Isle of Capri made little business sense to me. But then I knew that the old saying "the business of business is business" would, in Louisiana, be more aptly put as "the business of business is politics." The way it looked to me, the sale had been made to the contender that was best connected to get itself licensed and not necessarily to the group that had made the best financial offer.

I also felt that Edwin had possibly given Players a lesson in the art of manipulation—that maybe in the meeting in his office, he had sensed Howard's motive to cut Ed Powell out of the Players venture. He had labored the point that we should associate with reputable local businessmen; and the intent of his screened gesture could have been to dupe Howard into thinking that he wanted Players to shun Ed. The more I thought about it, the more I realized how difficult it was to decode your way to the inner Edwin Edwards.

I was almost expecting to hear Howard say, "Elementary, my dear Brotherton." But I think he was as dazzled as I was by Edwin's footwork. I also felt chastened. Back on the night I first arrived in Lake Charles, after I had cleared my hurdles in the bar of the old Downtowner, I thought that my experience on the ground in Louisiana and Texas gave me an upper hand in the game of southern politics. Now I could see that I was, at best, a little boy lost.

Before packing it at the Royal Sonesta, I wanted to call Bobby and thank him for the Saints game. He was sorry to hear that the Shreveport scheme had fallen through. "But look at the sun also rises aspect," he advised. "I don't see you smeared all over the front page yet."

I knew he was trying to console me. But his remark made me think of a sunset I had seen years ago, When I first arrived in Lake Charles. Moments before, I had seen a body lying beside a wrecked, burned out white car, along the exit to Lake Charles. I hadn't thought it was remarkable then, but I now recalled that the interior of the car was blood red.

CHAPTER 15

The Austin Protocol

＊

There were two things I wanted to do as soon as I got back to Lake Charles. First, I'd drive out to the new LeeVac shipyard and gather intelligence on the progress of the barge that was being constructed, to allow Players' Marine Operations Department to conduct its covert dredging runs. Then I'd prep the two rooms I had reserved at the Downtowner. I had requested adjoining rooms, both at the eastern end, with a clear view of Lake Charles. From this post, I'd be able to watch the illegal operation.

My directions to the new LeeVac yard, which was located along the Mermentau River, led me along a network of back roads, deep into the bayou hinterland that bordered the river. The brooding, primordial black water swamps edging out into shadow lands from either side of the dirt road took me back to my oilfield days. I remembered restless nights sleeping on floating barge accommodations, worried that a cottonmouth might slip under the sheets with me.

I could tell I was approaching the old shipyard. Abandoned hulls of boats and barges of all sizes lay ghost like, discarded and rusting, all along the entrance road. As I neared the river dock, I could see a flurry of activity around a single barge in the working dry dock. This would be the instrument of the "night run." It looked to be about fifty feet long and thirty-five feet wide.

At that size, it might not be as conspicuous as the Loch Ness monster in someone's back yard swimming pool; but I couldn't see how anyone could expect it to be covert, even at night—especially considering that it would be pushed back and forth by a tugboat. Far from being an out-of-the-way backwater, Lake Charles was the site of the Lake Charles Industrial Port, the fourteenth largest foreign shipping port in the United States. The Calcasieu River, which flowed into and out of the lake, was designated as a US Navigable Waterway, tied into the U.S. Intercoastal Waterway System.

I parked my car, walked over to the construction site, and looked around for Captain Ken Murphy. He was on the deck, supervising the twenty-five or so welders that were at work. He saw me, waved, and walked down the gangplank.

"Hey, buddy, so what's up?" I asked as he approached. "What do you call this thing?"

He looked back at the barge and then leaned over, put two fingers to his mouth, and spit his chew of tobacco at least fifteen feet. "Well, this is it, our dredging barge," he said. "We'll be done on 'er by this afternoon. Tonight, she loses her cherry. Follow me. I want to show you something. You're gonna love it."

Ken took me around to the front of the barge. The front steel plate had been cut open just under the waterline. On the bottom, several steel teeth had been welded into place. The front looked like a dinosaur's jaw. Running along the length of the inside bottom plate of the barge were several long pipes that ended at the teeth, where they were cut at a slant. On top of the barge was a large pump and diesel engine.

"Once it's in the water, nobody'll be able to see nothing," Ken explained. "That front plate covers it. I'll just scoop a load from the bottom and take it out and dump it in the big hole out in the middle. You see that pump up there? If I need to loosen the bottom up, I'll start it up and sparge the bottom out in front of the barge."

"No shit, Ken," I said. "What about all these welders. Do they know what you're going to do with this thing?"

Ken looked around and spat out another dark-stained wad. "These coon asses, we all know each other. They're working for me, the way they see it. They'll keep their mouths shut long as they get paid. I ain't worrying about it."

"Any idea what this monster is going to cost?"

"It ain't gonna be cheap.   It'll be about seventy thousand, the way I add it up."

"How do you think Players intends to cover that?"

"From what I know, it's been lumped into the whole entertainment barge project. The way I see it, those guys are so screwed up they'll probably cut the check for it and not even know what they're paying for."

I didn't want to pump Ken any further. I genuinely liked him. He was a dying breed of river rat who had spent most of his life in these bayous, on one type of boat or another. I knew he was uneasy about the operation he'd be starting tonight, but that he was going for some of the big money he had noticed flowing generously in Players' upper echelons.

I couldn't blame him for wanting in, and I hoped he wouldn't get burned for his part in this numskull scheme of Players.' But I didn't like his chances. I didn't see how he'd be able to make multiple runs, from the berthing site to the middle of the lake and back, without attracting notice. Thinking about Ken as an incidental casualty griped me. It occurred to me that it would be a great idea to weld David, butt pointing forward, to the front of the barge as a figurehead.

My security measures for my rooms (513 and 514) at the Downtowner wouldn't have impressed Ian Fleming, but they'd be effective. First, I installed a single-cylinder deadbolt on the door to each room. Next, I placed short strips of clear filament on the upper corners of each window, on the dresser drawers, and on a dummy briefcase that I'd leave in the room, filled with inconsequential documents. Before leaving, I'd sprinkle baby powder on the threshold of each door and in a grid on the carpet and attach filament to the upper corners of each door. When I returned later, I'd plug in my black fluorescent lamp and turn out the lights. If anyone had paid a visit, I'd be able to see the trail.

I knew that Howard, David, and Labov were in town for a meeting and that I'd probably be able to find them at either the Players office or the corporate house. Before I left, I thought of something I needed to check. Using the Phillips head tool on my Swiss Army knife, I removed the bottom plates from the bodies of the phones and found the wiring normally configured. The diaphragm under the mouthpiece in the receiver could only be energized if a call came in and if I lifted the receiver.

I found David and Howard sitting in David's office. Labov, they said, was at the barge construction site.

"Just in time," Howard said, as I walked into David's office.

"Just in time for what?" I asked Howard. Then I asked David, "What's up, sir?"   I was hoping to hear that life had been discovered on another planet and that they wanted me to start up a new casino there. If not that, I'd settle for another continent.

"We want you back here, full time," David said. His tone was stern.

Fuck you, I thought.

Seeing my expression, Howard threw in, "Yes, John, we need you to parachute yourself back into the project."

To me, all this had a Labov stink about it. "What's Labov telling you?"

"I don't want to talk about it," David snapped. "I don't like anything I've heard today at all. Get into this project and find out where it's at, now!"

"Are you telling me to take the project over? Did you fire Labov? I need some specifics here."

"No, we haven't done anything with Steve," Howard answered.

Before he could say anything more, David cut in. "You need to get your hands around the project and take charge. I'm not happy with anything—nothing at all."

My first thought was for Ken Hagan. I didn't think his contract had been documented yet, and I knew that Labov was holding stubborn in his refusal to take account of the implications of an oral agreement in Louisiana. I was beginning to see a bad moon rising on this issue.

I looked at David, then at Howard. "I want this straight up. You're telling me I'm now in charge of this project and Labov is gone? If that's the case, then it's my responsibility entirely. I'll gladly take it over, but I have to be in charge. I want it back to the way I had it before—everything on time and under budget. I don't want any bullshit with ambiguous scopes. We define the scope and stick to it. That sounds simple enough to me."

I could see that I had found David's soft underbelly. He looked at me in pure contempt. "You're going to work *with* Labov," he said. "You'll *both* be in charge. Anything about that you don't understand, John?"

For a moment I said nothing. I was too overcome by raw anger. I looked at the wastebasket and thought of kicking it. I looked at David, swollen with authority, and thought of back fisting him across the bridge of his nose. I looked at Howard and thought of saying, "You at least know better than this sort of nonsense." Instead, I took a deep breath. Then I looked at Howard and said, "*You're* my boss, Howard. I take my orders from *you*."

His reply was, "We expect you out at the barge construction site tomorrow."

I left the office in a cold rage. You jerks want me on site? I thought. Well, on site's where you'll get me. But it won't be tomorrow; it'll be right now. I didn't have a moment's doubt about what I was going to do when I got there.

As I approached the construction site, I could see the red iron of the barge-building framework reaching up into the sky. It looked gargantuan, even from a half mile away. I felt my edge drawing keener. I had expected the construction to be much farther along than the skeletal framework.

The security guard recognized me and waved me through. I drove a little farther in, stopped, and looked at the monstrous barge against the corner bulkhead, about two hundred feet in front of me. The road continued, running along side the barge. Across the road were the fabrication sites. A large crane was positioned so that it could pick up the fabricated pieces and lift them over to the barge for assembly. I recognized Ken Hagan's hand in the efficiency of the layout.

The ATCO office trailers were located along a dirt road off to my right. I looked for the one that was signposted "Labov" and pulled up to it. Inside, Ted Frazier, a new lackey manager whom Labov had taken on, was sitting behind a desk in a small office to my left. Labov had terminated his earlier manager, Rick Bernardini, over what I had heard was a budgeting glitch. Rick discovered that he had been carrying a ten million-dollar addition error that was not in Players' favor. He had been sacked just after he had caught the error and brought it to Labov's attention.

I had met Ted, Rick's replacement, earlier at the casino facility. I hadn't been impressed with him then; and, from what I could see of him now, I was impressed even less. On a construction site, you dress the part, out of regard for safety regulations and to let your colleagues know you're one of them, that you have no reservations about working up a sweat and getting yourself dirty. But here was Frazier in a dorky looking pair of soft-toed dress shoes.

He looked up from his computer as though startled. "Hello, John. Can I help you?" he asked. His tone sounded defensive, which was fine with me. He was Labov's man, and I had him in my sights.

"Not really," I answered. "So you can calm down. You look like someone just walked over your grave."

"Oh, no. No problem. I thought you were in New Orleans, or in Shreveport."

"Think again, Ted. I'm here. You have the budget for the project? I want to look it over."

"The budget? Well… well, I don't think I can do that, John. I mean, it'd be difficult right this moment."

"Then I'll see if I can make it easier for you. You either have it or you don't. Either I can see it or I can't. One or the other. You tell me which."

"Well, John, I don't have a *final* budget yet. I can't show you anything that's final."

"I suppose I can understand that. This project has been going for only seven months. Where's Labov? Can you get Labov?"

He pushed away from his desk, turned his back to me, slid his chair over to the phone, and placed a call. He was told that Labov wasn't in. He asked for Labov to call him back as soon as possible. Then he hung up, paused for a moment, and turned back around to me.

"The problem is… the problem is many things. All these additions, for one thing. And we can't get a contract negotiated with Hagan."

"Negotiated" is what I had expected to hear. I wished that Labov were here. There was a bright and shining light that he needed to see.

"Negotiated? What do you mean negotiated? Bernardini negotiated the deal a long time ago. They shook hands on it. Let me see the last bill that we paid to Ken Hagan!"

He slid his chair back to his credenza on the sidewall of his office and picked up a stack of papers. He reached over and handed them to me.

I looked at the invoice on top. What I saw had me praying that Labov would walk in the door. "Look at this, Ted," I said, handing the invoice back to him. "You can see for yourself that Ken's billing in accord with the agreement. But look at the paid-to-date amount. It shows you're already close to the total budget amount. You've burned the budget, and the construction's nowhere near finished. This has shit creek written all over it."

Ted looked at the invoice a moment and then replied, "Steve's not worried about *that*. He says we can negotiate Hagan down on the final costs."

Oh, for a miracle! Oh, for Labov here right now! I thought, feeling the adrenalin surge in me. I asked Ted, "Do you and Labov know what state you're in?"

"John, Steve says we have the upper hand. Hagan doesn't have a written contract with us."

"To hell with what Labov says! You tell me! Is this what they teach you up in New Jersey? No written agreement, no deal?"

Ted answered, "John, I've been doing this for a long time. It—"

"It what, Ted? Tell me how it is in Louisiana? Tell me!"

"It doesn't matter much, from state to state."

"It doesn't matter. You're telling me it doesn't matter? Have you hot guns from up north ever heard of Napoleonic Law?"

Ted sat dumbfounded.

"Take notes, Ted, and make sure Labov gets them. Better yet, you just listen up. There's one state that didn't adopt English Common Law. There's one state that chose instead to operate under the old French system, in which a verbal contract is just as binding as a written one. What state do you think we're in Ted? Let me hear you say it."

"I see," Ted said, slowly.

"About time. At least we know now you don't need new lenses. What's Ken Hagan saying about all this?"

"He's being difficult. He's hired some bohunk lawyer from Lake Charles who's moved into his construction trailer. Some guy named Austin, Eddie Austin."

I went numb, feeling like a left hook that I hadn't seen coming had caught me flush on the side of my head. I knew about Eddie Austin, Jr. I knew that if you were his client you were shitting in tall cotton but that if you were his adversary your ass was grass and he was the mower. I had met him a long time ago at a social function in Lake Charles. He was gray haired, wide shouldered; and at a casual glance he looked overweight. A closer look, however, told you that he was just plain big and powerful. To me, he looked like the classic immoveable object.

He was also unpretentious and outgoing, with an open smile that went across his whole face, making him look as happy as an innocent kid at the teddy bears' picnic. But once during the evening I saw him look across the room at someone. I noticed his hands at his side drawing up tightly into fists, the slight bend in his arms, and the forward lean in his posture. Joe Frazier used to come out of his corner like that; and after a minute's work on you he'd have you urinating blood for the next month. I also noticed Eddie's forehead angled slightly forward and down but his eyes looking straight ahead, with the intensity of a laser sighter. It was then, standing at a distance from him, that I noticed how shockingly blue his eyes were.

Later in the evening, when I had been introduced to him, he took my hand and paused a moment, to make sure we exchanged a firm, honest, manly grip as he looked me square in the eye. At that moment, I looked deep into his own eyes, into a soul that was at once simple and profound. I had taken an instant liking to him and had felt that we could, if circumstances favored it, become good friends.

Now I could be sure of this much: if Ken Hagan had Eddie Austin in his corner, Players would be well advised to throw in the towel before the bell for the opening round.

To Ted I said, "Let me paint a picture for you so you'll know just where we are. Have you ever read Brer Rabbit?"

"Brer Rabbit? Ya, I know the story. What's that got to do with this?" he answered defensively, crossing his arms and leaning back in his chair.

"Right now, Ted, we have both hands and feet stuck to the tar baby. It's Eddie's job to hold a knife to our last remaining appendage and to cut deeper and deeper, until his client gets what he wants. If you have any use for the balls between your legs, you should understand that. "

Ted had had enough stress. "Leave me alone, John. Please? Just leave me be. You need to talk to Steve. Go find him and let me get back to what I'm doing." Then he put his head down and began working on his computer, trying to ignore me.

I walked out of the Labov trailer, slamming the door behind me, and headed over to Ken Hagan's two trailers. I found him in his second trailer, sitting behind his desk in his office. As I came up to his door, I saw Eddie Austin standing beside him, arms folded, staring down at something on the desk, his blue eyes fiercely intent. I stood a moment outside, not knowing whether I was a friend or an enemy.

Ken looked at me through his thick glasses, surprised. "Well I'll be damned," he said. He then stood up, came out, and swallowed my hand in his.

I distinctly remember the dry, hard feel of the skin on his palm whenever we shook hands. My grandfather's hands had been the same, toughened by years of day in and day out work.

"I thought you'd disappeared," Ken said, "that you'd forgot about us little guys."

"Little guys, my ass, Hagan," I replied. "You're making a fortune building this abortion."

Ken and Eddie looked at each other, neither of them smiling. Eddie bent his eyes on me, with his forehead angled down slightly. I knew the meaning of this expression and looked over at Ken.

"You remember John," Ken said to Eddie. "He was in charge of this project before David and Labov pushed him out. Back then, it was just John and me; and we got things done. Don't blame him for being with Players. Let him live. He's the only professional thing they got going for them."

I extended my hand to Eddie and said, "Good to see you again." Then I asked Ken, "So where does this goat show stand?"

"If this Labov has his way, I'll go broke here. In fact, I think that's what he's trying to do, run me broke. He won't cooperate for shit, and I can't get any blueprints to build by. All I ever see is this stupid fucking balsa wood model that David parades around the site with. You ask him a question about this or that, he holds up the little model and says something like, 'There, build it that way!' Labov and his group are working against me everywhere. Looks to me like they want to take the project over, maybe to put a huge ration of egg on my face. Who knows?"

"You could be right," I said. "But it won't happen that way if I have anything to say about it. I came in to tell you that David and Howard have ordered me back on this project. But don't let your hopes get wild. I'm supposed to work with Labov. So I've got to wear him around my neck."

"Oh?" Ken grunted. Eddie stood silent, taking mental notes.

"Any chance we can get it back the way we had it? Think we can get this thing finished like we used to get things done?" Ken asked.

I looked at Ken, then at Eddie. "Any other way'll be over my dead body. I was just over giving Labov's manager a taste of religion."

Ken laughed. "Frazier? He couldn't find his own ass if he had to. Anything I can do to help you out, John? I gotta do something. I got a deal brewing to sell Lake Charles Construction, to an outfit called American Eco. They're pretty big, publicly traded. It could be good for me; it could be better than good. That's if Labov doesn't break me first."

"And that's not going to happen, John," Eddie said.

"With you for a corner man," I said, "I don't think it's going to be Ken who's short changed. Not from what I've heard about you, Eddie. Ken, can you find me some kind of trailer and set it down the hill, closer to the barge? I'm going to put the black hat on around here, and I don't want my office near Labov's."

"You got it, first thing tomorrow morning," Ken said. He then added, "And welcome back, buddy."

It was getting on to ten by the time I finished dinner and returned to my rooms. The seal was still intact on the door to room 513 but had been broken on the door to 514. I opened the door, turned on the light, and took a wide step across the threshold. I could see that the seals on the dresser drawers and on my dummy briefcase had also been broken. I placed my live briefcase on the floor, opened it, took out my black fluorescent light, plugged it into a wall socket, and turned off the lights. The baby powder footprints described a trail to the dresser, to the couch, then to the nightstand, where the phone was located.

Is this place an insect farm? I wondered. With my hand-held scanner, I swept the walls, giving careful attention to the wall between the two rooms. But I didn't detect any signals. Not a good sign, I thought. Whoever this was could be good. I sat on the bed, turned the phone over, and used the Phillips head device in my Swiss Army knife to remove the screws for the bottom plate. The wiring had been altered to allow the diaphragm under the receiver mouthpiece to sense and relay signals whether the receiver was lifted from the cradle or not. The phone was now an eavesdropping device.

Goddamn ears! I thought, as I cut the jump wires and reassembled the body of the phone. But who? I wondered.

I walked over to the window and stood looking out at the lake. I needed to think this out. Was Players keeping an ear on me? Or was it someone more professional—someone either staying at or stationed somewhere in this hotel? And were there eyes on me as well?

Far out in the lake, I saw two lights moving closer, slowly, toward the berthing site for the entertainment barge. I recalled that tonight was the maiden voyage of the covert dredging barge. The lights were from the small tug that Players was using to push the barge. I took my binoculars from my travel bag and focused on the lights. When the tug had the barge positioned over the berthing site, I heard the diesel engine start; then I heard the at first thumping and then steady humming sound of the pump as it ramped up.

It took about half an hour for the barge to excavate a load of bottom sediment. The pump engine shut down, and the tug began pushing the barge out into the lake. Out of habit drilled into me during recon training, I slowly panned from the barge back toward shore. I stopped at a point along the seawall outside the civic center. I could see the vague image of someone standing on the seawall. I turned the focusing ring to sharpen the image and saw a man looking out into the lake with a small pair of binoculars. He was following the progress of the barge.

I watched him for well over half an hour. As the lights of the tug, looking like pinpoint eyes from the middle of the lake, began to move back toward us, the observer used his cell phone for a brief call. He stayed at his watch until the barge was once again stationed over the berthing site, dredging up another load of toxin-rich sediment. He then turned and walked toward the parking lot. I watched him until he opened the door to a white sedan. But I wasn't able to make out the license plate. What the hell? I thought, as I closed the curtains. I had no idea of who could be snooping on me as well as on the dredging operation.

I had thought about the Reverend often since I had met him in Belize. I could tell from his eccentricities—some genuine, others postured—that he was a complex man. And I also knew that in his day he had been one of the bricks of the US Intelligence Community—that he hadn't gotten the lead he carried in his body from sitting at a desk, chewing pencils. I had no doubt that he was on a first name basis with the elephant and could recognize the myriad faces it showed in the smoke-and-mirrors jungle in which an operative must work his tradecraft. All he had known about me were the details of my military background; yet he had accepted me, almost paternally—in an instant sounding me more deeply than had anyone I had ever known before, with the exception, perhaps, of my father and mother. I had been flattered by his endorsement and what it meant—that he would position on my flank without question if I felt I needed him.

I restored my security measures and left to find a payphone. On the second ring, a voice that I recognized as the Reverend's answered "Hello."

I briefed him on my dilemma.

"How do you see your own situation in all this?" he asked.

"I can't give you a precise sit rep on my own position, sir," I explained. "I know that someone's been through my room and that the phone had a greedy ear."

"And you think it might be someone from Players?"

"I'm not sure, sir. As for Players, agendas are proliferating."

For a moment, the Reverend was silent. Then he said, "Meet me at the Lake Charles airport tomorrow afternoon. We should get in around 1400."

"We, sir?"

"I'm bringing some ugly friends."

"I hope you all aren't coming up here in that handy man's special you call a plane."

But the Reverend was in no mood for humor. "Young man, don't concern yourself with *my* arrangements. Get a good night's sleep. I want you on your toes when I get there." Then he hung up without saying goodbye.

The prospect of meeting the Reverend and his colleagues had me too restless to even think of sleeping. I was particularly intrigued by the man I had seen earlier this evening observing the dredging, which would be continuing past midnight, into the morning. Would he be back, or had he gotten all the INT that he needed? Was there any way that I could see more of him without alerting him?

Actually, there was a way, a perfect way. It was close to 1100 now. One of the riverboats would be casting off soon and would be returning a few hours later. I was sure I could talk the on-duty captain into letting me accompany him for his shift.

On the outbound leg, I saw nothing that impressed me as strange. But inbound, as it was getting close to 0100 and we were approaching the dock, I barely made out a figure standing in the parking lot, next to a white sedan. Once I had the focus ring for my binoculars adjusted, I could see that the figure was a man; he was wearing a dark t-shirt and probably jeans. He was looking through a pair of binoculars out into the lake. When the boat had been maneuvered into position for mooring, I looked back to the parking lot. I saw the white sedan backing out of its space.

In the lobby of the Downtowner, I encountered David and Howard, who had come looking for me. At this hour, I knew that they must have had something in the order of the momentous on their minds.

Neither of them looked overjoyed to see me. Howard spoke first. "Glad we don't have to wake you up, John. There are some things we want to talk to you about."

"We've got a lot of things that need talking about. Important things, John," David added in an accusing tone.

I had to admit that they were right—lots needed to be talked over. But I didn't like David's tone, and I wasn't in a mood for his authoritative blustering. I decided to completely ignore him. To Howard, I said, "You guys sound like you're serious. Hope I don't need Eddie Austin."

"That's not funny," David snapped.

"Touchy, touchy," I replied.

"First thing, John," Howard said, "never mind the move to Atlantic City. We want you living here. Your wife and kids can move there without you."

"Maybe I can get Eddie to tell me what to do about you guys driving my wife crazy."

"You seem to be getting a kick out of this good old boy Eddie Austin," David said. "You work for Players, don't you? Or do you think you pick your paychecks up in Hagan's trailer?"

David's implication triggered me. To Howard, I said, "If you heard what I just heard, David here is asking me whether I know whom I'm working for. I have no problem answering that, Howard. I'll tell you right now, before this sorry spectacle is over I'll make it clear just who's working for Players and who isn't, if you get what I mean by 'working for Players.'"

"Calm down, John," Howard urged. "No one's suggesting—"

"Horseshit, Howard. Horseshit! You too, David. Horseshit! You want to talk about responsible positions? Let's talk about Hagan's contract, then. Better yet, listen! I'll tell *you* about Ken Hagan's contract. If you don't have sense enough to finalize based on a realistic budget, if you can't see that, especially after all the money you've paid into this so far, you have no business standing here questioning my loyalty. It's a fact that I handled the last project state of the art. Ken Hagan himself knows that. You get Labov out of my face now and I'll do it again. It's not too late. But you leave Labov in the picture and you'll see one fuckup piling on top of another. And you let Labov play tag, or whatever he calls it, with Ken Hagan, and you'll be licking your wounds."

"Steve will take care of Hagan and his lawyer," David said. "We see nothing in Eddie Austin to be impressed about."

"Howard?" I asked, in exasperation. "You going to stand by and just watch this? You're a lawyer. Do you hear anything I'm saying?"

Howard looked at David, then back at me. "Steve's got the right view of this, John. Open your eyes. You think we're going to roll over for Hagan and his hired gun? Hagan's the one who's fucking this project up, and we're not going to let Austin and him skin us alive."

I threw my hands in the air and turned toward the elevator. As I walked away, David said, to my back, "You're with Players, John. Remember that."

"John!" I heard the Reverend call, before I was able to spot him in the line entering the arrivals lounge. In his khaki slacks and white shirt, he looked deeply tanned. Though he was carrying his cane in his right hand, his step seemed full of perk.

His four colleagues followed behind him. They were indeed ugly and also very big. I was about to ask the Reverend who the Brothers Grim were; but he said straightaway, "Let's go to baggage. We've got work to do." He didn't introduce me to his bricks.

As we entered baggage claim, the Reverend pointed to an available dolly. "You see the big box sitting over there, young man? I'd appreciate it if you'd get it for me. I'm not the man I used to be."

Off to the side of the conveyor belt, I could see a huge steamer trunk. "Anyone ever recommend traveling light to you, sir?" I asked.

"Just my gear," the Reverend answered. "All in the chip, you know. I'm renting from Avis. You know the way, I assume."

As I pushed the Reverend's trunk full of electronic gear toward the Avis counter, he walked beside me, with his colleagues following behind. Each had picked an outsized rucksack off the conveyor and was wearing it on his back. There was no conversation between them.

"This won't be social, young man," the Reverend said. "That pleasure will have to wait another day. In fact, you won't even see me while I'm here. I'm flying out the morning after next. Meet me near check in no later than 0900. We'll talk before I go. Now, good day to you. My men and I will be fine from here."

I shook hands with him and left him by the Avis counter. I didn't have to ask him how he'd be able to move around Lake Charles without my seeing and recognizing him.

He was alone when I met him at the airport at the time he had specified. Again, he saw me first. "We've got about fifteen minutes," he said before I had a chance to greet him. "Let's just walk about and I'll talk."

"Anything that'll make my hair stand on end, Sir?" I asked.

"A bit of this and that," he answered. "First thing—it looks to me like Ken Hagan and you are not getting any cooperation in what you're doing to keep this moving along. And I don't think it's any coincidence that there's a lot of money to be made by other parties if Hagan's company is forced off the job. Hanging a marker of sorts on him would be an obvious first step in that direction."

"That's more or less the way I see it, sir. At least now I can be sure I'm seeing it the way it is."

"As for you, young man, you're being painted as a Hagan ally. That's not helping your credibility in Players. Where do you see that getting you?"

"Credibility, in Players, sir?"

"I thought you'd see it that way."

"Where does it get me? Your guess is as good as mine. I know what I want to do."

"What's that, young man? I'm interested in hearing this."

"I want to get this project done right. But I don't know how to do that without making big waves in Players. The more I do that's right, the more they see me as a turncoat. What do you think I should do, sir?"

"I think you should think and act the way you were trained. You should have started thinking that way a long time ago. Jungles and deserts aren't the only places wars are fought. Whom do you see as your ultimate bosses here?"

"David and Howard may be my immediate bosses. But ultimately it's the shareholders."

"Right, young man. Spot on. It's a bind of sorts, actually. You can do a good job and get yourself fired. Or you can observe the party line and keep your job. But consider this: this whole mess is going to implode on itself sooner or later. What good is it having a job in a company that may not survive?"

"You're right. It is a bind, sir. But I'm a construction man at heart, a project manager. The way I see it, there's only one thing I can do."

"And you're military, too. Don't ever forget—they put the wings on a good man. I knew that a long time ago." The Reverend looked at his watch. "I'll be going to board now. You just go out to your car and get back to work. I've done all I can here. Your room's clean; and I'll doubt you'll be seeing the birdwatcher. But I'm leaving my handsome friends around for a few days, for presence and a few other things. You'll notice that they'll keep their distance. That's as it should be. Let them do their work. But you'll also notice a difference when they leave. You won't have to worry about security. What you do with Players is something you'll have to decide. You knew there was nothing gilded about them before you called me up here."

I thanked him for his help.

He replied, "Goodbye for now, young man. You know my number. Anytime."

I watched the Reverend for a moment as he walked toward the departure gate. I still couldn't figure whether his limp was real or feigned, and I wondered whether I would ever see him or need his lethal aid again.

During the time they stayed in Lake Charles, the Reverend's bricks kept among themselves, as the Reverend explained they would. I'd see them together walking around the barge construction site or in the evening, having dinner at Merv's. They gave me absolutely no sign of recognition. On the site, their presence seemed to unsettle Labov so entirely that his appearances became rare. On a few occasions, I walked into his trailer and asked Ted Frazier something to the effect of, "Ted, you know anything about those big, silent men I'm seeing outside the trailer all the time? You think they know where you live?"

Ted would fixate on his computer and answer, "I don't want to talk about them. I don't know what they want. Just let me be, John, will you?"

Blessed by Labov's scarcity, I was able to focus on construction of the entertainment barge. Ken and I knuckled down and started putting in long hours. Lacking blueprints, we roughed out our own sketches and then handed them to the subcontractors, on an hour-by-hour basis. Ken and I split the scope of work into distinct sectors and divided them between us; then we set ourselves in a friendly competition, to see which of us could get our sectors completed more quickly.

One morning, we set up a PA system; and I called a meeting of all the union workers. I presented myself as a Players man, but as one who had their interests at heart. I told them that I had supported union help as long as I had been with Players and that Players needed their best efforts now to complete this work on a respectable timeline. Also, Ken and I made sure that we spent as much time as possible out of the trailer, in the trenches (so to speak). And our workers responded: the project gathered so much momentum that we could foresee completion well ahead of our estimates.

But there was still the contract issue between Ken's company (Lake Charles Construction) and Players. For Ken, it was a source of high anxiety. He was counting on the sale of his company to American Eco but knew that Eco's principals, Phil Clayton and Terry Garth, would lose interest if the dispute with Players ran on and bled his company dry. From my vantage point within Players, I could see that the conflict was getting more and more polarized.

Labov clung stubbornly to his strategy to negotiate Hagan down. As a counter to Eddie Austin, Howard placed Daniel Ojserkis, one of his Atlantic City lawyers, onto Labov's flank. For additional firepower, Pat Madamba was called up. Before long, it was clear that, in Players' mind, the fight card read the elite unit from New Jersey against the good old boys, Ken Hagan and Eddie Austin.

The way it looked to me, Players was inflated with arrogance— counting on greater numbers and sophistication. For their parts, Ken and Eddie kept relatively low, doggedly sticking, without elaboration, to their position that Ken's fee volume and contract should be based on the scope of work being actually performed, inclusive of all the changes that David had heaped on the original design.

The only disposition that Eddie showed was that he simply wanted to bring a properly documented contract to the light of day. Week by week, however, he directed Ken to submit invoices for work completed. I knew Sun Tzu's *Art of War* well and was fully aware of Eddie's strategy. He would not respond in kind to Players' show-of-force. He would present an almost submissive, simple-minded masking posture. At the same time, however, with each weekly invoice that Players paid for work that was now out of the original scope, he was building precedent upon precedent.

In effect, Eddie was acting on two essential principles of warfare conducted guerilla style: let your enemy think it has the strength, so that it'll swell in arrogance; at the same time, keep on the retreat, but in a way in which you lure the enemy ever closer to a killing ground of your own choosing.

At one point, Labov came close to igniting a show of force from Ken Hagan. Howard's man Ojserkis had asked Eddie to formalize a contract that would represent a fair resolution. Eddie was to fax the document to Howard's Atlantic City office; Ojserkis and Madamba would get together with Labov and review it; then, if they approved, they would contact Eddie to schedule a meeting in Lake Charles.

Ojserkis and Madamba then scheduled the meeting in Merv's Bar and Grill, at a large table that was often reserved for Players' high-level executives and their guests. Out of necessity, I sat on the Players side, with Labov and Players' legal wizards, Ojerkis and Madamba. Across from us sat Eddie Austin and Ken.

Eddie started off thanking the Players reps for making the trip all the way to Lake Charles just to put a blessing on the contract. Abruptly, Labov stood, interrupting Eddie, threw his copy of the contract across the table at Ken, and said, "We're going to start from scratch."

I felt the sting in Labov's condescending tone and manner and could see Madamba's smug expression. I felt like standing, to say something that might defuse what looked like a firefight in the making. But Ken, his face red and his eyes bulging, had already jumped to his feet and was heading around the table to get at Labov. Fortunately for him, Eddie was up too, standing in Ken's way. Eddie placed his hands on Ken's shoulders and politely nudged him back a step. Then he turned to us and said, "Gentlemen, this meeting is over." With that, he put his documents in his briefcase and herded Ken out of Merv's.

Labov smiled sadistically and started to speak. But I had seen and heard more than enough.

I said good day and left, remembering what I had read about the famous gunfight at OK Corral. Wyatt Earp wasn't deadly because he was fast on the draw; he took his time and placed his shots carefully. And in the three-minute showdown, each of the few shots he took found its mark. The soldier in me knew that Eddie's shot was coming; but I didn't know when or in what form.

Labov and Eddie met several more times in an attempt to hammer out a contract. In his blustering manner, Labov persisted in trying to haggle

Ken's fees down. In his quiet, non-confrontational manner, Eddie held his ground. As the negotiations dragged on, Ken continued to submit weekly invoices; and Players kept paying. I knew that the issue would detonate when the project reached a critical milestone—the point where the accumulated cost to date came even with the originally estimated total cost.

When this pass came, Labov, counseled by Howard, Ojserkis, and Madamba, issued a statement that Players would refuse payment on further invoices and that construction work was to be shut down. Players' position was that no further money was owed: the changes David had wrought had not been documented in written change orders and were not, therefore, substantive.

Following the Players statement, two days passed with no reply from Eddie. Labov scheduled a meeting for Wednesday afternoon, to be held at the Players office, with the two principals of American Eco, Phil Clayton and Terry Garth, who were now managing the affairs of Ken Hagan's company. From the attitude that Labov carried, it was apparent that his strategy was to grind Ken Hagan into the ground once and for all.

Late Wednesday morning, however, Eddie and Ken met with Phil and Terry, who had flown in earlier from Houston. Neither of them wanted to see work at the site shut down and Ken's company drastically devalued. And both felt they had to rely on Eddie, on the stroke he carried locally. Eddie explained that Players' New Jersey lawyers probably had no idea that he could have the barge seized and then sold off at a Sheriff's auction, to pay off Ken's invoices. He would prepare the paperwork immediately and could, if Players didn't fall into line, order the Sheriff's deputies on the site in five minutes.

The meeting in the Players conference room started at 1400. Howard opened, taking Labov's stance that the work David's changes had forced on the project had not been documented completely in written change orders. No payment, therefore, was owing to Lake Charles Construction beyond the initially agreed on budget total and a few small items that Labov had agreed to reluctantly. That, in a nutshell, Howard said, was the line Players was drawing.

Not liking a word of this, and sensing that Players had dug themselves into position, Phil and Terry rose and left the meeting. Howard sat, gloating, it seemed to me. He knew that he'd be hurting both Ken and American Eco by withholding payment. Also, I thought, he was probably expecting them to come back begging.

About a half hour passed, and we drifted into small talk. Howard rose and went into an adjacent office to call the construction site. Within a few moments, we heard him yell, "They've what? They're already headed back to Houston?" He then closed the door to the office. I could hear his voice, but it was so low that I couldn't tell what he was saying. It was my guess that Phil and Terry had given Eddie the go ahead to have the barge seized and had then left town, disgusted with Players.

Howard came out a few moments later. He looked to me as if his spirit had been broken. "We have to fix this," he said, not looking at us, rather staring down at the floor. I'm sure he realized that Eddie had brought the contest to endgame. Maybe he even appreciated how formidable a tag team Eddie and Ken Hagan made.

In short order, Players caved in to Eddie's terms. Ken would finish work on the entertainment barge; the scope would include David's add ons; and Ken would hold any additional costs under five million—assuming no further design changes from Players.

Back at the site, Ken and I stepped up the pace; and our crews were able to finish the barge in two weeks. On the day that the completed entertainment barge was to be towed to its berthing location behind the Downtowner, thousands of people were lined up along the seawall waiting, and the media was out in force, with live TV remotes set up to capture the grand event. I was aboard the barge, next to the navigator. As we made the turn into Lake Charles, I loaded Wagner's *Ride of the Valkyrie* into the stereo receiver and tuned the speakers to full volume. When the barge docked, I locked it in place by knocking the first steel pin in with a sledgehammer. Then I took a bow as the audience clapped and cheered.

Soon after, however, I was told that I had taken my last bow on Players' time. Whipped into religion by Merv Griffin's appointments to their ranks, the board called for an investigation into the barge fiasco. Though the enquiry was supposed to be impartial, Madamba arranged for Players to retain Adams and Reese, a New Orleans law firm with which he had tight connections. For the financial inquisition, Players brought aboard Ernst and Young, a big six accounting firm that had, among its higher ups, a close friend of Howard's. I wasn't a brain surgeon, but I didn't have to be one to get a good idea of what was going on. The way I figured it, the investigation would probably amount to a hunt for a sacrificial lamb to offer in place of Howard and David.

Labov removed himself from any line of fire by taking sanctuary back in Atlantic City, and David imposed the cosmetic measure of hiring a new construction manager.

Soon after the investigation was finished, Howard and David summoned me to a meeting at the corporate house in Lake Charles. Though I was hoping they wanted to explain new lines of responsibility for me, my paranoia was at its most wholesome.

David opened by telling me that he was retiring. I told him that I'd miss him.

"No you won't," he said. "You're retiring too."

I asked him who was behind the decision to point me toward the pasture.

His answer was vague to an extreme. "Let's just say that it was a mistake giving Merv such a big stake in the company. His people aren't happy with the way things have been going."

Then he told me that my retirement agreement would amount to eight thousand a month for a year. "We think eight thousand a month for a year is fair for you, John."

I thought that the offer was insulting, nickel and dime considering that my family had been called on to move repeatedly, to live for extended periods with me absent most of the time. There had also been all the corporate hype—the assurances that my sacrifices and tireless dedication would, in time, pay off in a secure, long-term career. So I'm the lamb, I thought. And so this is how Merv takes care of his lot. Well, so much, then, for all my good work. So much for working for Players. But I didn't want to debate money with David now; I'd take it up later, by going over his head.

I asked David about Howard and Madamba. He answered that Howard would remain on as President, with Pat at his side. Having heard as much as I could stomach, I said goodbye to David and left the house.

Right away, I contacted Merv's top man on the Player's board, Tom Gallagher, and negotiated a revised agreement. My regular salary would continue from now (September of 1996) until next January, when I'd receive a final bonus. For two years after that, I'd be on a consulting fee plus a retirement package; together, they'd amount to ten thousand per month. But I'd have to confirm the details with Pat Madamba.

I didn't relish the dose of humiliation I knew Madamba was holding in store for me, but I had no choice other than to call him. I had nothing in the pan for job prospects, and I had bills to pay and a family to support. Madamba confirmed the amount and duration of the agreement but added that it would be canceled if I took employment at a casino in the Lake Charles area.

"Tom and I didn't agree to this," I objected.

Madamba replied, "Take it or leave it, Brotherton. I don't give a shit myself. And Gallagher's not going to get involved. He's helped you all he's going to."

As I hung up the phone, I thought of something Eddie Austin had said to me weeks earlier. He wouldn't disclose how much Ken stood to get out of the contract dispute and the sale of his company. But he did say, "If he works again it'll be only for pleasure." He then handed me his business card and commented, "It pays to have enough sense to hire a good attorney."

CHAPTER 16

POUND OF FLESH

＊

Within days of my phone conversation with Pat Madamba, the realization that the time would soon come when I'd be no longer functionally employed began to load on me. It wasn't so much a matter of being financially pinched. My consulting fee and retirement package would run for two years, starting from next January, when I'd stop receiving regular salary. So I'd have money coming in for the foreseeable future—that is, as long as I didn't take a job with another casino in the Lake Charles area.

Weighing on me more were the frustration of being effectively hobbled and the depressing prospect of being idle. Sure, I could look outside of Louisiana for work. But that would require me to uproot my family again, after a series of relocations that had been bewildering, to say the least. First, we had been moved from California to Metropolis, then to Lake Charles, and then to Houston—with me working in Lake Charles, Evansville (Indiana), Maryland Heights (Missouri), and Las Vegas and traveling back and forth. Next, it had been to Atlantic City (with me reassigned to Lake Charles and unable to regularly travel back and forth) and finally back to Lake Charles. We had now been here slightly over seven months, and Derek and Macie were just getting to feel settled in.

Also, working with Ken Hagan on the entertainment barge, under tight timeline and budget demands, had reminded me of how much real work—the kind that tires both your body and your mind and that proves itself in tangible results—meant to me. However much I once thought that politics was in my blood, I was now learning, with the passing of each day with nothing to do, that it was a challenging job assignment that really made my system sing.

Of no small consequence was the resentment I felt toward Players' management, the sense of betrayal and the feeling that I had been cast out. In lucid moments I knew I had no reason to feel rejected; but at times when depression came calling I was nagged by self accusation, a self-inflicted guilt that maybe I hadn't been up to standard.

But then I recalled something my training officer had said on my first day at Fort Bragg back in 1983: "Be loyal to that which is true to you." I had been true to Players' best interests; I had accomplished results that had advanced those interests; and I felt it had been the Players executive crew that had been disloyal both to the company and to me.

I remembered Major Robert L. Howard, the first day I had seen him at Fort Bragg, just after my sixty-four man stick had completed a tactical jump at 600 feet, each of us fully loaded out. To a man, we had landed close to the aim point. As we gathered up our parachute canopies and stuffed them into our kit bags, I noticed a senior ranking officer standing near the muster point. I rucked it into the formation that was gathering in front of him, pulled my rucksack off my back, placed it neatly in front of me, and then snapped to attention.

The officer now standing in front of us, looking us over with a face set in stone, was dressed in impeccably crisp fatigues. Among his decorations I noted the Medal of Honor bar. He walked up and down, scrutinizing us with the attention I was used to from the black hats back at Fort Benning. When he completed his inspection, he stood in the middle of our formation facing us. For a moment, he stood silent, expressionless. Then he announced, "I am Major Howard. I will escort you on a short walk to the training barracks. You are to follow me."

The short walk turned out to be an extended ruck in the full heat of a southern summer day. Ahead of us, the Major set an inhuman pace. Loaded out, we followed, at first trying to keep up. Then we settled for simply trying to make it. We knew that any of us who didn't would be dropped from Special Forces. By the time we reached the barracks, the attrition rate was nearly fifty percent. Those of us who were left were in severe oxygen debt, many of us throwing up.

Sweating heavily but not out of breath in the least, the major walked among us and then ascended a small platform. He didn't need a microphone.

"You can get as sick as you want—as long as you make it. Fail to make it, today, during any exercise here at Fort Bragg, or during any operation and you will no longer be Special Forces and you will no longer be entitled to wear the Green Beret."

As the Major spoke, I felt motivation course through me. Gone were the concrete legs, the screaming joints and tendons, and the burning lungs. If he had asked us to load out again and ruck it to the North Pole, I'd have followed him; and I'd have pushed myself to the point of death rather than drop by the wayside.

Major Howard continued. "Make your life stand for something— something on which you will one day look back and be proud. Never fear those who wish you harm. Destroy them if you must. You are now a part of the most elite military unit in the history of mankind. The well being of our nation and of any oppressed people depends on the fighting skills you will acquire here. Listen when I tell you this. Remember it: when there is trouble anywhere in the world, the phone always rings first at Fort Bragg.

It is an awesome responsibility that you will bear. Bear it well, but with humility. You will be forged into self-sufficiency, but you will cherish as a sacred trust the lives of the men with whom you will serve. You are to bear a pride that you will never let down, and you are to be loyal to that which is true to you."

I then thought of the Reverend, how he had seen the soldier in me the moment he met me and how he had commended me as a member of the First J.F.K. Special Warfare Battalion and of the 82nd Airborne Division. And I realized that for me to admit self-doubt and even a hint of suspicion that I was inferior would be for me to let down the opinion I had gained from men who in character far surpassed the morally bankrupt, corporate crowd I had recently been working with. I would, I resolved, bear a pride that wouldn't let me down; I'd bear it with humility and with gratitude to the peers who had instilled it in me.

On a morning toward the end of my first week as a nominal consultant, the phone rang. It was Ken, calling because he was worried about me. He wanted me to meet him come evening on Player's own turf, at Coconuts, the bar on the new entertainment barge. "You with me? Or you lost your nerve?"

"Anyone ever tell you you're a master of mischief?" I replied. "Of course I'm with you."

When I walked into the bar a little past seven, Ken was waiting at a table he had appropriated. "So you're one of us now, a retiree," he said as I took my chair.

"Looks that way, Ken. Maybe I should start looking for an assisted living facility." He laughed as I sat down. It felt great to see him, and his brand of humor was pure therapy. "Can't say I'm nuts about the way this whole thing feels," I said. "I know I did the right thing, but I sometimes feel like I failed, like I should have been able to save the shareholders from all the personal agendas. I know that's bullshit—that I alone wouldn't have been able to stop it—but I still feel that way now and then."

"It's pure bullshit. The jerk around you got is supposed to make you feel like that. You did exactly the right thing. And you didn't fail. So where does this leave you?"

"Pretty pissed of at Player's," I answered. "But right now I can't afford to let myself think of what I'd like to do about it."

Ken smiled deviously. "You know, wouldn't it feel great to tell them to place their agreement where they normally lodge their heads?"

"It would. But it's not that simple. I need the money until I line up another job. And I may have to move to find one. That's a whole can of worms in itself."

"But what if you did take a job with another casino around here?"

The thought was almost too delicious to contemplate. But the conditions that Players had built into the agreements were designed to discourage me from approaching the competition. I explained the complications to Ken, emphasizing that the agreements, as they now stood, would give Players a basis to sue me into the Stone Age if I were to violate their terms. There was, I pointed out, a chance that I could approach Howard and ask for his clearance if an opportunity to work in another local casino cropped up. But I had no idea right now how Players would react, and I certainly had no reason to regard them as abounding in the milk of human kindness.

"I was asking about it," Ken said, "because you never know what'll happen once word of this gets out. Keep in mind you're on the wrong end of a bad opinion that exists only in Players. There's no telling when you might get an interesting phone call. People 'round here have a way of closing ranks. Obviously right now you're between a rock and hard place. So maybe just take things as they come and cross bridges when you have to. "

Two mornings later, as I was halfway through my sit-ups, working up an appetite for breakfast, the phone rang. After the pep talk Ken had given me, I was feeling upbeat despite my circumstances. The caller introduced himself as Chuck Miller, a name that jogged my memory. I recalled that I had met him briefly at a social event last year and that he had been introduced to me as the general manager of the casino now operating on the Coushatta reservation. It was still welded into my memory how Players had treated me like a scapegoat when the backers—Minnesota-based Grand Casino—had been able to obtain licensing.

At first, I thought that Chuck might have heard of my imminent parting of ways with Players. He seemed to know nothing about it, however. I was surprised to hear that he would soon be vacating his position as general manager because Grand was transferring him to its casino in Tunica, near Memphis. It surprised me even more that he was calling to ask if I'd mind if he threw my name into the hat as a candidate for general manager of the Grand Casino Coushatta complex. In fact, I was stunned, speechless.

"John, you still there?" he asked.

I thanked him for his consideration and asked him if there was anything he'd like me to do at my end. He suggested that I fax him my resume as soon as possible, by tomorrow if I could. He'd pitch it to Pat Menche, Grand's vice president of operations at corporate level, who'd likely be calling me to schedule an interview. I thanked him again and said I'd get my resume to him immediately.

"Don't mention it, John," he said. "Just do a good job for them."

I hung up feeling a surge of energy—a conflicting mix of exhilaration at my new prospect and anger toward Players. I thought again of what I had accomplished for them, at least for their shareholders, and then of Madamba's *I don't give a shit about what happens to you attitude* in our last conversation. My hostility toward Players, especially toward Madamba, took on a raw edge.

Then I calmed down and realized I'd have to bide my time and look after payback to Madamba in a way he'd recognize as effective. More importantly, right now, I had to update my resume and fax it to Chuck Miller. As it happened, I was planning to meet with Robert Wooley in Baton Rouge the next day, at Stephen Edwards' new law office, located just off College Street. Edwin, now no longer incumbent as governor, shared the new office suite with his son. Also, Julie had moved her office into the same building. My meeting with Robert would give me an opportunity to fax my resume to Grand's office on a form headed by "Stephen Edwards: Attorney." I knew by now not to turn down any chance to capitalize on available political clout.

The next morning, the best part of going out onto I-10 was heading east, away from Lake Charles. As I accelerated onto the interstate, I began to review my situation. I needed to keep a cool enough head to put all the factors pressing on me into a balance-sheet perspective. Sure, it would be great to stick it to Players in any manner I could. Also, I liked the challenge that the new job would present. Though I didn't have any experience as a general manager of a casino, I had shown myself to be a skilled materials, equipment, and human resources manager in all of my previous positions. I was a manager at heart, I felt, and could apply my abilities to any management situation.

All that, on the plus side. But there would no doubt be politics in one form or another. And I'd still be in the casino industry, which had shown itself to be a special sort of demon country. Did I want to go this route? Would I be retreading a path I had already followed? And where would it get me ultimately?

I thought of my situation with Kathy. If the stress that had been a given in my life with Players had been hard on me, it had no doubt beat the hell out of her head. A leap into the unknown now would surely run my marriage on the rocks. Best, I thought, to go for a tangible prospect.

I met Robert outside of Julie's office, briefly explained my status with Players, and told him about the job lead I had gotten from Chuck Miller. "You should be happy the whirlwind of cash spit you out," he said and laughed.

"Robert, give me a break."

"Sorry, John. I don't mean to say it's funny. I know it must have come as a shock. What I mean is that you were better than they deserved."

I thanked him and went up the hall to find Charlene, Stephen's secretary, whose office was across the hall from Stephen's. I knocked at her door, poked my head in, and asked her if I could talk her into sending a fax for me. She was happy to see me and agreed with enthusiasm.

Whether because of a good word from Chuck Miller, or because my resume was impressive, or because it bore Stephen Edwards' name at its top, Pat Menche called promptly, within a few days of my submittal. We agreed that next Monday morning, around ten, would be suitable.

"Fine, see you at ten," he said, then hung up, without saying thank you or that he'd look forward to meeting me. Nor did he ask me if I knew the way to the Coushatta casino. I sensed that his lack of manners was a protocol in its own right and that I'd be going to a stage-managed meeting. My best guess was that I wasn't the candidate whom he preferred.

I remembered that the Reverend, when he had visited Lake Charles, had told me to think military—something he thought I should have done from the outset with Players, who had in effect politically ambushed me. As for Menche, in case he was planning to cycle me through a lip service interview, I'd use maneuver tactics. In my meeting on Monday, I'd act as the fixing force, coming at him direct, distracting his attention from his flank, which I'd arrange to be overrun from a direction he might not expect. I'd make my best effort to meet with and make a positive impression on the chief of the Coushatta Tribe of Louisiana, Mr. Lovelin Poncho. To predispose him positively, I'd arrange for him to receive a host of references from unquestionably impressive sources. If Menche were to show himself indifferent in our interview, follow up pressure from the chief of the tribe on whose behalf Grand was supposed to be managing the casino would no doubt warm up his interest in me.

It took me about forty minutes to get to the Coushatta casino, which was located on State Highway 165, a few miles north of the town of Kinder. The casino was visible from a good half mile away, signaled by the "Grand Casino Coushatta" sign, atop a post that was at least fifty feet tall. Then came the expanse of the complex itself. It was huge, with its gray parking lots stretching in all directions from the main building—a three-story, aqua- colored structure fronted by a Caesar's Palace style awning extending from the glass entrance doors. Even from the road, I could see the lights shining brightly inside.

As I turned left into the parking lot, I noted the trolleys, bright pink (looking newly painted), picking up and dropping off patrons. Already, at nine thirty in the morning, the parking lot was over half full. To my right were newly built administration and warehouse facilities, and beyond additional buildings were under construction. I wondered how much clearing it had taken to allow construction of this complex.

As I pulled up to the valets standing under the elaborate awning, I began to collect my thoughts. Before I'd go to Menche's office, I wanted to do a quick recon, to see how well Grand Casino was managing this enterprise on behalf of the tribe

There were very few tribal members among the employees I saw as I walked about the ground floor. And they held only menial jobs. The pit bosses and the floor managers, all neatly dressed in suits, were Caucasian, probably imports from one or another of Grand's out-of-state operations. If I could arrange to meet with the chief, I'd be sure to ask him if he'd be interested seeing this misallocation overturned.

The lady at the courtesy desk told me that the executive offices were located down the hallway to my right, through the first door on the left. Inside the door, a receptionist was sitting at a large desk, sifting through a stack of papers. To her right was a large rectangular room with offices along the perimeter and cubicles in the open floor space. I introduced myself and told her I was here to see Mr. Pat Menche. She stopped shuffling through the papers in front of her, looked me over thoroughly, then picked up her phone and whispered something I couldn't make out.

Within moments, I heard a pleasant female voice from my right ask, "Mr. Brotherton?" I turned to meet a young, heavy set, but pretty lady with shoulder length blonde hair, who introduced herself as Marla, the general manager's assistant. She asked me to follow her and led me to an office at the far corner of the room. On the door, I saw Chuck Miller's nameplate. She knocked, opened the door, looked in, and then opened the door farther to let me in. In front of me, sitting at a small conference table and studying a document was a man I took to be Pat Menche. He was dressed in a stylish suit, and his hair was gray, long and brushed back to a small ducktail. He looked to be in his mid to late forties. As he stood and extended his hand, I could see that he was well over six feet. He gave me the impression that he cultivated the image of a lady's man.

"Hello, John. I'm Pat Menche," he said in what I recognized as a northern accent. He motioned toward a chair, asked me to sit, and moved toward the door. "Give me a moment, I want the casino controller to join us." He then left the office and entered one of the adjoining offices.

I looked around the office that would be mine if I landed this job. It was larger than what I had been used to and was elegantly appointed. Behind the large wooden desk was a pair of wood cabinets. On the wall to my right was a twenty-five inch color TV monitor that was connected to surveillance cameras. As I watched the views of the action on the casino floor, I thought, I can do a lot with this, if I get the chance.

Menche returned with a young man who was about five foot ten and noticeably overweight. His dark hair was cropped short and combed to the side. He wore thick, metal-framed square glasses. He introduced himself as Jeff King and took a seat.

Menche then began the interview. He was politically nice but led me through the most structured and unimpressive line of questioning I had ever experienced even in a cursory screening session. I had the feeling that this was a stage-managed meeting, that Menche was simply going through the motions so that he could say that he had talked to me about the job, and that I was not the candidate he preferred.

When I got a chance to speak my piece, I tried to emphasize that my record would verify that I was a worker's manager, also one that always kept the investor's interest in mind. When I finished my statement, Menche looked at his watch, signaling that the interview was over.

 I decided to permit myself one last word that would, I hoped, lift the veil from this charade. "Pat, do you mind if I ask how many other candidates you are considering?"

"Several," he replied abruptly and then stood and walked toward the office door. Outside, he thanked me for coming, told me he'd be in touch, and escorted me to the receptionist's desk. There, he wished me a good day and turned and walked back to Miller's office.

I thanked the receptionist for her own courtesy and hurried down the hall, anxious to get to my car and my cell phone. The sooner I deployed my strategy the better.

First, I'd find out how I could arrange to meet with Chief Lovelin Poncho. For this purpose, I had been thinking of calling an old friend, Jack Hanks, who had done some business with the tribe and who might, I thought, know the network I should follow. Jack was close to Sheriff Wayne McElveen, whom I had backed in the past, and had been associated with some businessmen that had, with a good deal of support from me, obtained the payphone concession for the Players Lake Charles casino. When I ran into him from time to time, he always thanked me for my assistance and said he'd take the first opportunity to return the favor. The opportunity was now at hand.

"Where've you been, John? It's been awhile," he said after we exchanged hellos. Then he added, "Word is there's some sort of falling out between Players and you. You might want to know that anyone I've talked to sees it as Players' loss."

I thanked him for his vote of confidence and told him that I was taking a run at the general manager's job at the Coushatta casino. "I've just been interviewed and have the feeling that the management doesn't see me as the sweetest gal in town, so to speak. I need some leverage to apply. Anything you can suggest?"

"Yes, definitely. Grand's management has to get the tribe's permission to hire top positions at the casino. So it would make sense to present yourself to the tribe."

I thanked him and explained that I was hoping to get a meeting with the chief. "I reconned the casino and couldn't help noting that job distribution is not helping the tribe any. I thought I'd use that observation as my approach. At Players I did establish a reputation for being conscientious about localizing benefits."

"It'd be difficult to get a meeting with Lovelin straight out. You'll have to meet first with his tribal manager, a white man, Paul Ruppert. He's been there for quite a while, and the chief trusts him."

I asked him whether it would make any sense to contact another tribal member, Bertney Langley.

"I'd stay clear of him. He's not in the same camp as Paul and Lovelin. In fact, they don't get along at all. I'll give you Paul's number. Better yet, I know a lot of people in the tribe. I'll see if I can arrange for you to get together with him. I'll get back to you soon as I can. No need to thank me, John. This is how it goes with people like us."

I gave him my cell phone number and told him I'd be anxious to hear what he could put into motion. Then I opened my briefcase, took out a notepad, and started listing the names I would use as references. My strategy was to bypass both Grand's management and Paul Ruppert and have them contact Chief Lovelin Poncho directly. Then, if I could meet with Paul and Lovelin, I'd emphasize the need to better manage the casino on behalf of the tribe. If I could present myself as a general manager who would be the tribe's advocate, Pat Menche might find a hiring decision being imposed on him.

As it happened, I was able, through friends, to get a commitment for US Senator Bennett Johnson's office to call in an endorsement of me to the tribal office. US Representative Chris John and Sheriff Wayne McElveen were to do the same. In response to my own direct requests, State Senators Jim Cox, Greg Tarver, and Francis Heitmeier submitted formal letters of reference backed up by personal telephone calls.

As I was looking over my list, my cell phone rang. It was Jack Hanks calling back. "You busy tomorrow?" he asked.

"If you call trying to get the GM job busy, then I'm busy."

"Then we'll make you even busier. I talked to Paul Ruppert. He's knows who you are. He'd like to meet with you tomorrow at noon. Would the Jennings Holiday Inn be okay for lunch? I'll be there too."

"You bet I'll be there, Jack. That was quick. Just the way I needed it. Thanks."

"Don't mention it, John. See you tomorrow."

I arrived at the Jennings Holiday Inn early and found Jack waiting for me in the lobby. "Thought it might help if I gave you a heads up on Paul," he said, as we took seats in the lounge.

"Good idea," I said. "It's important that I handle this right."

"Just so you know, Ruppert, though he's close to the Lovelin and has his ear, is not at heart what you'd call a Native American rights advocate. He's pretty well a political animal and interested in his own skin. A self-preservationist is what I'd call him. He's also pretty serious minded. No jokes with this guy, John. Keep it strictly business. I'll help it along as best I can. That's why I came."

At about twelve thirty, I noticed a black Chevy SUV pull into the parking lot.

"That's Paul's car," Jack said.

As he walked toward the hotel entrance, I noticed that Paul Ruppert was tall, about six foot three, and lean, looking to be in his late thirties or early forties. His short, wavy red hair matched his beard. He was dressed in western boots, jeans, and what looked like a Tommy Hilfiger, long-sleeved cotton dress shirt. His strides were long and determined, and he looked intently from side to side as he walked. He entered the lobby and stood, looking around for us. I could see that his eyes blazed with intensity.

Jack introduced us. I reached out my hand and said, "It's good to meet you, Mr. Ruppert."

"Paul. Call me Paul, John," he replied. "Good to meet you too. Let's go in and have lunch. I'm starved." With that, he turned a sharp about face and started toward the buffet. Jack and I had to step double time to keep a huge gap from opening between us.

There were only two other parties in the restaurant; so we had our choice of seats. "Let's sit by the window," Paul said, turning back to us just as we caught up with him. He then turned and covered what looked like fifteen yards in two steps. When we took our seats, he snapped open the menu and studied it intently.

As the waitress was walking away, after having taken our orders, Jack opened the discussion. He explained how I had managed construction of both phases of the Players Lake Charles operation and emphasized how I had been able to solicit and maintain support of the local community. Then he reviewed what I had accomplished in lobbying the legislature and pointed out that I had established several valuable contacts in the capitol.

Ruppert, I noticed, was listening closely. Jack passed on to the role I had played in a recent election in Calcasieu Parish to determine whether to allow gambling to continue or to abolish it. I had, Jack explained, spearheaded a campaign to keep gambling. I had established media contacts and had kept in touch with them day by day. In the end, largely due to my tenacity as a campaigner, Jack said, gambling was endorsed by a two vote to one margin.

Ruppert was sitting erect, his eyes blazing. "You know elections?" he asked.

"I'd say I do," I answered. "I not only know how to run a campaign, I know how to read polls and how to focus essential messages. I also know how to erode the opposition, how to find their soft underbelly. I think I know how to win, Paul."

Paul lightly slapped both hands on the table and leaned toward me. "We've got an election coming up in May. Lovelin, the tribal chairman, has to run against an asshole named Bertney Langley. This son of a bitch is giving us a hard time."

I recalled how, back when Players had tried to sabotage the licensing of the Coushatta casino, Pat Madamba had tried to enlist Langley. An idea began to take shape in my mind, something that would put an iron in Madamba's side and that would, at the same time, erode Langley's standing among his constituency. "As I remember it, Paul, he conspired with Players to sink the casino."

Paul's eyes narrowed. "You know for a fact that he linked with Players?"

"With Pat Madamba. But as I remember this Langley was pretty harmless—not very effective at getting the tribe to listen to him."

"That was then. He's been working on his act. Also, he's learned to go down and dirty."

"Must have learned that from Players. How so down and dirty?"

Paul looked out the window, then back at me. His eyes were not only intense, they were murderous. "He's learned well, then. He's got a friend of his, Joe Duenas, an FBI agent, nosing about, looking for muck to throw at the chairman."

"Any muck to be found?" Jack asked.

"Nothing you guys need to know about," Paul answered. But you know how it goes with the FBI. You don't have to be guilty of anything for them to fuck up your life."

"Really," I said. "One of the plain facts of life is that you can be the cat's ass one minute and the crap that comes out of it the next. I'm going to recommend something, Paul."

"I'm listening."

I looked at Jack, then at Paul. "This Langley knows I was with Players. If I were hired as general manager, and if I were to get better job distribution, the tribal members might see the casino as being managed in their interests, to their benefit. That might hamstring Bertney, with his moral bullshit."

Paul slapped both palms on the table again. "I know what you mean, John. I can see you've got a mind for this sort of thing. What I need to do is get you together with Lovelin. I want to see if I can do that soon. He'd be interested in this. You got any proof of collusion between Players and Langley?"

An idea began forming in my mind. But I didn't want to explain it fully here. All I said by way of reply was, "I've got something you guys will love. And I'd be happy to meet with your chief. But can I suggest something?"

"Sure. But get used to calling him chairman. He prefers that to chief."

"Let's let this sit for the rest of the week, if that's not too long. You should be hearing some good things about me from some very impressive people."

"As John said," Jack added, "he knows how to run a campaign, his own included. John was also in the military, you know. US Army Special Forces and 82nd Airborne Division. Wasn't Lovelin in the Army?"

"He's a Vietnam veteran," Paul said. "I heard that he was awarded the Medal of Honor, but I've never heard him talk a lot about it."

"I think I can understand that," I said. "You don't get the Medal of Honor for doing KP. He must have been in a world of shit."

"I did hear that he was a tunnel rat," Paul said, "that he was stuck wounded in one of those tunnels the VC practically lived in. Fought his way out with his knife, I was told, and saved some of his men. I like working for him. All in all, he's a pretty quiet. He'll let me call the plays, unless he feels strongly about something. Then there's no mistaking what he wants."

"Well, let's work on getting together, the three of us, Paul," I suggested.

"I'll start on this right away. But I need to tell you, John, there's no pretense in the chairman. Leave that suit of yours at home. He can't stand the sight of a suit."

"Fine with me, Paul. This suit's a costume. It ain't me."

"Didn't think so," Paul said, turning to greet the waitress, who was approaching with our orders.

As soon as I arrived back home, I set myself up in the small room I used as an office. From my desk, I took a blank Players memo form and inserted it into my typewriter. I knew that Madamba had met with Langley and his wife in Eunice, back in the fall of 1994. So I dated the memo September 24, 1994. I opened with some incidental information and then wrote the second paragraph:

"On another matter, I just had a conversation with… They tell me that Burt Langley has almost a third of the tribe's voting signatures to stop the Indian project. However, he has told them that he had done enough of Players' work for free. I will be flying to Vegas tomorrow and stopping to meet with him… in Eunice, La. on Saturday. I am concerned about paying him directly and will probably use… to see to his needs."

Fresh off the typewriter, the memo looked too crisp, too new. I placed it in a file folder and went to Alphagraphics, where I made a copy and then a copy of the copy. I repeated this process several times. Back at my house, I folded the live copy several times and wiped coffee on the back of it. Now it looked real.

Much later, in September of 1999, as the date for the trial of Edwin Edwards was getting near, the memo would be cited in an American Press feature by Hector San Miguel. Langley would be quoted as confused over the matter. Nothing would be said about Madamba's reaction. Even now, I often wonder whether he enjoyed the article.

Toward evening, Jack called to tell me that Ruppert had gotten in touch with him, wanting to know more about me. From what Jack could gather, I stood a good chance of being the tribe's preferred candidate for the GM position.

I was feeling even better about my prospects three days later, when Ruppert called. Lovelin, he said, wanted to meet with me. "How does lunch tomorrow at the Jean Lafitte sound to you, John?"

I knew that the Jean Lafitte was in Lake Charles. "Lovelin and you are coming down my way? I'd have no problem driving up there."

"It's no problem," Paul said. "The chairman likes it there. So it'll be noon?"

"Yes, fine with me," I replied.

"Good. Oh, John. Remember not to wear a suit. That's important. Also, this'll be *the* meeting for you. Lovelin believes he can look into a man's eyes and see all the way in. He'll decide tomorrow whether you're the man for the job. And that'll be it, either way. You understand?"

I replied that I understood perfectly. What he said about Lovelin reminded me of my full blooded, Native American grandmother.

"By the way," Ruppert asked, "if you were running the election, what would you be doing right now? We already have a campaign strategist, a guy named Sandy Kaplan. Can you think of anything we should be telling him?"

I knew that Sandy Kaplan had worked on US Senator John Breaux's campaign and suspected that he might not fully understand Native American culture and protocols. "I'd suggest you tell Sandy to stay away from polls before he gets the itch to get one going. You probably know that tribal members don't think much of them. I grew up near a tribal culture, Paul, and I think I know what you're dealing with. What you need is ammunition against Bertney; and you need it bad." I had in reserve, of course, a high- impact round in the form a coffee-stained, simulated memo.

Paul thanked me for my counsel and wished me luck tomorrow. Before I hung up, I reminded him, "It's not about luck."

I arrived at the Jean Lafitte early, to make sure I'd be comfortable in the surroundings and to get my main points in order. Paul and Lovelin were already there, however, waiting for me at our reserved table. Good, I thought. They're as anxious as I am.

As I approached them, they both stood to meet me. Lovelin Poncho had every appearance of being a full-blooded Native American Indian. He was stout—not fat, but with wide shoulders and short legs. His dark brown hair fell to shoulder length. His nose was wide, almost flat looking against his face. The handlebars of his mustache dangled on each side of his mouth. He was wearing a long-sleeved, western shirt, jeans, and western boots. Under the thick lenses of his wire-framed glasses, his brown eyes opened into a man who did more thinking than talking.

As Paul reached out to shake hands with me, Lovelin stood silently, looking down at the table, then at Paul, then back down at the table. From having grown up near a Choctaw reservation, I was used to the polite, reserved mannerisms of Native American Indians. So I wasn't surprised when Lovelin reached out his own hand tentatively and accepted mine with only a light pressure.

"I'm honored to meet you, sir," I said as I took my seat next to Paul, across the table from Lovelin. Then I thanked him for taking the time to meet me.

When the waitress brought a plate of bread to the table, Lovelin took a slice, put it on his plate, and looked briefly at Paul.

"John?" Paul asked, "I don't have to tell you that Players is no friend of ours. Lovelin and I need to know if you have any relationship with them."

I answered, looking directly at Lovelin. "Mr. Chairman, sir, I normally think it's imprudent to speak ill of a past employer during an interview. I want to make that clear first. I hope you know that I was one of the people who was responsible for Players' success and that I always upheld and acted on the policy of keeping benefits local. I achieved good results for Players and was rewarded with what you could call an invitation to leave the company. I'm pissed, to be honest. I'll be pissed for a long time. I have no respect for the Players executives. I have solid reasons for feeling this way. And I have no reason to have any loyalties to them."

Lovelin looked at me for a long moment, then looked to Paul and nodded. Before Paul spoke again, I said to Lovelin, "Sir, I understand you were decorated in Vietnam, that you won the Medal of Honor. My full respect to you. I have a military background myself. I'm proud to mention that I was infantry, too, US Army Special Forces and 82nd Airborne. We prefer to call ourselves a band of brothers."

"Thank you, Mr. Brotherton," Lovelin said, his voice soft.

"Tell us about yourself, John, about who you are," Paul said.

I covered my childhood, briefly mentioning my Native American Indian blood relatives. I told them that they already knew about my time in the military. Then I covered my oilfield experience, emphasizing that I had appreciated the opportunity to immerse myself in other cultures.

"As I told you, John, we have an election coming up," Paul said. "I've told Lovelin about your public relations and campaign management backgrounds. Can you tell us some more about this?"

I explained that I was accustomed to dealing with political issues, to making contacts with politicians, and to communicating with the media. I also filled them in on my efforts in obtaining what had turned out to be a temporary monopoly for Players. I added that I had effectively countered an earlier attempt to pass a bill that would have allowed a referendum on whether to eject Players from Calcasieu Parish.

"How would you suggest we handle Bertney Langley?" Paul asked.

"What do the members of your tribe think of mudslinging?" I asked him.

"They don't like it if they know it for what it is."

"Then we should make sure it gets around that Langley is getting desperate. Emphasize that he can't come to terms with you on issues, so he has to nose around looking for dirty laundry. You do this right and his low down tactics will leave a residue on him. That, and in your own campaigning stick to issues that are important. Be Langley's counterpoint."

"We can make him look like a hypocrite without really trying to," Paul said.

"You'll make him look worse," I added. "He'll show himself plainly as all pretense."

"As I said, John, you have a mind for this sort of thing," Paul commented.

"I have a mind for something else too," I said. "I have a memo from Madamba to his boss at Players. It mentions how Players was planning to pay Langley for the effort he was making to try and put a stop to your casino."

Lovelin looked at me with flat, hard eyes.

"What I suggest is that we hold the memo till the last minute, till just before the election, and that we then send it out to the tribal members, tucked in with other informational items."

"You mean a campaign package?" Paul said.

"Right," I answered. "By that time I'll have had a chance to put some of the policies I'm working up for the casino operation into place. The tribe should be able to see that the casino's being managed more to their benefit. We could say something about that. The timing should be perfect."

"I like it, John," Paul said with enthusiasm.

Lovelin's eyes narrowed as he sat looking at the table. He looked at Paul, at me, then back at Paul. "I need to talk to Mr. Berman," he said.

"Lyle Berman is Grand's Chairman," Paul explained. "We make our own decisions, but it's best to refer them to Mr. Berman."

Following the interview, I felt as certain that I had landed the job as I could without having a formal offer in hand. Several days passed, however, with no word from Ruppert; and I began to chew my liver. By now, I had my sights set on the position and was prepared to resort to my final solution. If it were going to be so strictly a matter of politics, then I'd deploy strict politics as a tactical weapon. I'd use the system that seemed to get things done most reliably in Louisiana.

I called Rick Shetler and suggested that we get together. We met at his office, and I briefed him on my campaign to win the GM position. Then I told him I needed his help. It didn't surprise me that he offered to do anything he could. Rick and I had gone through stormy periods in the past, but I knew he went into his prick mode mainly when he was involved in this or that scheme to fatten Stephen's or Edwin's stash. Otherwise, I had always found him to be openly warm and generous, even sympathetic, as he had been when he had offered Kathy and me the presidential suite in the governor's mansion, back during Edwin's last term.

"Let's go and get you that job," he said. He reached for the phone, called Stephen, and asked him if we could meet with him this afternoon, at his law office.

"That's set," he said to me. "We'll go in a bit here. I've just got to take care of something first." He picked up some papers from his desk and called for Sue, his secretary. Among the papers I saw a check from Jebaco. He handed them to Sue and told her, "Go to the bank and cash these. Bring me back the money."

When she returned, he took the cash and waited until she left the office. Then he took what I could see was a large stack of hundred dollar bills and placed them in a white envelope. He stood, put the envelope in his back pocket, and said, "There. Let's go."

Stephen was sitting at his desk when we arrived in his office. He stood and we shook hands. Then Rick asked me, "John, could you excuse us for just a minute?"

Before I left the office, I set my briefcase on the floor. Rick closed the door behind me. I walked down the hall to Julie's office and stopped in to say hello. The whole office was, she told me, celebrating a victory. The fifteenth riverboat license had just been awarded to a partnership between Hollywood Casinos and Eddie DeBartolo, Jr. Stephen's firm, Julie said, been involved in the process, and employees were jubilant because their horse had won.

I congratulated her and walked back up the hall to Stephen's office. I peeked in through the door and looked at Rick. He motioned for me to join Stephen and him. I then entered and shut the door behind me. As I passed my briefcase, I paused a moment, bent over to pick it up, and said "my briefcase." I had, of course, no way of knowing that the FBI had planted a bug in the office. Later, I'd have occasion to wish that I had made the door scream on its hinges when I left and came back in and that I had roared something like, "I'm John Brotherton, coming back in the door and picking up my briefcase, which I placed there when I walked out."

As I walked over to take an empty chair in front of Stephen's desk, I saw on the desk a plump white envelope that looked to be a duplicate of the envelope that I had earlier seen Rick stuff with hundred dollar bills. For about a half-hour, we talked about a number of topics, including

Grand's contract to manage the Coushatta casino. We even kicked around the idea of taking it over when it expired.

On our way back to Lake Charles, Rick explained that Stephen had suggested we contact Cecil Brown, who ran an auctioning business in Eunice and who, Rick pointed out, looked after Edwin's interests in the area in which the Grand Casino was located. "Stephen thinks he may be able to say some helpful things for you to the right people," Rick said.

The next morning Rick and I drove to Eunice and met with Cecil in his office. Again, I had no way of knowing that the FBI was maintaining surveillance, in this case of both the parking lot and the office.

Rick advocated my cause with vigor, and Cecil agreed to talk to Lovelin on my behalf, but under one condition. If I were hired as GM, he said, he'd expect me to exert influence on Ruppert and Lovelin regarding $250,000 he said the tribe owed him for helping get the casino through the regulatory process. Pointing to several pictures of Edwin Edwards and him on his wall, he said the majority of this amount was supposed to go to the "big man."

Before I had a chance to reply, Rick assured Cecil that I'd look after the matter to his satisfaction. On the drive back to Lake Charles, I sat silent, thinking about what I had stepped into. I had contacted Rick to play the political card, and now I was certainly reaping an abundance of what I had asked for. Again, I asked myself if getting the job with Grand was worth immersing myself in a slough of political antics. Again, I thought of how Players had hung me out to dry. I thought of walking point on patrol through enemy territory. I had routinely done the equivalent for Players. Then I thought of risking a glance behind me, only to find that my slack and drag elements had stayed back at the firebase. Players had routinely done the equivalent to me. I thought again of my final talk with Madamba, not the wisest thing for me to do because it brought back what he had said. In fact, I could almost hear his sniveling voice—"Take it or leave it, Brotherton. I don't give a shit myself." Do I really want this job? Is it really worth all this crap? I asked myself. I do, I answered. Damned right I do, and damned right it is.

A week after Rick and I had met with Cecil Brown, I received a formal offer of the position of general manager of the Grand Casino Coushatta directly from Grand's president, Tom Brosig, acting on directions from the company's chairman, Lyle Berman. The offer came at a meeting that was held at the Grand Casino in Biloxi, Mississippi.

On the morning of the meeting, I met Paul Ruppert and Lovelin at the Jennings airfield. From there, we flew to Biloxi in the tribe's B-200 King Air. In the course of the meeting, I was interviewed briefly by both Lyle Berman and Tom Brosig. Pat Menche was present but had little to say. I could tell by his body language, however, that he was less than thrilled that I had sabotaged his strategy to eliminate me from the running.

After we finished lunch, and as we were walking into the lobby of the casino complex, Paul stepped me to the side and said, "John, I want you to wait here for a minute. Lovelin and I need to talk to Lyle and Tom."

Paul then led Lovelin, Lyle, Tom, and Pat into the bar. I watched the ad hoc conference through the glass wall that separated the bar from the lobby. Lovelin sat next to Lyle and addressed him directly, without so much as a glance toward Tom or Pat. For a moment, Lovelin and Lyle appeared to be in a heated dispute. Then Lovelin leaned back in his chair, folded his arms, and stared Lyle down. Lyle made a statement to Tom and Pat. Then both Tom and Pat stood up and walked toward me, with the others following. When Tom reached me, he held out his hand, and said, "Congratulations, John. You are the new general manager of the Grand Casino Coushatta."

On the return flight, I thanked Ruppert and Lovelin for their help. I didn't ask anything about what Lovelin had said to Lyle Berman. But I assumed that it took something carrying magnum force to so quickly bend the chairman of a corporation as powerful as Grand. Back in Jennings, after we had gotten off the plane, I let Lovelin walk ahead of Paul and me. Then I handed him the coffee stained memo that he hoped would blow Bertney Langley's chances in the election out of the water.

Later that afternoon, I called Ken Hagan and asked him if we could get together early that evening, at Coconuts again. Now that I had been officially hired by Grand, I knew he would be all for raising more than a few victory toasts on Players' own domain.

Ken was there when I arrived. As I came up to the table, he pulled a chair out and raised a saltshaker in his right hand.

"I'll need more salt than that for what I have in mind," I said, as I sat down.

Later, after we had run up a tab that I wouldn't be charging to a Players account, he said, "Hope you're not too mannered to tell your former employers where they can ram their agreements."

"You know me better than that, Ken. You'll see, my friend. It's coming—sooner than later."

CHAPTER 17

TEN YEARS GONE

Thus piteously love closed what he begat:
The union of this ever-diverse pair.

– George Meredith, *Modern Love*

＊

At the same time that my professional life looked to be moving toward steady state, my personal life was heading for a setback in the form of a shipwrecked marriage.

Back near the end of 1995, Howard had directed me to move to Atlantic City. I had completed that move and had my family living in a house I had bought there when Howard then assigned me full time to try and salvage the expansion of the Lake Charles casino. So for the first three months of 1996, I had been living at such a distance from my family that I had been unable to see them regularly. In March, Howard told me to relocate my residence to Lake Charles.

To prepare for my family's move, I had undertaken an ambitious house hunt and had chosen a one-story, 4,000 square foot home located on four acres, south of Lake Charles, on the outer edge of the suburbs. To the south and the west, thick woods extended from the borders of the lot.

To the east, the lot sloped down to a bayou that connected with the Intercoastal Waterway.

I had selected this home carefully, preferring it for its tranquil setting over several more ostentatious alternatives, and had pledged every cent I had in my Merrill Lynch account to guarantee the mortgage. I wanted a place to live where I could slow my life down and spend long overdue quality time with Kathy, Derek, and Macie. In April, I completed the deal on the house and moved my family from Atlantic City.

Kathy, however, had already launched herself on a course that could best be described as Homewrecking 101. When we had bought a house in Atlantic City, we had hired two contractors—named Liam and David— to do some remodeling work. This work was still in progress when I was shifted back to Lake Charles. When I would talk to the kids, I'd get bits and pieces of information to the effect that Kathy was indulging in drinking bouts with the contractors and that they were staying up late together. Now and then, I was also told, she was taking overnight trips with them to Philadelphia. Because my INT was coming mostly from Derek and Macie, I had to be careful about confronting Kathy; I didn't feel that it was fair to put the kids in a compromising position.

When she moved into our new home outside of Lake Charles, Kathy insisted that I hire Liam and David for renovation and remodeling work that she wanted done. She even went so far as to insist they live with us, to save accommodation costs. My suspicions that Kathy was carrying on with the contractors would leap toward a gnawing certainty whenever we were all together in the house. Kathy, Liam, and David would give me that "We know something that you don't" look that is a world of revelation in itself.

In hindsight, it's always much easier to see the conclusion of a crisis rearing itself like a neon signal in the complex of events that made up the crisis. When you're caught up in the immediacy of those events, however, you can be blind to the message on the wall. So it was with me. I had my suspicions, as I say; but I also had my hopes that my family life would stabilize once we had settled into our new house—once we had turned it into a real home.

About three months after the move to Lake Charles, Kathy started hanging around with a new friend, Mary—an officer employed in the Drug and Alcohol Resistance Education (DARE) program run by the Lake Charles Police Department. Initially, it amused me that Mary would call Kathy and enlist her company for a night of bar hopping and heavy drinking after driving about all day in her department's black van (with the DARE wordmark in red letters on both sides), preaching to school children about the pitfalls of substance abuse. But as the length of their drinking sessions extended into the morning hours and as their frequency increased to several nights a week, I began to object to Mary. Kathy's reply was that Mary—whose husband had recently left her and taken up residence with another woman—needed the support of a friend.

My concern turned to alarm when, during one of their visits to their favorite bar, Cocktails, in downtown Lake Charles, Mary introduced Kathy to a truck driver named Tony Hay. I didn't like anything I heard about Tony; and from its outset the situation smelled of big trouble. As Kathy insisted, Tony was, as was Mary, a friend in need of a shoulder to cry on. He had just been through a nasty divorce in which his wife had, she claimed, cleaned him out financially. He was in such dire straits that he didn't own a car and had no place to live other than a trailer that his company offered to let him use temporarily. The trailer was located inside the plot of his company's office complex.

I knew that big trouble had arrived on my doorstep when Kathy started staying out all night with her new friends and when Tony started calling the house, asking for Kathy, who would take the call in our bedroom, with the door closed.

Two incidents brought the gathering crisis to its final head. The first took place the morning after Kathy returned home, after having stayed out all night for the third time in a month. I was pretty sure she had been out with Tony, and I was waiting for her when her car pulled into our driveway. As she tried to enter the back door quietly, it didn't register on her, in her hung over condition, that I had secured the chain lock. Her eyes were glazed over as she shook the door back and forth, trying to open it. I walked up to the door, unfastened the lock, and stepped back to let her in. She stood staring at me stupefied; she looked like death warmed over.

"Looks like you had a rough night," I said. "I was worried. I called the police and reported you as a missing person."

"You did what?" she shrieked.

"Where were you? I tried your cell phone and beeped you at least twenty times."

Quickly, she shook herself out of her stupor, gathered her wits, and shot back, "I was out with Mary. We stayed at a friend's house, down in Cameron Parish. My cell phone and pager don't work down there."

I knew that the cell phone and the pager did work down there and decided that it was time to confront her. "I think you're lying to me, Kathy. I'm learning to tell when you're lying these days. It's whenever your lips are moving. You're involved with this Tony, and I think you should have the decency to tell me. You were out with him all night."

Her arms went straight to her side and her shoulders hunched into an attitude that feigned outrage. "Maybe I was. But Tony is just a friend, and that's all he'll ever be. You think I'd be interested in a fucking truck driver. John, please? I'm smarter than that."

Her insult to my own intelligence stung me. "You're not as smart as you think you are or you wouldn't assume I'm so stupid. You think I deserve this kind of treatment? I don't for the life of me know why you have to act like a slut."

"Fuck you!" she roared at me. "You don't know what you're talking about."

No, Kathy," I replied. "Fuck you. You need to get the kids up so they won't be late for school."

Twenty minutes later, I watched her load the kids into the Rolls Royce I had bought for her some time ago. As she pulled away, I noticed a new dent that extended about two feet across the back bumper. It looked to be the result of a run in with a telephone pole. I didn't have to stretch my imagination to figure out how the dent had been inflicted.

The second incident was a week-long rafting trip on the stretch of the Rio Grande near Terlingua, Texas, that Kathy was determined to take with, as she claimed, Mary and a number of friends, including Tony. Months earlier, Kathy and I had thought of buying a company that ran river tours near Terlingua. At that time, Kathy and Mary had gone on a float trip to assess the operation, so they said. The rationale for the present trip, as Kathy explained it, was to encourage the present owner to consider partial owner financing as part of our offer by demonstrating that we would be able to market the touring service effectively.

Macie and Derek, who were out of school for Easter break, were to stay with Kathy's parents, who were vacationing at their camp on the Toledo Bend Reservoir. Kathy would pick up Tony in her new, four-wheel drive truck (which I had just bought for her, to accommodate hew new image as a rafting aficionado), and they would drive to Terlingua, where they would pick up Rob and Becky, two friends who'd be flying from Houston. Kathy would find out the hard way that Rob and Becky were close friends of mine.

Then Mary and most of the friends dropped out; and I sensed that the rafting party was narrowing to Kathy and Tony, and Rob and Becky. I would find out later that Kathy had paid Rob and Becky's travel costs, probably to insure that at least someone else would come along with her and Tony on the trip for appearances sake. I made it plain to Kathy that I thought she was pushing the envelope in her association with Tony.

"Fuck you, John," she replied. "I told you before that Tony is just a friend. I'm getting tired of your paranoid nonsense. I swear that there's nothing going on between us."

The night she left, she tore out of the driveway in such a hurry that she didn't even stop to help our little dog, Cowboy, who had apparently just been run over by a car. She didn't even stop to tell me of the accident. Instead, she called me on her cell phone, on her way to get Tony. She was at least humane enough to let me know where I could find him—in a ditch on the east side of our driveway.

As it turned out, the two of them were in such a mating frenzy that they ditched Becky and Rob, leaving them on the highway in Terlingua, where they had to hitch hike a ride to the local airport, so they could get back home to Houston. Angry at being dumped and offended by Kathy's and Tony's openly touchy-feely antics, Becky called me and reported the whole story. Kathy was referring to Tony as her new boyfriend, and the two of them were sharing sleeping quarters—first the same tent and then the same motel room. Becky didn't hesitate to give me the name of the motel. For a moment, I thought of loading up my Spas Auto twelve gauge with double O buckshot and paying the lovers a surprise visit. I had read an account of a Texas judge charging a husband who had surprised his wife and her lover and who had shot them both to death with nothing more severe than disturbance of the peace. Instead, I placed a call to the motel and asked for Tony Hay's room.

I was surprised that he had registered under his own name. He either figured I wouldn't call or hadn't thought of taking even elementary measures to cover his tracks. Whichever the case, he impressed me as being quite an amatuer when it came to management of a dangerous liaison.

After two rings, Kathy answered. "You've got a notion of friendship that I don't think I can live with," I said. The line went dead immediately.

When she returned from her rafting trip, Kathy rented a small, wood-framed house in central Lake Charles and told me that she was moving out, that she was taking Derek and Macie, who were both numbed by the suddenness of this change in their lives. I was reluctant to let them leave with Kathy but had, at the moment, no legal basis on which to stand in Kathy's way. I felt that she was hell bent on any measure that would hurt me and that she viewed the kids as little more than resources to be deployed to achieve her vendetta.

I don't think I'll ever be able to forget the day she came over to move her belongings out of the house I had chosen for my family. She had the audacity to bring Tony with her. Then, when I first met him, Kathy's knight errant looked to me like a bum. He was wearing a soiled T-shirt, a pair of dirty, loose fitting jeans, and a baseball hat. His bowling ball gut hung over and covered his belt buckle. It also struck me that he had to be a lot dumber than he looked. On his thick black belt, in a leather sheath, he wore a jack knife that was large enough to be used as a hunting knife.

For a moment, I felt like confronting him—to make it clear that he was never to wear the knife in my house or around Derek or Macie. But I could see Kathy's mind at work here, bringing him to what had been our home, openly armed. She was hoping that I'd lose my self-control and do something she could use to get me into trouble. So I kept cool headed and simply took note that she would go to wild extremes in what I was beginning to see as her holy jihad against me.

I turned away from Tony and followed Kathy as she proceeded through the house. I almost had to laugh at the care she was taking to turn any pictures of us face down before Tony could see them. She also quickly threw all of our old Hallmark cards into a drawer to hide them from his view. As I watched her, she knew she was busted, but she didn't care. It was apparent that she was trying to make it seem to him that our marriage had been over much earlier. It took her about half an hour to gather what she wanted. Then she was gone, with Tony. Later, I'd learn that she had moved him into her rental house almost immediately.

Living alone, in a dead quiet house (no longer a home), with no more tucking my children in at night, was disorienting to an extreme. Every morning for the first week after Kathy left, I woke up expecting to find the kids asleep in their rooms. My routine was to wake them up and muster them to breakfast. Then we'd sit at the kitchen table, where I'd drink my first cup of coffee while they ate their cereal.

Now the house was so empty that I began listening to the echo of my footsteps. It was the closest thing I could hear to a sound other than my own. I fell into a morbid state, in which I lost all track of time and in which I also lost any sense of distinction between what was normal and what was aberrant. At first, I would call Kathy and ask to come to see the kids. She'd demand me not to; it would, she insisted, be unfair to Tony; and I'd feel that I had no choice but to go without seeing them. Then she deployed a strategy that was nothing short of diabolical—contemptible, in fact, because of its impact on the kids. On the one hand, she started insinuating to Derek that I didn't really think of him as my son. If I called and by chance asked to speak to Macie, she'd holler, "So you don't want to talk to Derek?" On the other hand, she took any occasion to try to alienate Macie from me also. If, for instance, I called and wanted to speak with Derek, she'd yell out that I didn't want to talk to my daughter. As the weeks passed, it got to the point where I was afraid to call at all; to do so gave Kathy a chance to twist whatever I said to serve her demented campaign.

Terrified of waking up in the morning to a deserted house, I was unable to sleep much at night. My appetite vanished and my weight dwindled and I fell into an ennui so deep that I lay in bed fully awake but inert for hours at a time. It was at this time that Harlan Duhon, with whom I had faced off in the old Downtowner bar my first night in Lake Charles, showed himself to be a stalwart friend. Worried about the depth of my depression, he started coming by to check on me, to see if he could buoy my spirits. Though I appreciated his support, it didn't help much; I was too much in the grip of my black study.

And then it came.

For some reason, I didn't notice that the world had changed. All had transformed to become structured shadows of wrought iron—houses, walls, people, walking away, flattening, becoming almost two-dimensional, but not quite. Pastels of olive green and dark mustard filled the gaps in the shadows. The sky was dark and finite. There were no stars to gaze at anymore. No reason to even consider the sky. It all made sense and, in another corner of my mind, it made none at all. But that corner I lived in didn't object.

At the center of this world, was a shining, happy, giggling little girl, excited with life and with me. She was everything and everywhere. Not made of wrought iron, she contrasted this bleak world with a radiant glow of sun yellow. She was my baby; she was my Macie.

The home we now shared was a large, two-story Victorian manor from the nineteenth century. It was just the two of us; everyone else I previously knew didn't exist anymore. Macie's room lay at the top of the stairs, where I tucked her in each night. My bedroom was at the bottom. We threw large parties for no reason at all. I seemed to know most of the guests that came, but I didn't talk to them. I just watched as Macie prepared and served them her latest hors' de oeuvres. I didn't know or even care where they lived. They were from beyond the barrier of our world.

Macie and I played, talked, and laughed out loud. We had no cares, and I had no reason to concern myself with work or with bills. My mornings were spent watching her play in the yard. My afternoons were of tea and crumpets, prepared by my little sunshine. Our Cheshire cat hung lazily from the tree in the yard, watching us with a big, curious grin. Each evening was rich with good stories, read to her in front of the warm and dark fireplace.

I loved her and she loved me and all was wonderful in this world.

Then we decided to throw another party. The usual guests attended, wearing their black shadows accented again with olive green and mustard yellow. But this time there was something different—something that made me feel uncomfortable. Somewhere in the room of guests, I could feel the presence of an unwelcome stranger—a dangerous stranger. As I watched the crowd, I could barely make out an unfamiliar shadow from time to time, meandering back and forth among the guests. For some unknown reason, I didn't pursue.

When the party was over, the guests left in an orderly fashion as usual, showing themselves to the door. Macie and I were left alone again. We cleaned up and I tucked her happily in for the night. But the sense of dread still hung in the air. It made the hair on the back of my neck tingle as I lay in bed, looking up at the dark ceiling.

In the dead of night, I was stirred by a cry from Macie. I ran up the stairs to discover that she was not in her bed. The sheets were strewn across the floor of her room. I screamed as I spiraled down into a vertigo panic—absolute terror, cascading with rushes of pure adrenaline—and fell to the floor. I frantically searched the house. Then I wandered out into the abyss beyond our yard, searching for the inevitable.

Panic turned sour, becoming overwhelming sadness. All was now black—no more mustard yellow; no more olive green; no more sunshine girl. In some way that I can't explain, I knew what had happened. The mad logic that ruled this world whispered the answer to my soul—Macie had been taken by the terrible stranger and killed. He had snuffed out her happy little life for his own sick pleasure. I got angry. I reverted to what I knew best. It was time for "the Lord's work."

The same creature of mad logic had whispered something else to me. "He'll come back again, once more, this time for you."

I pulled a .308 from the closet and removed the Starlight scope. Wouldn't need it at such close range. I fastened a single bullet to the drill press and guided the bit slowly but deeply into the lead. Pouring in just enough mercury, I sealed the hole with a small bit of wax, smoothing the tip for good ballistics. I filed the burrs from the rest of the bullet and then made four deep scores down each side so that it would burst open on impact. I loaded the bullet at the top of a full clip. I took a plastic Coke bottle from the fridge and emptied it, tying it over the muzzle with black electrical tape. No need to wake the neighbors.

I decided that I would deal out my punishment in the same room that my sunshine had slept—the place from which he had taken her to perform his sick ritual. I cleared out a space in the back of her large closet and cracked the door open just enough to stick the Coke bottle through. I leaned my back against the wall and brought my knees up so that I could rest the weapon on them. I had a nice clear shot. I pushed the clip in, then locked and loaded, chambering the deadly round. Then I waited, for months. I didn't need to eat. I didn't need to sleep. I only needed justice.

Then one night, very late, it happened. I could see the door to Macie's room slowly and quietly open. A head appeared in the doorway; then a man's body came fully through. I could see that he held a knife in his hand as he looked back and forth from one end of the room to the other. I waited for him to walk slowly to the center of the room. When he was directly in front of me, I moved the sights from below his ear and re-aimed them on his left knee. I ever so gently squeezed the trigger.

"Ssss-thunk" the projectile quietly reported as it entered the left knee, exploded out the other side, and then cleanly severed the adjacent knee from the leg. The mercury had performed well. The murderer dropped to the floor like a sack of potatoes, in shock, not realizing what had just taken place. Before he could scream, I was out of the closet, slamming the butt of the weapon down hard on his head with full force. He went limp long enough for me to get the baggie-tie on his hands behind his back. I rolled him over and rested my ankles in his armpits, his head propped face-up between my knees. Then I slowly began recognizing the face of the killer. It was Tony the Trucker.

I was certain that the man knew his own death was imminent, so I began my interrogation with the belief that I would get to the truth.

"What did you do with my little girl?" I asked through tightly gritted teeth.

"She's dead, been dead," he replied in a groan of pain. Then he grinned at me through his bloody teeth.

I reached one hand into his right armpit, clasping the pectoral at the tendon, then lunged my four fingers into the pit while clamping hard. He shrieked in pain. I had to act fast before the loss of blood faded his consciousness.

"How?" I asked with a seething growl.

"Slowly and painfully, you motherfucker! I enjoyed every minute!" he screamed.

He shouldn't of pushed me.

I reached behind my back and pulled my long knife from its sheath. As I did, the killer laughed again in defiance.

"You know what kind of knife this is, asshole?" I asked with a cute slur. "It's a skinning knife."

The killer shrieked again as he began to understand his fate. After a little bit, he stopped and began gasping for breath. He was probably beginning to lose his grip on reality. Just as well; no one could go through what I had in mind for him and last very long.

I reached into my side pocket and pulled out my mini acetylene cutting torch. I lit it. The moment I touched the flame of the torch to the blade, *I awoke and sat upright in the bed and screamed, "She's alive! Thank you, God, she's still alive!"*

Macie wasn't dead, she was alive. It had all been a bad dream.

The application of the nightmare was clear enough to me. Tony had lost his own daughter as a result of his divorce. Now I felt he was coveting my family as a replacement. Deliberately, I figured, he had chosen Kathy—a disillusioned housewife with a ready-made family, a convenient target for him. Worse, he and Kathy were drawn together into a conspiracy against me that would victimize both Derek and Macie, that would sentence them to an existence in which they'd have to contend with a live-in stepfather and Kathy's persistent alienation effort, in which they'd be separated from me from day to day, and in which they could only see me during permitted visitations. I didn't need to be a child psychologist to imagine the long term, year-to-year stress load that would be imposed on my children. I had read and seen enough to know that the contemporary iteration of the American tragedy is a generation of children and young adults to an alarming extent rendered dysfunctional by the angst inflicted on them by their broken homes.

I had also been letting the stress of my marriage breakup have at me like a vampire—its fangs fastened to my jugular, glutting itself on the blood that should be sustaining me, while I lay a passive victim.

Victim? I thought. Me, victimized? Am I beginning to sound like Tony? Is he my shadow self? Is that why I hate him? No, there's more to it than that. I realized that my dream had also warned me of something brutish and primitive in Tony that would bear watching.

The image of myself as prostrate, defeated by stress, sent a surge of rebellion through me. I had to get out of my black hole, now. With every moment of time I lost I was losing more of myself. I threw off the bed covers, jumped to the floor, and stood looking out the window. It was a beautiful day, still very early. I'd put on shorts, a T-shirt, and my runners and get my butt back into the full PT (physical training) routine that had been a daily given in my life at Fort Bragg. It wouldn't be just fifty push-ups and sit-ups; it'd also be five miles of roadwork. And I'd do it today even if it made by body scream all over with the pain of it. If you hurt, I'd been told, you heal. I was certainly hurting. Time now, I realized, to see to my own healing. And part of that, I resolved, would be bending no farther to Kathy's wicked brand of tyranny.

Back from the run, which went more easily than I had expected, I was about to step into the shower when the phone rang. I didn't have to guess who it was.

"I've changed my mind," Kathy said, smugly. "What we agreed on for child support just won't cut it. I want five thousand a month. My friends tell me I can get almost your entire paycheck if I take you to court."

I laughed and thought, How's this? This woman distributes herself in New Jersey, Texas, and here in Louisiana and thinks she can specify to me a sum like that, as if I don't know the overgrown child she'd be really supporting? I said, "You'd better get yourself ready for a fight, Kathy. That includes who's going to be keeping the kids."

My first move was to find an experienced divorce lawyer. I called Henry Liles, whom I knew Rick Shetler had used for his own divorce, and made an appointment for the next day. We met at his office, just south of Lake Charles. I was a half-hour into explaining my marriage breakdown and its aftermath when I heard, coming from the lobby, a voice I couldn't help but recognize. "Where is the motherfucker? I know he's here! I see his fucking car out in the parking lot!"

Then Kathy stormed into Henry's office. "There you are, you motherfucker! I saw your car out there. You think you're going to use Rick's lawyer to fuck me? Fuck you! I'm a woman. The judge will give me everything—everything, you motherfucker!"

With effort, I kept myself calm. Also, I made a decision. I'd get Kathy out of Henry's office, somehow get her on her way, then I'd make a call I maybe should have made in the first place.

I apologized to Henry, walked out of his office, and out into the parking lot, with Kathy following me, cussing a streak that established a personal best for her. Up ahead, I could see Macie and Derek sitting in her truck, staring at us, in shock. I stopped, turned, and walked back toward an advancing Kathy. I wanted to get far enough away from the kids that they wouldn't hear what was sure to be a caustic exchange.

Kathy and I came together about twenty feet from the truck. "I'll fuck you over so fast your head will swim," she said. "I'm the woman. I'm in charge here. The judge is going to take my side no matter what. You'll see, you stupid motherfucker."

"Kathy," I said, "the kids can probably hear you. You don't want—"

"I don't give a fuck!" she screamed, pointing toward her truck. "I'll destroy those kids if that's what it takes to get your ass, you motherfucker."

At that moment, a Lake Charles police cruiser turned into the parking lot and approached us. I could see Henry waving at me from his office window. As a thank you gesture, I waved back.

One of the officers got out of the cruiser and walked toward us. I raised my hands and shook my head, as Kathy continued cussing. The officer got my message and walked up to Kathy. "You need to settle down," he said to her, politely.

She glared at him, at me, then back at him. "Oh, you don't scare me. I'm going to get that motherfucker, that Mighty Mr. John Brotherton. He's a motherfucker!"

The officer removed his handcuffs from his belt and took a step toward her. "I mean it," he said. "One more word and you're going in."

That sunk into Kathy's seething brain. She walked to her truck, got in, started up, and tore off. As she turned out into the street and sped by the parking lot, she rolled down her window and shot the finger at me.

I apologized to the officer. "That's my soon-to-be ex wife," I said. "She's acting a little strange."

"A little?" he asked.

"Well, maybe more than a little," I answered.

"He was smart enough to hire a good attorney," Eddie Austin had said of Ken Hagan, when Players was trying to shove him on the real cost of constructing the entertainment barge. Kathy was now living with Tony—a situation that, when I thought about it, sent nausea through me. Though Macie was only eight and Derek thirteen, they weren't so naïve that they didn't know Kathy and I were still married and still their mother and father. But they wouldn't be able to rationalize fully that the rupture in the marriage relationship was strictly owing to antagonisms between Kathy and me. I feared they would—as would any young child—burden themselves with guilt, feeling that they had done something to cause the breakup.

I was particularly worried about the kids being exposed day in and day out to Tony. I couldn't see a single thing about him that I regarded as wholesome, and there was little that I would put past him. I knew, moreover, that Kathy would try everything she could think of to push me out of the picture and to substitute Tony as the father figure. I had seen her do this before, when she had met me and had discarded her first husband, Eddie Strysik. I had never heard her explain to her son that being in jail may have been the reason that he didn't come around afterwards. What worried me most was that I knew Kathy wasn't rational enough to realize the damage she'd be inflicting on the kids by demonizing me.

It was time to see if the Austin protocol was available to me. I knew Ken Hagan would have Eddie's home number. Besides, it would boost my morale to talk with my good friend.

Ken had caught wind of Kathy's antics and had, he said, mentioned them to Eddie Austin. "Did he offer to act for me?" I asked. "I know he doesn't practice divorce law."

"He didn't say anything concrete other than, 'John has my card. He knows how to call me,'" Ken answered.

I told him about the visit I had just received from Kathy and added my impressions of Tony.

"If I were you, I'd call him right away. This has gone far enough. You want his number at home?"

"You bet your ass I do, buddy. Think he'll mind?"

"If I know Eddie, he won't. And I think I know Eddie."

So far from minding my calling him at home, Eddie was thrilled to hear from me. "I'm not just a lawyer, you know," he said after I apologized for any inconvenience I was imposing. "I like hearing from my friends. You're a friend of Ken's; you're a friend of mine. So why've you been making yourself so scarce?"

I explained that my deteriorating marriage had gotten the better of me and that I had crawled into my cave.

"I don't normally deal with divorces," he explained, "but in your case I'm willing to make an exception. Ken's filled me in on some of the happenings, for lack of a better word."

I told him *happenings* suited the context perfectly. I also told him I'd be on thin ice financially until I got another check from Players.

"My fee is something we can discuss later, when you're on your feet," he said. "If she's living with this Tony Hay, you have adultery, given that the two of you are still married. But you have to prove they're spending nights together. Do you know her address?"

I gave him the address of Kathy's house and listened as he dialed a number on another line. "I need surveillance and pictures—the adultery beat," I heard him say.

I asked him if he needed to go that far.

"The pictures are important, John," he said. "They can prove to the court that a man spent the entire night with your wife. Prove that, and the court'll assume adultery. The court assumes that and you get an immediate divorce, no alimony."

I thanked him and told him I knew I had come to the right place.

"I was telling you this is the right place back when I gave you my card," he said. "I think we ought to get together to talk more about this. I think, in fact, that it's time you got social and invited me over to your place. If you have no problem with it, I'll be over this Saturday, about noon. Crown will be fine. That okay?"

I told him it was more than okay, that I'd love to see him. After I hung up, I felt like I had put the black dog that had been snapping at my heels miles behind me.

My talk with Eddie reminded me of another matter that had the potential to get legal—the status of my agreements with Players. Because Grand had offered me the job as general manager of the Grand Casino Coushatta complex, I needed to clear the matter with Howard. To accept the appointment without formal clearance from Players would make me vulnerable to litigation. I called Howard the next morning, and he agreed in principle to change the agreements, to remove the "non-compete" provisions. But he wanted me to finalize the matter with Pat Madamba.

I was unable to reach Madamba until late in the afternoon. He had already discussed the agreement with Howard and was ready with what he thought would be an effective spanner. "Well, John," he said, "I think everything is pretty well in order except one item."

I asked him to put me in the loop.

"We want you to get Players out from the contract with CMMS. Do that, we have a deal. Otherwise, John, no deal."

CMMS was an electrical contracting enterprise that was owned by Harlan Duhon's wife. During the construction phase of the Lake Charles expansion, Madamba had, as part of Players' effort to add businesses owned by women to the vendors' list, negotiated a contract with her. Players, however, had as yet not met its payment obligations to CMMS. Nor, as I understood it, had Players met its requirement to inform the Louisiana Gaming Commission of the contract. Madamba, I figured, was trying to coerce me into taking advantage of my friendship with Harlan to in turn coerce his wife into ditching the contract, thus relieving Players of the need to pay up and of the chance that the commission, if it were to get wind of the contract, would have cause to review and maybe suspend their casino license.

I smelled what amounted in my mind to blackmail. "And what if I can't do this?" I asked.

"Well, John, let me see now," Madamba sniveled. "As I see it, you're dead in the water. You've let Players know you want to go to work somewhere else. Technically, then, you're not a loyal associate of the company anymore. You have a job with Grand, who probably doesn't know you still have an existing agreement with us. Dead in the water, you see?"

"What I see is blackmail," I answered.

"John," Madamba pontificated, "I'm just telling you where you are at right now."

I kept myself calm, asked him to think very seriously about what he was proposing, and told him I'd call back in a few days. Fortunately, when I did get back to him, he had for some reason backed off his scheme. We finalized the changes to my agreements with Players, and I was free to take my new job.

About mid way through Saturday afternoon, Eddie and I were sitting in my living room, listening to classical music and discussing the complications involved in a father trying to gain sole custody of the children of a marriage. As Eddie explained it, unless radical evidence could be shown to demonstrate beyond all requirements of logic that Kathy was totally unfit to be a parent, the court would most likely grant joint custody but designate her as what's called the Domiciliary Parent. In effect, my rights—which would consist of visitation privileges—would be very similar to what they would be if she were to be given total custody. "In other words," I said, "joint custody doesn't mean shit."

"Probably as good a definition as I've heard," Eddie commented.

Our conversation was interrupted by the screeching sound of a vehicle tearing down the driveway; then, in moments, I saw Kathy's Rolls Royce careen around the back of the house, into the parking area between the back porch and the garage. She came to a grinding stop, jumped out, and ran toward us. Her eyes were bulging, and she had a leering grin across her face that I had never seen before.

I got up and closed and locked the French doors that opened onto the back porch. Exasperated, she stood on the other side of the glass shrieking, "You pay me, you son of a bitch! I own you! I own your sorry ass! I want it all! I want everything! You pay me now, motherfucker, or I'll break the glass!"

I just looked at her and shrugged my shoulders. I knew better than to say anything. She turned, ran into the garage, and started throwing around anything she could pick up. But that only seemed to fuel her frenzy all the more. She opened up the riding mower and pulled out all the wires she could get her hands on. Next she kicked over my motorcycle and tried pulling out the wiring from the side. Then she started spinning herself around and around, screaming out "Aaaaaagh! Aaaaagh" over and over.

"She's clinical," Eddie said to me. "Not just mad. I'm no psychiatrist, but I can tell you that what we're seeing now is some kind of psychotic episode. She's lost her connection to the real world."

"I know, Eddie," I said. "I suppose I've known for a long time. If I could only make her go the hell away."

"Where she is right now is a type of hell in itself," Eddie said.

"I know that too. I don't doubt she wants me in some sort of hell that she's prepared specially for me."

In court, the Austin protocol worked as effectively as I could have expected it to, given the divorce laws that prevail in Louisiana. Although Kathy initially petitioned the court, the judge awarded the divorce to me on grounds of adultery, with no contest from Kathy. As Eddie had predicted, Kathy and I were given "joint custody;" Kathy was named as the Domiciliary Parent; and I was given visitation rights, with additional dispensations for holidays and summer vacation. Thus a decree made official in seconds not only terminated a marriage of ten year's standing but also, as I feared would be the outcome, sentenced my son and my daughter to an emotional minefield of a life.

I'd be lying through my teeth if I were to deny that I have hard feelings even now. The final days of my marriage with Kathy were too traumatic—for me, and for Derek and Macie, I have no doubt. The best I can do is to remind my children that I love them every chance I get and to hope that Kathy will come to her senses enough to realize the sort of Russian roulette she has been playing with two developing, impressionable minds.

Almost everyone who becomes familiar with the history of my first marriage shows essentially the same reaction. First, the whole thing has the appearance of being so one-sided, with me more sinned against than sinning. Then there's always the question—Why did you put up with so much?

Strange as it may seem, anyone who knows me well can provide the answers far more readily than I can. (To be sure, I don't regard myself as being an infallible self-analyst.) Almost without exception, my close friends will point out two things about me of which I'm only vaguely aware. For one, I'm told I can't abide seeing anything to which I've committed myself fail. For another, it would be in my nature, probably because my own natural father abandoned my mother and me when I was very young, to persist to an extreme in holding a family unit together.

We've all heard about what's called the tragic flaw—not so much an imperfection in a person's makeup; more of a character trait that would propel one on a tragic course in specific situations. All I can really say here is that I have always refused to admit the word *quit* into my lexicon. It's that refusal to drop out of the ruck that's accounted for many of the successes in my life. I suppose it's also contributed to some of the unhappy outcomes. In that, then, I measure up to the human paradox that our strengths are also, often, our handicaps.

CHAPTER 18

THE RECKONING

✳

Watch me now, I sang to my reflection in the entrance doors to the Coushatta casino. I was reporting for my first day and was looking forward to biting into my new responsibilities. I certainly had enough on my plate. For starters, I'd have to master the financial reporting system. I'd also have to get myself on working terms with the vice presidents, managers, and staff.

As I approached the door into the lobby, I had a moment of self-doubt. You've never dealt a hand of Blackjack in your life, I told myself. You've never worked in the pit or managed one. You don't even know how to play craps. And here you're going to run one of the most profitable casinos on the face of the earth?

I thought of my break up with Kathy and of the despondency in which I had wallowed so recently. Then I looked out over the casino floor and thought of the reservation natives stuck here in low-paying, go-nowhere jobs. "Damned right you'll run this place," I said and opened the glass doors and walked into the casino.

Pat Menche met me at the entrance to the executive offices, gave me a friendly hello, and explained that I was expected at a meeting at ten, in which I'd introduce myself to the vice presidents and present my management strategy. As cordial as he was, I didn't appreciate having the presentation sprung on me at such short notice.

Just before I walked into my office, my secretary handed me a package. I noticed that it had already been opened and that it had been sent Fed Ex, by Players. It contained the final documentation of my revised consulting and retirement agreements. Madamba! I thought. I had told him specifically to mail the agreement to my residence, not to my office. Because Grand Casino Coushatta and Players Lake Charles were direct competitors, I didn't want anything to do with Players coming across my desk here. Looking at the package, I recalled that it was a standard precaution in most casino companies for security to open all parcels as a measure of protecting high-ranking personnel—regarded as priority targets among gamblers who had lost it all and were seeking revenge. But I also had to wonder, Has Menche read over the agreement? Will he keep it in the corner of his jaw and use it later to make it look like you still have ties to Players? No way to start your first day, John, I told myself.

I decided I'd have to short circuit Madamba's twisted sense of humor. Stored at home, I had my collection of tapes. I'd sift through them and find the ones that would scare his airs and graces right out of him.

I turned my attention to the meeting coming up in less than an hour. I wasn't ready with anything resembling an operating plan, and I felt Menche should have damned well known that. I had outflanked him before, however, and I knew how I'd do it again this time.

The conference was held in one of the meeting rooms adjacent to the casino's buffet restaurant. Menche signaled for me to take a chair at the head of the table and politely introduced me to the line up of VPs. Then he simply said "John" and took his seat. I first explained how pleased I was to be taking in hand the reigns of Grand Casino Coushatta's management team. Then I announced that, as my first initiative, I was appointing Jeff King as my new assistant general manager. I needed Jeff at my side, I explained, to break me in.

And I left it at that. I didn't see fit to introduce what I hoped would be one of my first and most positive initiatives—to open the higher employment ranks to reservation members, even if that meant extensive operations, supervisory, and management training. I wanted to discuss this

plan with Paul and Lovelin first and to then introduce it as a formal proposal. This way, Lovelin could work the plan into the fabric of his election
campaign.

Back at my desk, with noon hour coming up, I called Eddie Austin
at his office and invited him to come over to the casino as my first VIP
guest of honor. He accepted and arrived shortly after one in the afternoon.

As we were touring the floor, I mentioned the package from
Madamba.

"I wouldn't worry too much about him," Eddie said. "He'll push
you, but they won't be big pushes, just aggravations. But I'd keep an eye
on this Menche here. Guys like that won't meet you in the street. They
won't meet you anywhere. If you don't watch them, you won't know what
they're up to until you see it happening."

"Reminds me of a venomous ex-wife we both know," I said

"And how's Kathy behaving?" he asked.

I explained that she was probably in strategic pause, planning what
she'd do next to get in my face. "The last thing I need is for her to show
up here. Is there any chance you can arrange a restraining order?"

"I can," Eddie answered. "I'll file for it tomorrow morning. But,
from what I've seen of her, I won't guarantee that she'll abide by it. Then
you'd have to have her arrested. You'd have to think of the kids in that
case. But I'll see to it, and we'll just hope it works."

Eddie spent the afternoon reveling in his VIP status on the floor
while I tended to financial reports in my office. At five, I met him in the
lobby. He was standing just inside the glass entrance doors.

"I don't see your pockets bulging," I said as I walked up to him.

"No, you don't," he said. "I see that VIP treatment here only goes so
far. Tonight'll have to be on you, my friend.

A few days later, we both drove into Lake Charles for the kickoff of
Contraband Days, an annual twelve-day festival celebrating the historic
capture of the city by the gentleman pirate, Jean Lafitte. Local yachts
would be docked at the seawall near the Lake Charles Civic Center all

during the festival, and live bands would be playing every night. I was looking forward to both Eddie's company and the carnival atmosphere.

As we approached the seawall, Eddie noticed a thirty-eight foot Sport Fisher that belonged to a mutual friend, Steve Mitchell, who was sitting on the deck with his wife, slowly sipping a drink. Eddie yelled to Steve, who launched his dinghy to bring us out to his boat.

As the evening drew on, the crowds gathered; and we relaxed on the deck, slowly drinking. Steve and Eddie were having a great time kidding me about being single. I dismissed their jibes and looked at the people massing along the seawall. One person in particular, a lady, caught my notice. I couldn't take my eyes off her, especially when she smiled. A smile like hers would have banished Job's miseries and inspired him to write an "Ode to Joy." For my part, I felt the choral movement of the *Ninth Symphony in D Minor* playing somewhere deep inside me. Luckily, I was sitting; but that didn't stop the warm rush up through my chest, the tingling down my arms into my fingertips, and the sudden paralysis in my head. I felt stupefied, as if my whole word had been overturned.

I was probably vaguely aware that I had fallen in love, completely, there, on the spot. For a moment, I couldn't figure out what to do. Then I realized I had to do something, anything, before the crowd swept her away. I'm usually very careful not to make a fool of myself. But now I didn't care. I stood, yelled "Hey!" and then raised my arms as if to say "What do I have to do?" She noticed and broke into a smile that amplified the one that had smitten me only seconds earlier.

"I think I see where this is going," Eddie said and starting singing, "Love is in the air."

I looked at Steve and asked, "The dinghy?"

"Yours for the evening," he said.

"Get it back before midnight or it'll turn into a pumpkin," his wife added.

I rowed the dingy backward, to keep myself facing the seawall, so that I'd keep my lady and her girlfriend in sight. Nor did I use the five-horsepower outboard. I thought it was more gallant of me to approach on my own power.

I pulled up to where my lady and her girlfriend were standing and stood up straight in the dinghy. I opened my mouth to speak but couldn't think of what to say. All that came to my muddled mind was, "Hi, I'm John… Brotherton. John Brotherton, I mean. I just wanted to say hello. So that's what I rowed in here to say. Hello."

My lady and her girlfriend looked at each other, looked back at me, and started laughing.

"Did I say something funny?" I asked.

"No," my lady said. "But you look like such a fool standing up in that little boat. Why don't you sit down before you fall overboard? I'm Susan Touchette, and this is my friend Charlotte Wynn."

Now I noticed Susan's eyes—brown, deep, and warm. To me she was stunning, as lovely as Jane Asher—lovelier even. I took her advice and sat down. But I still couldn't take my eyes off her. She was about five feet, nine inches tall, with fairly short, straight, dark brown hair, which she kept in bangs. And she was slender, elegant to an extreme—very European looking, I thought. I could picture her sitting at a sidewalk café just off the Avenue de Champs Elysee, looking far more Parisian than American.

From behind me I heard voices calling, "John!" I turned and saw Eddie, Steve, and his wife standing, holding their drinks in the air in a welcome aboard gesture.

"Those are my friends," I said.

"They look like very nice people," Susan replied.

"I think they'd like you both to come out and join us for a few drinks," I said. "You can come out in the dinghy here with me."

"Or we could swim," Charlotte said and laughed.

"You look harmless enough," Susan added. "We'd love to join you for a few, but just a few."

As the night passed, Susan and I moved to the deck rail. As we small talked about who we were and where we had been in our lives, I felt that the molecules under my skin were vibrating madly and that electrons were leaping out of their orbits, charging the space between us. At one point, she looked at the luxury yachts all around us, then directly at me.

Thrusting her finger into my chest, she said, "I'm into down-to-earth people. Money's one thing, but the most important thing to me is what's in your heart." She must have known then that my heart was in melt-down over her. I certainly knew. I had heard the expression that love is a sickness that is its own cure. I had never understood it before. But I did now.

It was close to midnight when I walked Susan and Charlotte to Susan's car. Susan and I had agreed to meet each other at the festival the next evening. As I opened the passenger door for her, she kissed me lightly on the cheek.

"You might be sorry you did that some day," I said.

"Maybe I'd be sorrier if I didn't," she replied as she got into her car.

South of Lake Charles, the traffic thinned to nothing except for a single car behind me. The car was still with me as I turned west onto my street and drove the last few blocks to my house. Instead of turning into my driveway, I stopped along the curb. I noted that the car was a plain white sedan, with no markings. In the front seat were two young men, both with short haircuts. As they passed, the driver accelerated suddenly. The car shot away too quickly for me to get a read on the license plate. As I turned into my driveway, I realized that my giddiness over meeting Susan had been replaced by the uneasy feeling that I had, for some reason, been followed home.

What now? I wondered, as I walked into my house through the back door. Would I need to take my phones apart? Would I have to scan my walls and every nook and cranny I could find in four thousand square feet? Would I have to get the Reverend and his brick men back up here to sort this out for me?

Who? I asked myself. And why? And why were there two of them? I thought of my nightmare, also of how Kathy had disposed of her first husband. She had been ruthless then. Would she be even more ruthless now? Would she really do anything, including bringing harm on the kids, to lash out at me? And would Tony help her? I made a mental note to cancel my life insurance as soon as possible, remembering that Kathy was still named the beneficiary on the policy.

I decided I'd keep my .45 caliber pistol loaded and under my pillow while I was sleeping; and I'd keep my Gerber on my night table. I'd have my Spas Auto twelve gauge in my bedroom closet, loaded with a nasty surprise. I'd fill the tube with shells I had hand loaded: an extra powder charge behind seven dimes (instead of double 0 buck), a seventy cent payoff that could take the entire quarter panel off an old Cadillac. If I had to use force to protect myself, anyone taking cover behind a wall or door wouldn't have a chance. As a deterrent, I'd hang my heavy bag on my back porch, where my two tails could see it if they came by while I wasn't in. If they didn't get the message, I could at least say I had given fair warning.

It also occurred to me that Madamba might be playing with my head. You've got an antidote to that, I told myself: the tapes. But I couldn't remember where I had placed them. I looked in my storage locker in the garage, in my desk, in my safe, in my briefcases, in my closets, and finally in every drawer in my house. But I couldn't find them. For a moment, I panicked. Had someone broken into my house and stolen them? If so, it could be Players or some of Edwin's friends who were taking an unwholesome interest in me. That, or it could be Kathy, trying to find something to use against me.

I forced myself to slow down, to stop racing through all the possibilities, to focus on what I knew: that I was being watched and that my tapes were gone. I couldn't change either right now. My best course was to keep myself forearmed against hostile intent until I could get a visual on the puppet master in this silly show.

I continued to see Susan all through the Contraband Days celebration. At first, I'd meet Charlotte and her, and we'd hang out with my own friends, going to parties, dancing to the bands, and socializing aboard Steve's yacht. Toward the end of the festival, we spent our evenings alone with each other. It was as clear to each of us as it was to Eddie—who, when we ran into him, insisted that he was the only fitting candidate for my best man—that we were falling deeply in love. But neither of us wanted to rush. For my part, I felt so strong and totally alive with Susan that I knew my feelings had to be serious. But I wanted to be sure that I wasn't caught up in a rebound syndrome. Susan was sensible enough to keep the flame on low and to let the feelings developing between us burn slowly. She was also pragmatic. As soon as she sensed that our attraction had the potential to become serious, she explained to me that she didn't come alone, that she was a twosome, a single mother, with a six-year-old son, Taylor. His welfare, she made it clear, was her first priority; and any man who would step into her life would have to accept that as a given.

Though I didn't toot my horn on this issue, I did assure her that I wasn't put off in the least that she had a son. What I felt and kept to myself was the admiration I felt for her; she certainly contrasted starkly with Kathy, who had initially resisted my wish that Derek, her son, be brought from her parents' home into ours.

On my way home after the last night of Contraband, I noticed the white car following me as I passed the city limit on the south side of Lake Charles. I had my trusty Gerber under the driver's seat, the blade honed to complete readiness. I pulled to the side of the road, put the Gerber on the passenger seat, and waited. The car passed, continued on for about thirty yards, made a U-turn, and came back toward me. I put my head-lights on high beam and could see the two occupants, both with short hair. As they passed me, going back toward Lake Charles, I rolled my window down and gave them the finger.

My phone was ringing when I opened the back door to my house. I was hoping that it was Susan, calling to say goodnight. Instead, it was Kathy. She didn't even bother to say hello.

"I see you're sport fucking around town, you bastard! I heard about your slut."

I told her that my personal life was really none of her business.

"You think you're Mr. Goody Two Shoes, you motherfucker! You want to go around screwing whores and make me look like an asshole? Fuck you, John! You think you can fuck with me? I own you. You'll see.

You think I'm stupid. You'll see, motherfucker. You'll see how smart I can be."

The drift of what she was threatening was beginning to alarm me. "What am I going to see, Kathy? Nutless wimps in white cars? If Tony and you have weird ideas about fucking with my life or with Macie's or Derek's, let me make it clear. I'm already talking about custody with Eddie."

"So you think your going to fight me for custody? Think again, you asshole! That would be the biggest mistake of your life. You'll see. You don't think I can fuck your life up? You watch me. I have the hotline for the New Orleans FBI right here, you stupid motherfucker. I don't have to fuck you up. I'll call them and let them do it for me."

Now she had my complete attention. I recalled that she had once said she had dropped the dime on her first husband and wondered if she had already acted on the threat she was making now. Maybe I could calm her down enough to find out exactly what she had in mind with the FBI.

"Kathy, I want you to think this over. What good would you be doing you or anybody? I haven't done anything illegal. You've got nothing to tell the FBI. You'd only make yourself look foolish."

"Fuck you, nothing! Wait till they hear how you bribed Edwards, you motherfucker. You call that nothing? I'm going to fuck you over like you've never been fucked over!" She then hung up. I thought of Robert's song about the whirlwind of cash funneling into Edwards' pockets. Are you some kind of asshole? I asked myself. You went and told her you suspected Rick was laundering? Brilliant. You gave her the match, the fuel, the whole fire triangle.

The phone rang. Again, it was Kathy.

"I just called them, the FBI! If you don't think your life is fucked up, think again. You won't be humping that whore behind bars. You won't be humping anybody. You'll be getting—"

I hung up on her and prepared myself for a sleepless night. I was less worried about having my rights read to me and being handcuffed than I was about the field day Menche could have if I came under investigation. There was also the matter of my licensing. If an investigation gathered head and went to a grand jury, the state could have cause to withdraw my license to work in a casino. I recalled a case in which a casino employee had testified to a grand jury about an incident in which he hadn't been involved. Nevertheless, he had to fight to keep his license from being revoked.

Kathy called me again, early the next morning at my office. This time she wasn't angry; nor was she swearing. She was scared witless.

"John!" she pleaded, "you've got to tell me what to do! I don't know what to do. They're on their way over here."

I asked who was coming.

"The FBI! Somebody named Joe Duenas called. He said he's coming over with a few other agents. My God, John, what do I do?"

I recalled that Joe Duenas was the agent whom Bertney Langley had supposedly enlisted to snoop into Lovelin Poncho's life. I told Kathy to figure out what she should do for herself, since she was such a genius. I hung up and decided I'd better be a genius and call Eddie. Before I could dial his number, however, the receptionist for the executive offices came to my door and told me that a very official looking man and woman were at her desk, asking to see me.

She was right that my visitors were official looking. Both looked to be in their early thirties, athletically built, and dressed in neatly pressed but plain suits. With her shoulder-length blonde hair, the lady would have been attractive if she had shown any willingness to smile. For the young man's part, his mouth seemed to be configured in a permanent smile. But it was the sort of smile you'd expect from someone you'd see attending state executions for amusement.

I walked out to the reception desk to introduce myself.

"I'm Special Agent Karen Worsham Jenkins," the lady said, without offering her hand for me to shake.

"And I'm Special Agent Shawn Stroud," the man added. "We're from the FBI, New Orleans. We need to have a word with you, Mr. Brotherton."

I pointed them toward my office and let them step ahead of me. I closed my office door behind me and motioned for them to sit.

"I need to come right to the point, Mr. Brotherton," Agent Jenkins began. "We have evidence that you've been involved in efforts to pass money to the Edwardses."

For a moment I was confused. I figured this visit had to be connected with the call Kathy had made last night. But I could also see that this Stroud looked, with his short hair, like one of the two men who had been tailing me the last few weeks. Either these two agents knew only what Kathy had told them or they knew something more. Whichever, I'd have to play dumb, get them on their way as fast as possible, and contact Eddie immediately.

"Why whatever could you mean?" I asked, laughing, trying to give the impression that I didn't think the implied allegation was worth consideration.

"Don't give us any good old boy 'I don't know what you're talking about' crap," Jenkins snapped. I noticed that her eyes were gray and ice cold.

"We have evidence, not gossip," Stroud said.

"So cut the crap right now, Mr. Brotherton," Jenkins added. "We want you to come in with us now and tell us what you know. You wait for this thing to go off like a grenade, you'll get hit by the shrapnel. You'll be guilty by association."

"So this is your chance now, your only chance," Stroud said.

I ignored them and looked up at the surveillance monitor, worried that this conversation was being recorded and that Menche would be feasting his ears on it before the day was over. "I have nothing to tell you," I said and walked to my door and opened it.

As they were leaving, Stroud and Jenkins each handed me a business card. (I have both cards to this day.) "You don't have time to waste, Mr. Brotherton," Jenkins said. "You don't have the luxury of time. Call us immediately. Our numbers are right there on the cards. You need to call before it's too late. I mean it."

Back in my office, I closed the door and dialed Eddie's Lake Charles number.

"Ain't love grand," I heard him say. "I can't wait to wear a tux. How many weeks you figure I have?"

I told him about Kathy's call the night before and explained that I had just received a visit from two special FBI agents.

"Not another word now," he said. "You're probably not on a safe phone. Get to a pay phone as fast as you can. I'd suggest right now. It's getting close to noon. Just say you're taking an early lunch. Keep in mind that these investigators are not losing any time themselves."

I drove to a gas station and used the pay phone to dial Eddie. His secretary told me he was with another call but that he was expecting to hear from me and that I should call back in a minute. I decided to call Rick Shetler at his office at Gatti's. Though I didn't at the time consider Rick to be my closest friend, I had no axe to grind against him, especially considering his recent help in landing me the general manager job at Grand. And I knew that his intestines had little immunity to the kind of stress I was now under. I thought it only fair to give him a heads up.

His receptionist answered. I told her who I was and that I needed to talk to Rick.

"John," she replied, "Rick's not taking calls. There are a bunch of men here. They came in and walked straight into his office. They knew right where it was. There are also a few out at his back door."

I remembered the first time I visited Rick at Gatti's. I wouldn't have been able to find his office without him leading me to it. Now he had been raided, and the team had known the layout of his shop, both inside and outside. What Rick's receptionist had told me didn't sound like cowboy-style surveillance. I thought about my tapes and wondered whether my nocturnal tailmen knew the inside of my house better than I did.

Eddie, when he took my call, didn't even say hello. "Here's what I want you to do John, right now. Call Players. According to your severance agreement with them, they'd have to provide counsel for you in this sort of situation, at their expense."

"What about you, Eddie? I want you on this."

"I'm with you all the way, wherever this goes. Players'll have to cover my fees, too. They'll know that. If they try to waffle, you know whose name to drop—mine. Now get busy, John. Call Players."

That night, the FBI was all over the news channels. I heard the anchorman describe the swoop on Rick's office. Edwin Edwards' home and the law offices Edwin shared with Stephen had also been raided. The agents had seized around four hundred thousand dollars in cash from a safety deposit box belonging to one of Edwin's associates. On a more general front, the report said, the FBI was conducting a covert investigation of Edwin and several of his associates; specifically, the agency was looking into his relationships with several riverboat casino establishments.

The FBI's interest in the casinos grabbed my close attention; when I heard Players mentioned, however, I came to my feet and hung on every word. The report said the FBI investigation was targeting any relationship it could establish between Edwin and the Hollywood/Debartolo casino in Shreveport, the Casino Magic in Shreveport, the Treasure Chest casino in Metarie, and the Players casino in Lake Charles. An FBI spokesperson explained that the agency decided to go public at this point because it had recently received information that could compromise the investigation.

Kathy's dumb luck, I thought. Does she have any idea of what she's started? I also wondered how many incidental casualties would result from her attempt to get at me. I recalled the hacked-over saying, "Heaven knows no wrath nor hell hath no fury like that of a woman scorned." In its application to me, I thought it was far from trite—that it was the most profound truth ever uttered.

I hadn't talked to Rick in a long time, but I needed additional INT on the report I had just heard and figured he'd be a reliable source. I called him at home, but he didn't answer. Nor did he answer when I called him at his office. Has he packed up and made a run for it? I wondered. Is the whole Edwards network using quail tactics, each flying to a different bush? There was only one way I could tell—by driving over to his house.

I found Rick in his boathouse. With the lights out, he was lying on the couch in just a pair of shorts. I tapped on the door and walked in.

"Looks like I'm not the only one who had a bad day," I said, as I turned on the light.

Rick sat up and squinted at me. "Bad day, shit," he said. "Everything's fucked up. I just got to my office and there was a bunch of guys with guns, flashing FBI badges, standing at the back door. They weren't cordial."

"Did they say what they wanted?"

"No. They took what they wanted. They cleaned me out. They got everything out of the safe."

"What did you have in the safe? Money?"

"More than money—records. I kept good records of everything. You know what I mean? Tape recordings too. It's not good, John. I'm fucked. And the damned TV station keeps showing a picture of my pizza shop with an empty parking lot. People probably think nobody wants to eat there."

I told him that Kathy could have prompted the raid by calling the New Orleans hot line to rat on me and that she was now talking to an FBI agent named Joe Duenas.

"That's the guy," Rick said and stood up, slowly. His entire frame was sagging. "He's the guy who grabbed up all of my stuff today."

"I can tell we're going to have a good summer," I said.

"Speak for yourself," Rick replied.

Halfway home, I noticed the nondescript white car behind me. I couldn't blame Rick for being despondent. Any kind of attention from the FBI was a good reason to sink into depression. Once the agency got its nose into something it regarded as suspicious, it would poke into every corner of your life.

It was obvious that Kathy hadn't started the initial investigation. I had noticed the tail on me at least a few weeks before she had called the New Orleans hotline. And the news reports had been suggesting that the investigation into Edwin had started over two years ago. At best, I figured, Kathy's disclosure had amounted to a weak allegation—certainly not enough to warrant on-going surveillance, lightening raids, and confiscations, but enough, perhaps, to give the government a reason to go public and to look more closely at me. It occurred to me that I had been in Stephen's office lately, that his premise had no doubt been under watch, and that I was possibly on tape. I couldn't think of anything I had said that would incriminate me; but I knew that my assessment wasn't the one that counted.

The white car was still with me as I approached my house. You call this covert, you assholes? I thought. For the last five miles we had been the only two vehicles on the road. As I pulled into my driveway, I noticed that the surveillance car slowed down. I stopped before turning into the parking area behind my house. If the night owls wanted to stop or pull up behind me, I'd get out and say, "You guys might was well come in; you probably already know your way around."

The next morning, from my office at the casino, I called Madamba in Atlantic City and told him that Players was obligated to provide me with counsel. I also specified that I wanted Players to retain Eddie as my local counsel.

"I don't know that I want to buy into that, John," Madamba said. "Eddie's not too high on our Christmas list around here."

I was in no mood for his affectations. "I don't really care what you think of Eddie Austin. I'm officially requesting him as counsel, and frankly I don't have time for your bullshit right now. One of the reasons I'm requesting Eddie is because he whipped your asses."

For a moment he didn't respond. Then he said he'd run my request by Howard and get back to me.

An hour later, he called with the name of an attorney, Cary Feldman, who would be contacting me. I asked him to be sure to have Mr. Feldman contact me either at home or through Eddie's office. I wanted to keep the business of the FBI investigation out of my workplace as much as possible.

Now I needed to take damage control measures. First, I called Grand's head office in Minnesota and was put in touch with Joe Galvin, the VP in charge of government affairs. I explained that the FBI had contacted me regarding an investigation that implicated Edwin Edwards and Players and that I was calling to let him hear the news from me first. I also told him that I didn't expect to be involved in any serious way and that I'd be happy to answer any questions he might be having on the matter.

Then I called Ruppert, briefed him, and scheduled a meeting with Lovelin and him. Paul suggested that it'd be smart to meet at his house and that I should come by early in the afternoon.

Next, I wanted to call Rick to see whether anything new had come in his direction from the FBI. Both his assistant and he, he explained, had been summoned to appear before the grand jury. He had, he explained, hired an attorney, who had advised him to take the Fifth Amendment. Edwin Edwards, moreover, had released a copy of the search warrant that had been served on him during the raids. The warrant specified over one hundred and seventy corporations and people—with the names ranging from Ed Fishman to Lovelin Poncho. It interested me to hear that Pat Menche was mentioned—though his name had been horribly misspelled; and it scared the hell out of me that I was also listed. For the first time it occurred to me that there was a direct converse to the comfort zone—the discomfort zone. I couldn't think of a better term for the real estate in which I was now squarely situated.

On the overhead surveillance camera in my office, I noticed Bertney Langley, Lovelin's rival in the election for the tribe's chairman walking around out on the casino floor. Because he had objected to the Grand Casino Coushatta on moral grounds, I was curious to see what he was doing here.

I watched him turn down the hall toward the executive offices. Then the receptionist called to inform me that Langley was asking to see me. I asked her to send him in and then opened my door to receive him. I wanted it to be seen that our meeting would be of the open-door kind.

I greeted Langley as he entered and waved him to one the chairs at my small conference table. As I took a chair across the table from him, I asked, "How can I help you today, Mr. Langley?"

He was just stopping by briefly, he said, to introduce himself, as a member of the tribe, and to congratulate me on my appointment. For a moment we chatted about my backgrounds. He said he was particularly impressed with my tribal ancestry. Then he excused himself. "I know you've got a lot on your plate," he said, "so I'll just look about the place and be on my way."

I thanked him for stopping in. As I watched him leave the executive office suite, it occurred to me how right he was. I did have a lot on my plate—a lot that I had no appetite for. Right now, I thought, the only visits I'd welcome would be from Eddie, Susan, Ken Hagan, or my mother. I couldn't think of anyone else I trusted.

Paul, Lovelin, and I met around Paul's kitchen table. I restricted myself to explaining that two special FBI agents had come to my office, asking whether I had been involved in laundering money to the Edwards family, and omitted anything about Kathy or Rick. My main concern, I said, was whether the FBI's interest in me would reflect badly on Lovelin among the tribal members. Neither Paul nor Lovelin was worried. From what they had been able to assess, the tribe had reacted with hostility to Joe Duenas' reported attempt to ferret out Lovelin's dirty laundry. The resentment toward Duenas, Paul said, would attach to the FBI itself. At the best of times, the tribal members would regard attention from any government agency as intrusive.

I returned to the office feeling relieved on at least one count, only to find that Kathy had launched the second prong of her offensive. On my desk was a message for me to call Joe Galvin, at the Grand corporate office.

As Joe explained, Kathy had called Tom Brosig, insisting that Grand should fire me because I would soon be in big trouble. Tom had refused to discuss me with Kathy and had turned the call over to Joe. Kathy then subjected him to a ten-minute harangue in which she insisted on reciting the details of what she alleged as my black deeds. From what he told me, Joe laughed her off. He was more than familiar with the black-widow syndrome, he said. But I knew that Menche was in the corporate office today and was worried about what he might do if he got wind of the call. I could see my image in Grand collecting stains, like a thirsty blotter, before I had a chance to prove myself.

Although Madamba had said that Cary Feldman would be calling me, I felt I'd be better off calling him myself. I found him to be professional and concise. I was impressed that his credentials extended back to Watergate. He asked me to brief him on my situation but made it clear that he needed to meet with me directly. Until we could get together, it would, he said, be pointless to get into a wealth of detail. If it were convenient for me, he'd fly to Lake Charles the day after tomorrow. He asked me to recommend a good place to stay.

"Players owns the Downtowner," I said.

"I want someplace else," he replied. "I'm your lawyer, in your camp, not Players'. I want you to understand that right now."

I recommended the Holiday Inn in Lake Charles, located on the shore of the lake, immediately east of the Players casino complex. We agreed to meet there for dinner the evening he arrived. I hung up feeling positive for the first time today. I might have Kathy, the FBI, and perhaps some of Grand's executives trying to overrun me, but I had a kick-butt lawyer on each of my flanks.

Cary's plane was to arrive late in the afternoon. Eddie and I planned to wait for him in the lobby of the Holiday Inn. He had already talked at length with Eddie and so was up to speed on everything that Eddie and I knew about the FBI inquiry and the grand jury investigation. Also, he had received a subpoena for me to testify.

"I think you'll like Cary," Eddie said. "I do already, and I've only talked to him. He's strictly business, I'd say."

"He seemed that way to me. Did he say anything about what he had in mind?"

"No. We talked the situation over, and he said he wanted to get to work as soon as he gets here. 'I don't like wasting time,' is what he said. I told him that was fine with me—that I didn't charge my clients for wasting their time."

"That's how I work," said an older man, who looked to be in his early fifties, and who had found us without our even noticing that he had entered the lobby.

"Cary Feldman?" I asked. "How'd you know it was us?"

Cary was tall, easily over six feet, large built, but not stocky, with short, curly hair. He was dressed in a tasteful but plain navy blue suit. He looked at Eddie and me, laughed, and held out his hand. "Eddie said you'd be the big guy and he'd be the bigger guy. Couldn't go wrong with that make."

"How 'bout dinner?" Eddie asked.

"Not for me," Cary said. "We've got work to do. I want to check in first. Then let's go up to my room. We can't make ourselves invisible around here, but we can damned well try."

I suggested that we order from room service. "Suit yourselves," Cary said. "But nothing for me. I don't like to eat when I'm working."

In Cary's room, Eddie and I sat on the couch; and Cary took an easy chair, placing it so he was facing us. He took a notepad, a pen, and a document from his briefcase and placed them on the coffee table. Then he pushed the document and the pen toward me.

"First thing," he said, "is my retainer agreement. I need you to sign that. Even though Players is paying, you are my client and my only interest. I am working for you."

"Thank you, sir," I said. Eddie glanced over the document and nodded to me.

"Now, here's my office number, home number, and pager," Cary said. "Call me anytime you need to. Right. Now, Eddie gave me a good heads up on your situation. But I need you to tell me: what do want me to do for you?"

I looked at the subpoena and looked at Eddie, who nodded again to me.

" I don't want to go before the grand jury," I said. "I think there are some people at Grand who'd love to have nails to put in my coffin."

"I know, Cary said. "Eddie explained that your license could get revoked. I'll have to talk this over with Eddie and see what we can come up with. For now, I need to know the entire story the way you see it. I mean the whole thing. You just talk, and I'll take notes."

"Go ahead, John, I'll do the same. Just take your time," Eddie said.

When I finished my account, Cary placed his note pad in his briefcase and Eddie stood to shake hands with him.

"I think you and I see this the same way," Eddie said.

"How's that?" Cary asked.

"Cover your own butt and kick theirs as hard as you can," Eddie answered.

"Right. That, and be ready to make your move, when and if you get the chance," Cary added.

CHAPTER 19

MISTAKEN IDENTITY

✴

As the D-day for the tribal election (in late May) drew near, I dedicated much of my time to Lovelin's campaign. First, I wanted to make it plain to all the tribal members that a sea change had taken place in the management of the casino. I reviewed the personnel file for each member who was presently a casino employee and, where I felt qualifications warranted, awarded promotions. I pushed especially hard to raise members from staff to supervisory or management positions. Next, I spearheaded into effect a new policy that required the casino to make its best effort to purchase goods and services from businesses run by tribal members. In a personal letter that I sent out to each tribal member, I pledged my assistance to any member who saw an opportunity to start up a new business. Several took me up on my offer, with the result that Susan and I spent a lot of our free time visiting members in their homes and running advisory sessions. It wasn't long before I had established myself as a general manager whom the tribe could trust as being its advocate.

My efforts got Bertney Langley's attention also. He started making it a habit to meet with me as often as he could. In our get togethers, he seemed to go out of his way to impress me as a candidate who genuinely had the tribe's interests at heart. At one point, I felt so conscience pricked over the coffee-stained memo that I was going to ask Ruppert to hand it back to me. The next day, however, Langley's camp sent to each of the tribal members a campaign letter that attacked me directly, both professionally and personally, going so low down as to insinuate guilt on my part because I had been mentioned in the search warrant for Edwin Edwards' premises.

In all, I saw the letter as a cheap trick. Although Madamba was, from my own personal perspective, the primary target of my memo, I decided that Bertney's sleazy scandal sheet made him a worthy victim also. I recalled Hamlet's callous attitude after he stabs Polonius, who had been hiding behind a curtain to eavesdrop on the highly intimate conversation Hamlet was having with his mother. If the old fool insisted on meddling in a dangerous business, there was, Hamlet said, no reason to sympathize with him if the business did him in. Same with Langely, I felt. I saw no foul play in forcing him to swallow a draught of his own vintage of poison.

Nor did I hesitate to use an age-old guerrilla strategy against him. I had Ruppert wait until two days before the election day to mail to the tribe an information package that included the coffee-stained memo. Bertney was caught flat-footed, with no time to react. When the results were in, Lovelin had prevailed. His margin of victory was narrow and by several assessments attributable to the impact of the memo.

A few weeks later, Jeff King, now my assistant manager, and I were directed to attend a three-day corporate retreat that Grand was staging at Hinckley, Minnesota, the location of another casino that it managed on behalf of a tribe. Initially, I planned to arrange for use of the tribal plane. I had just finished reserving the plane when I received a call from Pat Graham, who worked for Aviex, the Houston-based contractor that also maintained Players' aircraft. As I understood it, Graham was also involved in promoting development of a golf course on the Coushatta reservation lands.

He was calling to suggest that we use a larger plane for the flight to Hinckley. He was, he explained, trying to sell the plane to the tribe and thought that this would be an opportune occasion to demonstrate its utility for junket trips for VIPs. I agreed to his suggestion and canceled the reservation I had made.

The next day, however, a newspaper article covering the Edwards investigation put my nose in the wind regarding Graham. As the article reported:

"…an FBI agent testified that that Edwards had been the unwitting guest on an FBI-piloted undercover plane that ferried him from Colorado, where he has a vacation home, to his home in Baton Rouge."

Edwin's reaction to this disclosure was entirely in character:

"I find it hard to believe that they were FBI agents because they flew the plane so well and because they found Baton Rouge on the first pass. I… hope that if they try to set me up again that they'll give me a jet…"

Then came the wake up call for me:

"Edwards said the plane trip was arranged by Pat Graham, a Texas businessman who has figured prominently in the Edwards probe. Facing 20 years in prison for his role in an unrelated federal case [sic], Texas prosecutors have said Graham is cooperating with the Edwards investigation."

Though I didn't mind a ride on a larger plane, and though I didn't think I'd be talking to Jeff King about anything that would stimulate the FBI, Graham's motivation pissed me off. To me, it was obvious that he was trying to save his own skin by ensnaring as many people as possible in the Edwards imbroglio. As general manager of the Grand Casino Coushatta complex, I'd be a trophy he could brag about.

I called Graham just before the plane was to be sent for King and me and told him I'd be in my "ass kicking" mood if he were to come along. As it turned out, the trip up to Hinckley was more comfortable on the larger plane; it was also all the more relaxing for the lack of Graham's company.

On the second day of the retreat, I was mortified to find out that I had been paired with Grand's chairman, Lyle Berman, in a company golf tournament. I was pretty sure that I was the only manager in Grand's gaming operations who wasn't a golfer. I had, frankly, never liked the sport.

An anxiety attack laid claim as I approached the two long rows of golf carts that were waiting for the participants and saw the names "John Brotherton" and "Lyle Berman" written in black felt marker on a piece of paper attached to the windshield of one of the carts. It didn't help that Lyle himself was standing beside the cart waiting for me, grinning widely, holding a club with an oversized head.

"Look at this, John," he said, "my new Big Bertha driver. It just came in. Beautiful, isn't it?"

"It is," I fibbed, not knowing anything about what made a golf club beautiful and wondering why the head of the club was so huge. Then I decided to unburden my anxiety, to explain straight out that I had never played golf, that I didn't even have a set of clubs with me. At first, my confession didn't register; so I repeated it, feeling totally like a fool. Once he digested my meaning, Lyle reacted well. "You can drive the cart, and I'll be the twosome," he said. "I'll just take your strokes for you."

As we pulled up to the third tee, for a long par five hole, Lyle started to get curious about how far I might be able to drive the ball. "You're a pretty big guy," he said. "You should be able to knock it out there pretty far. Use my Big Bertha."

It was, I knew, a tall order; but I'd try. To decline would be politically incorrect. I took the grotesque looking club, addressed the ball, looked far down the fairway then down at the ball, wagged the club back and forth (as I had seen pros do on TV), brought the club back slowly, and then unleashed my swing. I felt a shock in my forearms as the clubhead bit into the turf, just behind the ball, excavating a six-inch gouge. Somehow the head continued on and made contact with the ball, launching it in a sharp breaking curve to the left, at a perfect right angle to the fairway. The divot flew straight ahead, nearly ten yards.

"My club!" Lyle yelled as he grabbed for his brand new Big Bertha.

I sighted down the shaft, which still looked perfectly straight. I handed the club back to Lyle and tried to make light of my blunder. "This is one pretty tough club. Doesn't look too bent to me."

Tenderly, he slid the "1" sock over the titanium head and placed the club in its tube in his golf bag. As he took his place in the passenger seat, he said, "John, that was the worst snap hook I've ever seen in my life. We'll just have you drive the cart from now on."

As we were finishing the front nine, Lyle turned our talk to business items. I decided to raise a topic that had been on my mind for some time. The Delta Downs horse track, located in Calcasieu Parish, close to the Texas border, was on the ballot for a vote, to be held in October, that would determine whether it would be permitted to run slot machines. I was worried that the operation, if it were to obtain public blessing and regulatory approval, would reduce the volume of patronage at the tribe's casino.

I mentioned my concerns to Lyle and asked him if he wanted me to go to work on defeating the election. "No. No, I don't," he replied flatly.

"But it could hurt our business," I pointed out.

Lyle looked at me seriously. "Look, John, we have a deal to buy the track, and we have committed money to help win the election."

"Does the tribe know about this?" I asked.

"I've told them," he said. "If it goes through, I intend to strike some kind of deal with them."

I was shocked. In Louisiana, Grand was supposed to be conducting itself in a way that would optimize the Coushatta tribe's interests. According to the terms of its seven-year contract with the tribe, Grand was receiving about forty percent of the revenue that the casino generated. What I was now hearing, however, sounded plainly like a conflict of interest. Also, the way I saw it, Grand would, if it were to consummate a deal with Delta Downs, have leverage to coerce the tribe into renewing its management contract. But I said nothing in reply, and we finished our round without further mention of Grand's participation in Delta's proposed expansion.

One afternoon shortly after I returned from the retreat, Pat Graham came into the casino office, supposedly to show Jeff King (an avid golfer) a new set of plans for the golf course he was developing. The real intent of Graham's visit, however, became clear when he walked into my office, after he had finished talking with King.

He introduced himself and stood waiting for me to offer him a seat. I let him stand, hoping he'd get the idea that I didn't care for his presence. Though he no doubt got the message, he remained in place. So I shut my door, waived him to a chair in front of my desk, sat myself down behind my desk, and confronted him. "You didn't come to see me about the golf course, did you?"

"No, not really," he answered. "We think you have something to say to us."

I knew whom he meant by us, but I wanted to make him say it. "Us? Us who?"

"The FBI," he said straightforwardly. "We think you might have something you need to talk to us about."

I told him I didn't want to talk any further without having my lawyer on hand.

"John," he said, "you don't need a lawyer. You need to talk to the agent in charge of the Edwards investigation, Jeffery Santini." He then took a piece of paper, wrote Santini's name and number on it, and handed it to me. "You need to act quick. You need to call him today and tell everything you know. You don't have much time."

I wanted to see if I could get him to elaborate on his assessment that I could do without a lawyer. "And you're really saying for me to forget my lawyer?"

"I am. They're too expensive. They cause too many problems. You're better off without them. Trust me, you don't need one."

I may have born at night, I thought, but it wasn't last night. I figured that Graham might be an FBI asset, but I had my doubts that he was following their script now, here in my office. I had too much respect for the FBI to believe that they'd instruct him to pressure me like this, to try to tell me that I didn't need a lawyer.

"I'll think about it," I said and walked to my door and opened it. "I have to get going. I need to take care of something in the casino."

"Okay," he said, following me. As he reached to shake my hand, he added, "You don't have much time. I mean it."

Later, the FBI would tell me that Graham had worn a wire during our meeting. Also, much later, the prosecutors would say that they had started their investigation of Edwin Edwards in April of 1996, prompted by Graham's disclosure to the New Orleans FBI that he had put up $845,000, in two payments that former Houston Mayor Fred Hofheinz had made to Cecil Brown, as a down payment to obtain state-level approval for Hofheinz's company to construct a juvenile prison in Jena, Louisiana. The prosecutors would also say that another $1.3 million was to be transferred to Edwards through Brown when project financing was completed.

When it came to dealing with the FBI, I'd have occasion within a few months to fully appreciate what Cary Feldman meant when he said you have to "be ready to make your move." In early August, he phoned me at Grand. I was out on the casino floor and so took the call at one of the courtesy phones. As I had come to expect from him, he got straight to business. "The government called me today. They say they have some recordings that they would like for you to hear. They want to know if you'll come to New Orleans so they can play them for you."

I hesitated before answering while my mind raced backwards, replaying a thousand conversations I wished I'd never had. I asked, "What do you think, Cary? Do they have me saying something stupid on tape or do they want me to hear someone else saying something stupid on tape? If they want to try to scare me, tell them to go screw themselves."

Cary wasn't amused. He answered, "John, I think you should hear them out. You've been put on the back burner for a while, but now I think they're concentrating on John Brotherton."

Now I wasn't amused either. "So what do you think the play is?"

"It could be many things, John. I recommend that we go in, hear what they have to say, and leave. I want you to say nothing and show no reaction to anything you hear. We're going there to gather intelligence, not to give anything away. What do you say?"

"I'm with you," I replied. "Go ahead and set it up. Any day's okay. I'll adjust my schedule."

Cary called me back the next day to say that he had brought Eddie up to date and that he had scheduled a meeting in New Orleans on August 18th, about two weeks from now. Given the objective that Cary had laid down, there was, I thought, little I could do other than sweat it out over what the government might want with me.

One morning a week before the meeting, however, Lovelin Poncho gave me an additional basis for anxiety. Jeff King stuck his head in my office and said, "The chief's in the deli restaurant, drinking."

I figured that if Lovelin was into the alcohol this early in the day he had probably been drinking all night. I also knew that he could, once he was on a binge, drink himself nearly senseless. "Let's go," I said. "We should probably take a look."

As Jeff and I approached the deli, I could see Lovelin sitting at a booth, facing away from us. He was alone, nursing a large glass of red wine. When we got to his table, he looked up at us, mumbled something I couldn't make out, and waved for us to sit down. Great, I thought, as the momentum of his arm motion nearly caused him to fall out of his seat, onto the floor.

King and I sat on the side of the booth facing Lovelin, who was rambling on with a slurred, incoherent speech. I leaned over and whispered to King, "He's in pretty bad shape. I've got to get him out of here, now. You go get a car and meet me around by the back loading ramp."

Once Jeff had left, I told Lovelin, "Sir, I've got to get you out of here. I don't want anyone seeing you like this."

He gave me an irritated look, glanced around the casino, kept silent for a long moment, then sluggishly shook his head in agreement. I got him to his feet and, with his shoulder next to mine, and with my arm around his back to hold him up, started walking him toward the handicapped ramp. He placed one foot out and missed the floor, nearly bringing us both down. "Easy, sir," I said. "Let's try it again." Slowly, one step at a time, I guided him toward the ramp, using my entire weight to keep us going in a nearly straight line. At the top of the ramp, I stopped, turned him to the right so that we faced down the ramp, and paused to see how many people were watching us. At the moment, we didn't have a large audience.

From behind me, I heard a waitress saying, "Sir, I need you to sign for the drinks. I'm sorry, Mr. Brotherton, but it's your policy that everyone sign, no matter who they are."

"I know," I replied. "Give me just a second here." I leaned Lovelin up against the wall of the ramp and placed his right hand on the safety rail. "Can you stand here for just a moment, sir? I need to sign this."

He slowly nodded. Gravity, however, overtook him just as I was signing the bill. He tried to gain his balance by placing one foot a little farther down the incline of the ramp. But his other foot immediately followed; then he was stumbling, wobbling, and weaving down the ramp, out of control of his body, helpless. He was halfway down, gaining speed, before I had a chance to react. He reached the bottom and lurched abruptly when he came onto the level floor. He then lunged about thirty feet out onto the casino floor before I could catch up with him. As I reached him, he came to a stop, and his legs were about to collapse under him. I shouldered up to him, reached my arm around his back again, and walked him toward the back service doors, whispering a silent prayer, Be there, King. Please!

As I stepped Lovelin down the long hall toward the loading ramp, we passed several groups of employees who were walking by us on their way to work in the casino. I frowned hard at any of them who looked at us and hoped they'd get the message to keep their mouths shut.

I kicked the door to the loading ramp open and maneuvered us outside. Straight in front of us was the employee building, which housed the uniform, investigation, and accounting departments. Just to the right of the employee building was the Indian Gaming Commission office. A few people were walking on the sidewalk that ran in front of the two buildings. They hadn't noticed us. But that would change, when the show began in earnest.

I walked Lovelin about thirty feet from the back door and stood us still, waiting for King to arrive. "I. . .I can stand now," he mumbled as he straightened himself up. When he felt to be steady on his feet, I took my hands away and walked to the end of the building, to look around the corner to see if King was coming with the car. I saw him barreling up the road on the side of the building, in our direction. Good, I thought.

I turned back around in the chief's direction. Shit! Not good! I said to myself when I saw what he was doing. He was standing in plain sight, facing the sidewalk, his pants dropped down to his knees, urinating leisurely. Now he had an audience. I didn't care to take note whether the onlookers were shocked or amused.

"Sir!" I said to him, "not here."

He turned to me with a confused look but kept urinating. It took him a seeming eternity to finish. Then he reached down to pull up his pants and wobbled back and forth, almost falling to the ground. I didn't help him this time. He was buttoning his pants when King arrived with the car. I put Lovelin in the front passenger seat and told Jeff to drive us to the chief's house on the reservation.

Thankfully, it was a short distance. But when we arrived, Lovelin insisted that we join him on his front patio. Realizing that it was bad protocol to say no, we took our seats while he went into his house. He returned with a fresh bottle of wine, opened it, and filled our glasses.

We sat, trying to be patient, as Lovelin stuttered through one incoherent statement after another. Then he looked at King and back to me and made a remark that got my attention. "He's going to kick your ass," he said, now pointing directly at King. "He's going to kick your ass."

I knew he didn't mean that King was going to try to take me on physically. I didn't know precisely what he meant. But I got the sinking feeling that there was something to what he was saying. I thought perhaps the FBI had talked with him or that something politically funny was afoot in Grand—that maybe King had been put in the on-deck circle and was waiting to step into my job. I also started feeling that the chief's loyalty to me didn't match mine to him. I thought of my grandmother, of how she had told me that loyalty is at the heart of the tribal bond and of how she would spit on a tribal member who betrayed that trust. I looked over at King. He was looking down at the ground flustered.

"Let's get back," I said to him and walked off the patio toward the car. I let King drive and sat in the back seat. As we headed down the long driveway, I turned and looked back at Lovelin, sitting alone in his chair, drinking himself into someplace beyond oblivion. I wondered what he knew that I didn't, what he had, in the midst of his stupor, been able to focus on enough to repeat a single, complete statement—"He's going to kick your ass"— twice over.

On the seventeenth, I arrived at the office early to get my work caught up so that I'd have the next day free for my meeting in New Orleans. Eddie and I would be driving over early to meet Cary at the airport.

Toward the end of the day, Tom Brosig called to tell me he'd be flying in tomorrow to meet with me. I noticed that his tone was dead serious and hesitated in my reply, trying to think of what to say.

"John?" he asked. "Are you there?"

I answered that I had planned a personal day off. "I let everyone know about it two weeks ago, sir. It's going to be hard for me to break my plans now."

His voice was stern. "Well, it's very important that I see you. Can't you make arrangements to take off some other time?"

I told him I couldn't. "I urge you, sir, to let me go ahead with my plans. I'll see you any day after that you wish."

He continued to press, and I had no doubt that there was nothing coincidental in his gravity and sense of urgency. But I was confused. I rarely ever took a day off and had so far been trusted to work with little supervision. As far as I knew, moreover, my performance since I had come on the job had been outstanding. In fact, the numbers for July had set a new record for the casino, and Pat Menche had just told me that I was doing one a hell of a job. My nostrils were definitely flared into the wind.

I held firm because I had no choice. Also, I had to keep my reason for taking the next day off close to my chest. Finally, Brosig conceded. I hung up the phone, looked around my office, and said out loud, "Well, it was good while it lasted."

On the drive to New Orleans to pick up Cary, I thought about the news coverage of the Edwards investigation over the last few weeks. According to the reports, the government had been bugging Edwin's house for a long period of time. That bothered me; I didn't think anyone was allowed to do that. I had also read about the Federal Judge and the US Attorney who were heading up the case. US District Court Judge John V. Parker of Baton Rouge had a distinguished reputation—both on and off the bench. And US Attorney Eddie Jordan of the Eastern District of Louisiana also had a sterling background. Jordan, I had read, was black, extremely intellectual, and specialized in Constitutional Law. I had no doubt that both Parker and Jordan were thorough professionals, utterly lacking any taste for shenanigans.

Cary and I dropped Eddie off at the Hilton and continued on to One Shell Plaza. In the elevator, Cary pushed the button for the floor on which the FBI was leasing offices. Nothing happened. He pushed the button again, with no result. He figured that a security key was needed to access the FBI's floor and suggested that we go to the next floor up and walk down one flight of steps. As the elevator started to move up, he briefed me on the rules of non-engagement. "Remember, say nothing, no matter what you hear. React to nothing, no matter what happens," he specified.

I replied that I felt I was ready.

When the elevator reached the floor we had selected, the door opened to a lobby. To the left we saw some offices. We stepped out and started walking toward them when we heard from behind us, "May I help you?" We turned to see a tall young man with glasses and short light colored hair, wearing a laminated identification badge.

"Yes, we're looking for the FBI office," Cary replied.

"Well you've found it," the young man said.

Cary introduced himself, then me, and explained that we were here to see Assistant US Attorney Steve Irwin.

The young man smiled and introduced himself as Agent Dennis Swikert. To me, he said, "John Brotherton, how do you do? I'm glad you're here. I have a lot of stuff you can help me with today. But you're supposed to report on the floor below this one. This is the staff office."

I looked at Cary and shrugged. He said, "We tried to go to that floor, but we couldn't get the elevator to work."

"Right," Swikert replied. "Let me go with you. I'll get you on the floor."

The three of us rode the elevator down one floor. Swikert then led us to a small seating area. On the wall in front of us, I saw a large FBI crest. To the left of it was a large glass wall; behind it a lady was sitting behind a desk. In front of the glass, near us, was a metal detector. Swikert asked us to take a seat and then went through a security door to the left of the metal detector.

Cary and I sat down and waited. Seconds later, Swikert returned with a slightly older man with gray thinning hair, who stepped in front of Swikert and stood in the middle of the seating area, with his hands on his hips, looking first at Cary, then at me. "I'm Agent in Charge Jeffery Santini," he said as he reached to shake my hand.

I stood, took his hand, but followed Cary's instructions and said nothing. Standing and extending his hand, Cary said, "This is John Brotherton, and I'm Cary Feldman. Good to meet you, Mr. Santini."

"Good to meet you too," Santini said.

"We were supposed to meet Assistant US Attorney Steve Irwin here," Cary pointed out.

"He's running late," Santini explained. "He had to go to court this morning to do some business related to the case. He called and said to begin without him and he'd join us when he got here."

"Okay with us," Cary said.

"Then why don't we put you two through the metal detector? Santini said. "Then we'll take you back where we can meet." He waved us toward the machine.

Cary went first and I waited a moment before following. Once we had passed, Santini punched the security code on the door and led the way down a hallway with small interrogation rooms off to the right every few feet. We came to another security door. Santini punched in a series of numbers and opened it. At the end of the hallway, he led us into a large conference room. The large windows on the far end gave a beautiful view of the city along the Mississippi River. Centered in the room was a long wooden table surrounded by about a dozen high-backed blue chairs with the FBI crest embroidered in bright gold on the cloth upholstery. Two men were seated side by side on one side of the table. Placed in the very middle was a large tape recorder with long buttons on one end and with a large speaker area on the other end. Next to the recorder were two cassettes in clear cases, stacked neatly.

"This is Agent Kurt Hemphill," Santini said pointing to one of the seated men. He was young looking, with short dark hair, and was wearing a pressed white shirt and tie. He nodded in our direction.

Santini pointed to the other seated man, who was also young looking and who was dressed in a suit. "And this is Jim Mann, with the US Attorney's office. He'll be sitting in until Irwin can join us." Mann didn't speak in acknowledgment of us. Rather, he remained seated, looking at us seriously, through narrowed eyes.

Cary reached over and shook hands with Hemphill and Mann, handed his business cards around the room, and waited patiently until he had received cards in return. Santini took a seat at the end of the table near the windows; I sat near the door, with Cary to my left, toward Santini. Cary looked at each member of the gathering and then patiently, obviously taking his time, took a yellow note pad from his briefcase, placed it on the table, and then arranged the business cards he had been given in a neat row in front of him. For a moment, he looked over the business cards and then looked to Santini and simply nodded. Cary's composure was a comfort to me, here, before what could very well be a tribunal of sorts. By his understated body language, he was signaling my inquisitors that he would, if he felt he had to, proceed in accord with his own drummer, in my own interests.

Santini caught Cary's nod and nodded back. "All right, gentlemen," he said, "let's get down to business." He reached over to a credenza on the opposite wall, picked up a stack of documents, and handed copies around the room. "I want you to take a look at this. It's a transcript from a meeting in Stephen Edwards' office on March 13 of 1997 between Mr. Brotherton, Rick Shetler, and Stephen Edwards."

I took my copy, quickly looked it over, and saw that it covered the get together in Stephen's office, the day that Rick had driven me to Baton

Rouge, to enlist Stephen's advice on how I could better place myself for the job with Grand. In Rick's office, before we had left, I had seen Rick cram a stack of hundred dollar bills into an envelope. In Stephen's office, Rick had asked me to excuse myself for a moment. I had placed my briefcase by the door and had gone down the hall to see Julie. When I returned, just after I had stepped in the door, I had picked up my briefcase. Then, on Stephen's desk I had seen an envelope that looked familiar. The next day, following Stephen's suggestion, Rick and I had driven to Eunice, where we had met with Cecil Brown, who offered to help me with the job I was seeking if I'd help recover $250,000 the tribe owed. Most of that money, I remembered Brown saying, was to go to the "big man." I also remembered my thoughts on the way back to Lake Charles. I had asked myself whether getting the job with Grand was worth all the political crap. Now, in this meeting with the government, I could see that my notion of the crap I was in for had been too narrow in scope.

Down the left column of the transcript names were entered against specific passages. The document was actually formatted in the manner of a movie script. I noted the names: Rick's, Stephen's, and mine. The passages attributed to me were highlighted and also hand annotated with comments such as "offer" and "acceptance."

The thrust of the annotations, I could see easily enough, was that I had been an active participant in making an illegal deal of some sort. I quickly turned through the pages, remembering the discussion—how Stephen had bashed Goldberg and how we had discussed disposition of the contract for management of the tribe's casino. I knew I wasn't a legal wizard, but I couldn't see anything in what had been discussed that touched on anything criminal. I turned back to the front page and started looking again. There it was, I saw, right in front of me. I had missed it the first time. The majority of Rick and Stephen's personal conversation after I had left the office, at Rick's suggestion, was missing. From what I could see in the transcript, it looked like the FBI thought I had been in the meeting during the period I was down the hall, talking with Julie.

The conversation I was looking at in the manuscript was formatted as being between Stephen and me. According to the dialogue, Stephen was asking me about an amount—twenty-seven eighty-three—and I was verifying the figure. Following that exchange, according to the transcript, someone had been whistling for quite a long interval. Then I had said, "My briefcase."

I could see a plain instance of mistaken identity. The transcript was assuming that I had been in the meeting when, in fact, I had been with Julie. It was also assuming that I was speaking instead of Rick. This part of the meeting had taken place just before I had stuck my head in the door, after I had returned from Julie's office. Rick had waved me in, something that the listening device would not have been able to pick up. Rick had probably been whistling while he had been waiting for me to get in the door and take a seat across from Stephen's desk. Of course, as I stepped in the door, I had said "My briefcase" and had then bent over to pick it up. Here, obviously, the government agents had concluded that my briefcase contained the amount of money in question.

A statement from Santini distracted me from the speciously formatted transcript. Sounding totally sure of himself, he said, "It looks like we have a lot to talk about. Seems like we caught you making a bribe."

Following the directions Cary had specified, I didn't answer. Instead, I reached over and scribbled "That's not me" on Cary's pad and pointed to the conversation on the transcript. He looked up at Santini with a puzzled look, but Santini didn't wait for him to speak. Probably figuring he had me with my pants down, he kicked into action. "Let's play the tape," he said, grabbing the cassette on top and taking it out of its cover.

He inserted the cassette and turned the machine on. I let the entire conversation play the first time without showing any concern. When it was finished, I reached over and wrote "Make them play it again" on Cary's pad.

"Could you play the tape again?" Cary asked. "It seems there is some disagreement as to who's speaking."

Santini frowned and then said, in a point blank assertion, as if he was laboring what he felt should be obvious, "I've been doing this for too many years to make a mistake like that. I know that it's your client speaking."

"Well, then, you don't have a problem playing it again, do you?" Cary asked, his voice calm. I could see Cary's own protocol at work. He would let Santini flourish his arrogance until the moment was ripe for undermining it in one fell move.

Santini played the first part of the tape again. I reached over and wrote "Make him turn it up and play it over and over" on Cary's pad.

Cary's politely framed request to have the tape played over repeatedly visibly exasperated Santini, but he complied. About the fourth time through, I heard what I was listening for. I could see that the sound had caught Santini's attention too. Between the end of the first conversation and my statement "My briefcase," there was a faint noise. Santini reversed the tape again and again, playing the strange sound several times. Then he got it.

He started to say, "That's a—"

"Door!" I threw in. Cary gave me a "shut up" stare.

But the point had registered around the room. Santini looked dumbfounded for a moment, then deflated. It was apparent to him as well as to everyone else that I had come into Stephen's office and shut the door behind me after the till-now incriminating discussion had taken place. It was obvious now that I hadn't spoken the words that had been attributed to me on the transcript.

Exhilarated, I began to drum my fingers on the top of the conference table. But Cary looked at me again. He knew that a pregnant silence was the best way to press home the victory of the moment.

For a few seconds, Santini stood, plainly flustered. Then he said, but in a tone less than blustering, "Well, we have another tape that your client will be interested in hearing." He pulled the second cassette from its cover and inserted it.

We sat and listened to a conversation between Stephen and Marion Edwards, in which Stephen was explaining what an opportunity it would be for me to be running the Coushatta casino. Stephen's remarks were a little forward—including mention of the possibility that he could "get some chips" (meaning business) from the casino.

But it sounded like everyday business world talk to me. At the time the conversation took place, Edwin was no longer governor. So Stephen wasn't the governor's son. What I was hearing was the *You scratch my back and I'll scratch yours* talk that's everyday in capitalistic business transactions. To the extent that the conversation implied me, I was a manager of a privately owned corporation; I couldn't be seen as obligated to the same regulations that apply to how employees of government agencies are to conduct themselves. If I did business with certain vendors and did not give or receive any under-the-table compensations, I wasn't doing anything criminal.

When the second tape had finished playing, Santini could see that neither Cary nor I were concerned in the least about what we had heard. Cary continued to deploy lethal silence: that is, until Santini handed him the moment he was awaiting. Assuming again his assertive bearing, Santini said, "Well I'm sure we have some other recordings that—"

And Cary struck, his tone calm but deft, like a surgeon's knowing probe, or like a "soft" strike that touches the one nerve ending that'll relay searing pain along the brain's synapses. "Are they here? If you've got them, were here to listen," he said.

Santini went dead silent as he and Cary stared straight at each other. Without breaking eye contact, Cary said, quietly again, "If that's all, then, I guess we can be on our way."

Santini said nothing in reply. He opened the door and led us all toward the waiting room. Just as we got to the elevator area, the doors opened, and a short young man with long brown hair with bangs stepped out. His arms were overloaded with files. With him were two younger men, athletically built, dressed in impeccable suits and ties. The three looked to be dead serious.

The man with the long hair put his files on one of the chairs, then walked over to Cary and introduced himself as Assistant US Attorney Steve Irwin. He ignored Cary's offer to shake hands.

Cary, still talking quietly, introduced me as his client. Irwin and his two associates quickly turned and walked over to me. The naked aggression I could see in their strides amused me. There was, I was aware, something they didn't know that would cut them off at their knees.

"Steve," Santini said, "we need to talk about something."

Irwin ignored him and spoke straight to me. "You're a target," he said and paused, no doubt to savor the terrified reaction he was expecting.

But I knew the script Cary had given me—that it had no lines for me. I just smiled and let myself savor Irwin's momentarily puzzled reaction.

"Steve, we need to talk," Santini said again, his voice insistent this time.

Instead of replying, Irwin said to Cary, "Come with me," and then turned and walked toward the security door. Cary took up Irwin's pace and was followed by everyone other than Santini and Swikert, who remained behind with me. Before he followed Irwin through the door, Cary turned to me and said, sternly, "You can visit now, but you know the rules."

Santini sat in one of the chairs across the room from me; I took a place at one end of the couch; and Swikert joined me, sitting at the other end. At first, an awkward silence prevailed. I broke the ice by asking Swikert where he was from, whether he liked New Orleans, and whether he was married and had children. Once he started talking, he impressed me as being personable enough. I turned to Santini and asked him about himself. He went on for a while, even telling me that he was once assigned to work with J. Edgar Hoover. He disclosed that once, when Hoover wasn't looking, he had snuck a peak in his briefcase but didn't "see any dresses." I didn't know for sure whether he was serious or just kidding, making small talk. But I did find him likable.

He laughed and said, "You know, we've talked to Pat Madamba. He says that John Brotherton is the type of guy that can get you to tell everything about yourself before he says much of anything. I guess he was right."

I just smiled and recognized the comment for what it was. They were trying to see how I reacted under pressure—in the manner in which a lawyer assesses how a witness will perform when placed on the stand. I felt I was doing pretty well.

"By the way," Santini commented. "We've talked to your ex-wife too. Man, I don't envy you—not at all. She's something else, for sure."

I had also recognized that comment for what it was—the absolute truth.

Much later, I would come to greatly admire and respect these two men. They would become my friends in the time I would soon be spending with them.

Cary returned and shook hands with Santini and then Swikert. "Well, gentlemen, I guess we'll be getting on our way," he said.

As soon as we were on the elevator, alone with each other, I asked, "So, what did Irwin say? Right now, I think the agents are probably telling him what happened."

"Yeah, he came on pretty strong. I just listened to him. He didn't much care what I had to say. I just asked him to send us a copy of the transcript and said we'd get back to him."

The transcript would never come. And I would soon learn that I had been an active target before Irwin had disclosed that unenviable status to me.

As soon as I arrived back in Lake Charles, I called King at the casino to check on things. "Everything's fine here, but there's something strange going on with the corporate guys," he said.

"Oh yeah? Like what?" I asked.

"Well, one of the secretaries from headquarters in Minnesota called down here this morning looking for Brosig. She said he was supposed to be here today. Then someone else called back and said it was a mistake. One of the staff coming on shift said that the Grand corporate jet is sitting on the Jennings Airport runway."

That is weird, I thought. I knew that there was no mistaking that jet. I hung up, both frustrated and apprehensive. It was too late in the day now to go out to the office. But I did call Ruppert to see if he knew what was up. He said he wasn't aware of anything out of the ordinary but that he wanted to talk to me personally the next day about something important.

The next morning, I went into work early. As I stepped into the administration offices, I could see that the door to my office was open and that the light was on. Here we go, wherever that might be, I thought as I walked toward my office. As I rounded the last corner, I saw Tom Brosig and Joe Galvin sitting in two of the chairs across from my desk. When they saw me coming, they both stood. I walked in, shook their hands, and took my seat behind my desk. "So to what do I owe the pleasure of this morning's visit?" I asked.

In an even tone, Brosig replied, "We at corporate do not believe that you have the skills necessary to run this casino." He then handed me a letter on Grand Casino stationery. As I looked the letter over, seeing that it essentially repeated what he had just said, he added, "You're more of a development guy."

I swallowed my shock and looked Brosig square in the eye. "So that's it then? July hits the best ever, while I'm at the helm, and in mid August I'm not management material?"

Brosig and Galvin sat in silence.

I let a moment pass, then asked, "So, is there any severance pay?"

"No," Brosig flatly replied.

I felt myself getting angry. I looked at my berets and medals that I had mounted in shadow boxes on the wall behind them and suspected that Brosig had seen fit to bring Galvin along with him because he was worried about how I'd react to his message. I looked at Galvin. He was certainly a big man, but he was no match for me. I decided to test whether he felt himself up to his probable role as Brosig's security measure. I rose to my feet as quickly as I could, leaned over my desk, and looked right at Brosig. Galvin made no move. Instead, he tilted his head and looked over at Brosig too. Lucky for you, I thought, looking at Galvin. Had he shown any inclination to physically interpose, I would have struck first.

Brosig relieved the menacing silence. "Sorry, John," he said. "I have to go talk with Jeff King now."

With that, he stood, opened the door, and walked over to King's office. I forced myself to remain calm—realizing that the letter in my hand had probably not been entirely Brosig's decision, that he had most likely been forced to take a role in a much larger drama.

To Galvin fell the unnerving duty to escort me off the premise. As we got close to the parking area, we ran into Tribal Councilman Horace Williams. I stopped and asked him, "Horace, what's going on? I've just been fired."

"I don't know," he said, looking over at Galvin. "But you bet I'll find out."

"As you can see," I said, "I'm being escorted off the property—*tribal property.*"

Horace looked at me, shocked, as I continued toward my car. And Galvin watched me the entire way as I made the drive off of the property out onto the highway. I didn't offer the courtesy of a goodbye wave.

On my cell phone, I called Ruppert. "So, did you know that I was going to be fired? Is that what you wanted to talk to me about?"

"No," he answered. "I knew the feds talked to Berman, and I heard that the feds said you should be fired. But I thought that the chief and the council had to approve any change like that."

So the feds fired precipitously, I thought—a lethal shot that found its mark, before, even, they had met with Cary and me and discovered the faulty assumption embedded in the transcript. I made a decision to take minimal action for the time being. To Ruppert I said, "Look, you're under investigation; the chief is under investigation; but I get my ass thrown out. I'm going back to Lake Charles and calling a press conference."

I staged the conference in the back yard of my home and was surprised at the large turnout and the high level of interest. I welcomed the reps and then read them the following statement:

I thoroughly enjoyed serving the Coushatta Tribe during my time at the casino. I am proud of my aggressive endeavors to develop and promote Tribal members as well as creating new Tribal business opportunities not previously present at the casino. The purpose of the National Indian Gaming Act was to provide opportunities such as these for Native Americans. As an employee of Grand Casino Inc., I felt that this was my top priority, and contractual obligation to the Tribe. Grand Casino Inc. and myself seemed to continually differ on this priority. At the same time, I became uneasy with Grand's apparent involvement with slots at Delta Downs, which would endanger the thousands of jobs I fought so hard to bring to Calcasieu Parish and those already existing at the Indian casino. Grand was very vague in its reasons for abruptly severing our relationship but I will refrain from any further comments until I have conferred with the Coushatta Tribal Chairman, Lovelin Poncho.

KPLC, the local NBC affiliate, ran the story as top news that evening. The next day, *The American Press* carried it on the cover of the Metro section. Grand, when asked, declined to comment. I guessed that they were waiting in the bunker. Smart place, I thought. For them, I definitely had incoming ordinance in mind.

But measures of retaliation against Grand would, I knew, have to take a back seat to more pressing concerns. I was now flat out unemployed and had to take quick inventory of what I saw as a narrow range of short-term options. I was really worried about my cash flow. The divorce had pretty well consumed any reserves that I had on hand and that Kathy hadn't already spent, and I hadn't been drawing a paycheck at Grand for a long enough period to allow me to recover. In accord with the terms of the divorce settlement, moreover, I was now faced with almost all of the community debt obligations as well as monthly child support payments. And the last thing I wanted was to fall behind on those. A default there would give Kathy ammo she'd readily use in the hearts-and-minds operation she was still running on my children.

I fully realized that my ability to job search locally would be hampered by the publicity that followed my abrupt exit from Grand. It had been an event of sensational order in the Lake Charles area. Moreover, though I was well known and respected hereabouts, both personally and professionally, my name had been listed prominently on Edwin Edwards' federal subpoena. Understandably, employers would be nervous about me.

One thing I knew that nobody could take away from me, my performance record, reflected in unequivocally hard numbers. The more I thought about how well I had done in observing bottom lines in both Players and Grand, the more I began to think I had the basics of a case for approaching Players. After all, I had demonstrated that I could function as a general manager for one of the largest, most lucrative land-based casinos in North America. I was, despite what Brosig had claimed in my exit interview, more than a development person. I had, in short, proven that I was a force to be reckoned with if I were working on behalf of Players' competition. Maybe, now that I had shown myself more versatile than they had known me to be when I was with them, they'd be interested in at least seeing me. It would, I figured, be worth a try—if for no other reason than that it was the only recourse I had to act on immediately.

I called Howard Goldberg in Atlantic City, and he seemed willing enough to get together on his next visit to Lake Charles, in about a week. When I came into the Player's office to see him, however, I noticed a chill. I was shown to the conference room and told to wait there for him. In a few moments, he walked in, said hello to me stiffly, sat down across the table from me, and said nothing. I got right to the point. "Well, as you know, I'm out of a job."

"Yes, that's unfortunate," was his dry reply.

I added, "Well, I lost it, you know, because of an investigation that involves the job I had here." He was looking so unreceptive that I thought better of explaining that I had gotten enmeshed in the affairs under investigation as a result of having walked point on so many of Players' forays into dubious territory.

Howard just sat and looked at me, saying nothing.

"I need some help," I said. "I'm living here in Lake Charles and I don't have any way to make a living right now."

He looked to his side, then up to the ceiling, then back to me. "Well, John, I'd like to help, but I think it wouldn't be the right thing for Players to give you a job. Not with the investigation and all."

We both sat silent. There was nothing more I cared to say. Then Howard's face brightened. "Wait a minute. Ed has some stuff going on with Chuck Norris over in Russia. He's in the next office, so why don't you talk to him? That's about all I can do."

I thanked him and stood, intrigued by what he had mentioned. Russia? Chuck Norris? I didn't know what to think. I decided to keep an open mind for the moment. .

Which I did as I entered the office that Ed was using. Surprisingly, he was ready with a solution that had no lack of intrigue value for me. He was, he said, working with Chuck Norris, who was, he explained, an active partner in various enterprises in Russia, in Moscow specifically, that could possibly use my project development skills. But before he could offer me a job in Russia he had something he wanted me to care of locally. He asked me to make sure that Delta Downs didn't get even halfway to first base in the forthcoming election regarding its proposal to install and operate slot machines. "You defeat the election, I'll get you a job over there," he said.

Though I knew precisely how I'd blow Delta out of the water, I said nothing more to Ed than, "You've got a deal." Then I thought hard about going to Moscow to work—about the problems it would help me avoid and the ones it might create. In perspective, at the moment, the positive side of the balance sheet, weighted by the prospect of an income in the short term, looked longer than the negative side. I decided to take on my immediate assignment and bide my time.

First, I put all of my furniture in storage and moved into Susan's house. I gave Kathy more of the community property and managed to come to an agreement with her to sell our house—an understanding that she'd later mire in complications.

Then I acted on an opportunity that Players had unwittingly handed me. I recalled my discussion with Lyle Berman on the golf course at Hinckley. At the time, I had been shocked at the extent of Grand's complicity in a scheme that would place them in what could easily be made to look like a conflict of interest situation. Now, I savored the irony of it— Grand's chairman had handed me a bomb that I could drop back on Grand. If I could work it, the fireball would spread to Delta and consign its expansion plans to nothing more substantial than ashes.

With relish, I started working my network of media connections, insisting that Grand had an undisclosed contract with Delta Downs to fund the election and to buy the track if the election passed. The current track owners, I maintained, were covering their trail with their bleak economic forecasts. Unless they could capitalize on the revenue surge that would result from the slot machines, they would, they were saying, be forced to close their doors and put their employees out of work. What they of course were overlooking to mention, I emphasized, was the amount of money they would make by selling out to Grand, their covert election financiers, if the election were to pass.

I had guessed it right that the media hounds were keen to the scent of a secret deal. When the reporters would call Grand, its spokespersons would dismiss the deal as a rumor. In turn, Delta Downs would flatly deny that there even was a deal.

Hector San Miguel, with the American Press, sensed corporate double speak and kept digging. In Louisiana, he knew, if you fund an election, you are obligated by law to report it. Whether by coincidence or out of necessity, Grand went public with an admission shortly after Hector probed them. On October 7th, 1997, Jaye Snyder, Grand's director of communications, disclosed to the media that Grand did indeed have an option to buy the track.

Then, on October 10th, Jim Beam, the Senior Editor of *The American Press*, scathed Grand and Delta on their clandestine intimacy. On October 18th, the public spoke its opinion by killing the slots issue at the polls.

"Get your bags packed," Ed told me, when I called to let him know I had met the prerequisite he had set.

The phone rang the next morning, as Susan and I were leaving her house. It was Kathy. Since I had started living with Susan, she had raised such a ruckus that Susan had filed for a restraining order against her even approaching the house. "I got a piece of paper here in my hand I think you'd be interested in seeing," she said.

"What's that?" I asked.

"The FBI just gave me immunity. Now you better start doing what I fucking say! If you don't, I don't know just what I might remember or say. You start by telling your little whore to drop her restraining order right now or I'm going to make your life a living hell!"

I didn't want to challenge her by telling her that she had already done her best at making a living hell of my existence. I decided to stick to what I thought were facts. "But Kathy, I haven't done anything illegal."

Her voice was seething. "Oh, you're gonna' see now, you motherfucker! You just wait."

In that instant I realized that my decision had been made for me—that I couldn't bear another tirade from Kathy, that I couldn't abide her "motherfucker" this and "motherfucker" that rhetoric any longer, that half way around the world was probably not far enough away from her. I said goodbye and hung up. To myself, I said, Russia here I come!

In the weeks preceding our departure, Ed started me working on the first project, the design of "Chuck Norris' Hollywood Stars Studio," a talent studio Ed said was to be built in Moscow, to attract aspiring Russian actors, who would be expected to pay a fee to cover the efforts to market them.

As departure day came near, I thought repeatedly about the relationships I'd be leaving here in Lake Charles. I planned to bring Susan over with me as soon as I was settled, but I'd be putting myself at a distance from my children that would be tough to manage. But it certainly won't be forever, I rationalized.

Forever, however, in the strictest sense of the word, is what it was to very nearly become.

CHAPTER 20

"A Chuck Norris Enterprise"

I traveled among unknown men
In lands beyond the sea.

– William Wordsworth, "I Traveled Among Unknown Men"

❋

And so it was late in the afternoon of November 5, 1997, that my Lufthansa flight began its descent toward the international runway of Sheremetyevo 2, Moscow's international airport, located approximately seventeen miles northwest of the city center. Ed and his interpreter, a lovely Russian girl named Anna Romanova, were also on the flight but were in first class seats. Ever in character, Ed had purchased a coach ticket for me.

It had been a long trip, fourteen hours in all, starting from Bush Intercontinental Airport, in Houston, with changeovers in the U. S. at Dallas-Fort Worth International and J.F.K. International, outside New York City. The longest leg, eight hours, had been from J.F.K. to Frankfurt. There, after a half-hour layover, I had boarded Lufthansa for the two-hour flight to Sheremetyevo 2.

During this last leg especially, I thought a lot about where I was headed. I was both excited and nervous. I was excited because I had always looked forward to immersing myself in a foreign culture. In the past—in France, Italy, Angola, and Saudi Arabia in 1981; in South America in 1980, 1981, and 1982; and in Thailand, also in 1982—I had found that my curiosity and my eagerness to take on a challenge had gotten me over the culture shock that immobilizes many North Americans when they first arrive in a far-flung foreign country.

But I also had good reasons for being nervous. I knew that the sector of the economy in which I'd be working in Moscow was obligated for its day-to-day existence to the Russian mafia. In fact, I was fully aware that, in the face of the reformist efforts of Boris Yeltsin, the mafia clans of the former Soviet Union—consisting in the main of the Russian mafia, the Chechen mafia, and the Russian-Jewish mafia—were thoroughly alive and well, still at the heart of and largely in control of anything that could be called a system, including not only the economy but also no less than the Communist Party itself.

As Robert Friedman describes in *Red Mafiya: How the Russian Mob Has Invaded America* (Little, Brown and Company, 2000), the present centrality of the mafias in Russia is largely the handiwork of the former KGB, which, during the Gorbachev period, covertly withdrew as much as $600 billion in increments from the funds of the Communist Party and stashed these amounts in out-of-country caches, under cover of shell companies and false-flag accounts (Friedman, page 112).

To help them in this megaproject, the KGB turned to the mafias, which, before Gorbachev, were relatively small and organized, Friedman explains, "along neighborhood, regional, and ethnic lines" (page 112). In effect, the KGB resourced the clans so generously that their ranks swelled and their power grew to the point where they became the logical employers of KGB operatives after the communist system unraveled. By the mid nineties, the leading mafias controlled from forty to eighty percent of Moscow's economy, extorting protection payments from businesses ranging from sidewalk kiosks to multinational corporations and infiltrating all levels of government, even Yeltsin's closest advisors and appointees (Friedman, page 114). As a Russian banker described the purchase of the mafias on Russia's economy, "In 1917 we had a Bolshevik revolution, and all the rules changed. In the late 1980's, we had a Mafiya revolution, and the rules changed again. If you're a businessman you can either pay the mob, leave the country, or get a bullet through your brain" (Friedman, page 114).

I had read interviews with Russian citizens in which they had responded to the question—What does the word *mafia* mean to you?—with statements that equated mafia lords with what we, in the states, call politicians and businessmen. This is to say that the ordinary Russian saw little difference between an Al Capone and a US President or the CEO of a major US industrial conglomerate. I was aware also of the central difference between how the mafias operate in the US and in Russia. In the states, they moved into and controlled the out-of-the-way, illegal sectors of the economy. In the land of the bear, to the contrary, they were the economy; they controlled every aspect of it, especially its supply sector. Any attempt to drive them out of their insidious prominence would result, almost overnight, in a panic-inducing, severe shortage of goods. You might be able to bribe a loaf of bread from a food store—but only if you were lucky. Otherwise, the shelves would be bare. Yeltsin indeed knew whereof he spoke when he characterized Russia as "the biggest mafia state in the world" (Friedman, page xix).

I had briefed myself, moreover, on the ruthlessly brutal temperament of Russia's mafia henchmen. It wasn't that they were violent for the sake of it. But, if they perceived you as in some way standing between them and money they saw as owing to them, they wouldn't hesitate to react with maximum force. And they didn't restrict themselves to light arms and legitimate targets. I wouldn't be long in Moscow, in fact, before the truth of this assessment would be verified only a few blocks away from the Palace Hotel, on Tverska Ulitsa, where I'd initially be staying. A main thoroughfare for shoppers (Moscow's equivalent of London's Brompton Road or Manhattan's Fifth Avenue), and once the processional route that the czars followed on ceremonial occasions, Tverskaya would be the location for a new Rolls Royce dealership. According to the reports that would come my way, the management would be too obtuse to see the need to take on a Russian partner. Their grand opening would last thirty minutes before the facility would be shut down by a shoulder- mounted rocket launcher.

I had been thinking about the dark side of Moscow as my flight drew closer to Russian air space. After my troubles in Louisiana, I had resolved to make my stay here a disciplined exercise in keeping a low profile, well out of harm's way. A resolution like that, of course, was easy to make, high above the earth and far from the Russian capital. It would be harder to put into practice on the ground, where, I would learn, harm's way had a mind of its own, where it also had a way of finding you.

As the plane approached the tarmac, I noticed the heavy snowfall—consisting not of softly alighting snowflakes but of pellets driven hard by what looked like a knife-edged wind sweeping down on Moscow, no doubt from eastern Siberia, where on a day like this the temperature would be somewhere around minus 40 degrees F, without factoring wind chill. I shivered, looking at the ground crew huddling into their hooded parkas. Before it went nuclear, Russia could easily claim its winters as the most potent weapon in its arsenal. They had certainly stopped at least two of the world's biggest, most determined, and most disciplined expeditionary forces—Napoleon's and Hitler's. Watching out my window as the wheels touched down, sending the snow pellets swirling in vortexes, I wondered how long it would take my thin southern blood to acclimate, to thicken.

"Anywhere in Moscow we can buy snowmobile suits?" I asked Ed, who was waiting with Anna just outside the plane's exit door.

"I think you'd have to part with more than a few US dollars for something like that," he answered.

"Right," I said, thinking that Louisiana wasn't the only place where the business of business consisted largely of bribery. Anna smiled as Ed showed his airport VIP card, which gained us access to a plush lounge, with a bar, where we waited while our documents were cleared and our baggage was collected for us.

Outside the terminal, a limousine was waiting for us. I looked at Ed. "It's from Chuck's casino," he said.

Ed sat in the back seat on the passenger side; Anna sat in the middle; and I took the driver's side so I could more easily ask the chauffeur questions about any sights we might pass on our way to the Palace. I liked this touch, the limo being here for us. Having just arrived in a strange country, it gave me a sense that I was well looked after. Also, every joint in my body was stiff from sitting long hours in the coach seat; and the accumulated jet lag had me feeling ten times my normal body weight. My eyes felt like lead balls, and I wanted nothing more than to stretch out and let sleep have its way with me. I asked Anna and Ed to let me know if we came to any significant landmarks and then leaned back and passed out with exhaustion.

I must have been dozing for about twenty minutes when I heard Anna's voice. "John, we're in Moscow," she said. The limo had taken us southeast from the airport along Leningradeskoye Schosse onto Leningradskiy Prospect then onto Tverskaya Ulitsa, which ran also southwest, ending at Red Square.

I rolled down the window. Immediately, the blast of cold air stung my eyes. Anna asked the driver to slow down. Now I had my first view of the legendary apartment buildings that Stalin had imposed on Moscow's skyline. They impressed me as gargantuan, monstrous, even grotesque. I could see why they were called the Stalin Skyscrapers. I could also see why many visitors to Moscow called them Stalin Gothic. All that was missing were the gargoyles leering out from the outside walls of these run down monuments to pure communist thinking.

In the weeks to come, I'd acquaint myself with some of Moscow's more positively aesthetic landmarks. There would, for instance, be the august statue of the nineteenth century Russian poet, Alexander Pushkin, on the north corner of Pushkinskaya Ploschad (square), on the northeast side of Tverskaya Ulitsa, a little less than a mile down from the Palace Hotel, going toward Red Square. There'd be Red Square itself—properly termed Krasnava Ploschad, with the *Krasnava* being old Slavic for *beautiful* (a synonym for red, in this culture considered as the most beautiful of colors). Always I'd find this four hundred-yard long square both fascinating and intimidating for its historical associations. Since the reign of Ivan the III, in the fifteen-century, it had been a center for major public and political events. Before that, it had also been the site for public executions.

There'd be the Bolshoy (great) Theater, home of the Bolshoy Theater Company, located in Teatralnaya Ploschad, about a block and half northeast of lower Tverskaya, near where it ends at Red Square. At any time of day or night, and in any weather, I'd find the front of this neoclassic building inspiring, with its eight columns supporting the portico topped by the sculpture (part of the original 1825 theater) of Apollo guiding the chariot in which, according to myth, he carries the sun across the heavens.

There'd be the Kremlin, of course, on the north bank of the Moskva and forming the northeast-facing wall of Red Square. Later during my stay in Moscow, I'd rent an apartment on the same side of the Moskva and would be able to look out my front window, directly down Red Square and the Kremlin, at the stately, gold trimmed Great Kremlin Palace, flanked on the east by the Cathedral of the Annunciation, with its resplendent gold onion domes.

And there'd be the metro stations, each an artistic triumph in itself, together forming the public transportation infrastructure on which most residents in Moscow depend. Today, I might be somewhat fuzzy on Moscow's street names; but I can still name and describe in detail each of the metros.

As the limo took us down Tverskaya toward the Palace, Ed explained that what he referred to as "Chuck's casino" was properly called the Beverly Hills Club. It consisted of a casino, a restaurant, and a discotheque and was located on Kudrinskaya Ploschad, a block north of the new and old US Embassy buildings (a detail that would later become critical for one of my American colleagues) and less than two blocks northeast of the Duma (the lower house of Russia's parliament), often referred to as the "White House." I recalled a statement shouted out by a demonstrator in front of the house: "That's where the mafia lives!" (David Remnick, *Lenin's Tomb: The Last Days of the Soviet Empire*, Random House, New York, 1993, page 125).

Today, Ed said, as soon as we arrived at the casino, I'd be meeting one of Chuck's three partners, Nikolaj Nikolaivich, who was a native of the United States but who had returned to Russia, seeking his ethnic roots, just after the fall of the Berlin Wall. Nikolaj was, hardwired politically, supposedly the first cousin to Boris Nemtsov, presently first deputy prime minister of the Russian Federation, Boris Yeltsin's right hand man, and, at the tender age of thirty eight, widely favored to prevail in the next presidential election. The second partner, Igor Ballo, was head of the Russian Gaming Business Association. And the third, Larry Miller, Ed added, was under prosecution by the US government on charges of smuggling and money laundering.

I watched out the window as the limo sloshed through the accumulated snowfall, which had turned to slush in the heat island of the city. From what I saw, I had a hard time believing that I was in the capital of a former superpower. Everything looked old, worn out, and rusted, as if the city had never graduated from heavy cast iron to steel. The newest buildings looked to me as if they had been built in the seventies. Prevailing against the backdrop of the gray overcast cloud ceiling were the cheerless profiles of the Stalin skyscrapers.

The traffic matched Milton's description of hell—"confusion at its worst confounded." As a consequence of Moscow's addiction to motor cars and speed, what had been constructed as a four-lane highway was now being forced to accommodate ten lanes. As I had seen in other countries where the sudden infusion of modern technology had outstripped people's ability to use it sensibly, here it looked like the drivers were being driven and like vehicles had been granted an open, no-bag-limit season on pedestrians. Even the sidewalks looked to be fair hunting ground. I had to pity the hapless *Moskvichy*. The bitter wind funneling in vicious gusts between the skyscrapers and the river of slush on the sidewalks gave them enough to contend with. They certainly didn't need the soakings they were getting from the jets kicked up by the cars mad-dashing by, sometimes within inches of them. I could also see that the Militia (Police) were out in force. Dressed in green, they looked very military.

After a few minutes, we pulled up in front of a large white building bearing the sign "Palace Hotel" in English. Ranked at the lower end of Moscow's luxury hotels, the Palace is typically described as being elegant in the direction of simplicity, with a congenial staff. To me it looked like what you'd expect at any respectable Hilton. The floors were light-colored marble; the counters had a rich wood finish; ornate brass and fine chandeliers were appointed throughout. Off to the side of the lobby were a bar and a restaurant. A grand staircase led from the first floor to a mezzanine, where another, larger, more formal restaurant was located. The section of the lobby facing the street was lined by large windows.

After I settled into the single room Ed had reserved for me, I walked down the hall and knocked on the door of the expansive suite he was renting for himself. (Soon, as a cost-conserving measure, Ed would move me out of the Palace into a tiny apartment, just across from the Beverly Hills Club. The apartment, which I'd be sharing with another American employee, was owned by the casino and would therefore be free.) I sat on a couch in the front room and watched as he started unpacking. When he was done, he sat in a chair across from me and crossed his legs in his usual manner.

"So what's Chuck's casino like?" I asked.

"It's pretty nice, but not like Las Vegas," he answered. "You'll see in about fifteen minutes or so. We're going over there for dinner now."

Again, a limo was waiting for us. It took us southwest, down Gruzinskaya Bolshaya, past Zoo Park, turned left on Barrikadnaya, and then right down a narrow alley that wound around toward Kudrinskaya Ploschad. Up ahead, I saw a large neon sign that read "Beverly Hills Club," with the caption "A Chuck Norris Enterprise" below. Underneath the sign was the entrance door. I saw two long white limos parked next to the entrance and several black Mercedes sedans parked across the alley.

As soon as we stepped inside, we were met by five young, very big, athletic looking men dressed in black tuxedos, with white shirts and black bow ties. Each had short hair, cut in flat top fashion, and the visage of each was hard set into an expression that gave me every reason to think that they wanted to kill me on the spot. They recognized Ed and let him walk by but stood in my way. I said nothing and returned their bad ass stare. So much for resolutions, I thought, as I felt the adrenaline shoot through me. By instinct, I dismissed the surge of anger that started to rise in me and felt the old, disciplined, fighting readiness take hold. In Moscow, I knew I could expect to run into apes like these almost anywhere, and I wasn't about to let them intimidate me right off. Actually, for the moment, I felt good, alive and clean. I had always regarded the instinct to fight back in the face of oppression as wholesome. If these wise asses wanted a generous helping of *De oppresso liber* right now, I'd gladly provide.

"He's. . .he's with me," I heard Ed say, from more than a safe distance. The simians didn't seem to understand, and we continued our staredown. I was sizing up the biggest of them, getting myself ready to drop him straight into his shoes as soon as one of them made a move, when Ed walked back. He put his arm around my shoulder and repeated, "He's with me."

Reluctantly, they stepped aside and let us pass. "Nice guys," I said to Ed.

"Security," he replied.

You mean mafia muscle, I thought as I looked back and noticed the telltale bulges in their jackets. As we walked down a long hallway, I saw that the walls were hung with pictures of Chuck Norris with all manner of famous and infamous people. At the end, we turned left into the casino. One large pit ran the length of the room, splitting ten gambling tables, with five on each side. The high ceiling resembled a night sky, black with thousands of tiny white lights. On the walls were large posters from Chuck Norris' movies. Directly across the room was the door to the restaurant. A casino service bar was next to the restaurant. The entrance to the disco was in the far corner of the casino. At the very end of the room was a steel door labeled "Private."

Ed and I walked over to watch the action at one of the tables. I looked at the chips and said, "Hey, Ed, they've all got Chuck's picture on them. Not bad."

He laughed. "Yeah, they came out pretty good."

"They know you pretty well here, don't they?" I asked.

"Well," he said, "I look after the casino for Chuck and find him people to work here. The Americans working here are guys I found for him."

Later, when I'd take on being general manager of this casino, I'd meet one of my American colleagues, Danny, who'd become my casino manager, also my apartment mate after I'd move from the Palace. Danny had been brought over from Nevada by the present manager, Ron Levy, whom Ed had recruited, using his contacts in Las Vegas. Ron wouldn't last long in his position. Nikolaj despised him from the moment he had met him. Within a few weeks, he'd call Ron into his office for a brief, early morning meeting. He'd show Ron some pictures having enough instructive value that he'd be on a plane to the states that afternoon, no doubt thanking his lucky stars that he was still among the living.

Ed and I watched the casino action for a few minutes and then went to the restaurant and took a table. "So, Ed," I asked, " what are the rules on the casino here in Russia? What kind of tax is there?"

Ed thought over the question for a moment, then said, "Well, there's a ninety percent tax on gaming winnings."

I was shocked. "No way," I said. "You can't pay salaries and run a place like this on just ten percent."

Ed looked around the room and I was sure his mind had drifted elsewhere. Ed was a pure marketing man at heart. No matter what his responsibilities were here, I knew they didn't include bookkeeping and government regulations–two things that he had always, ever since I had known him, found to be boring topics. I would, soon enough, find out for myself how the casino got around the tax problem–by skimming. There were two sets of books, one for the government and one that had the real numbers. I decided to try and press the issue with Ed.

"Wasn't Chuck involved in one or two Vegas Casinos? What happens if the Nevada Gaming Commission comes over to look around? What about the Foerign Corrupt Practices Act?"

Ignoring my curiousity entirely, Ed changed the subject.

"You know, there's a funny story about the casino's grand opening,"

Ed said. You can read about it in *The Exile*."

At the moment I didn't know about *The Exile*, an English language newspaper that I'd come to depend on for its candor of reporting and for its slice-of-life approach to goings on in Moscow. In fact, I'd find it to be the only thing printed in Moscow that was worth reading.

"Go on," I said.

"You know who Vladimir Zhironovsky is?"

I answered that I did. I was familiar with Zhironovsky's saber rattling, nationalistic rhetoric calling for the communist Russia to rise phoenix-like from its ashes and to re-impose the old Iron Curtain. I had always considered him full of little more than sound and fury.

As Ed explained it, a huge grand opening had been planned last year for the casino's opening night. The event had included a ceremonial dinner to which Nikolaj had invited several of the political dignitaries with whom he was connected, including Boris Nemtsov. Igor Ballo was also to attend, with a legion of his influential friends. Chuck's role was to serve as host and main attraction. The event would be covered live by the Moscow news station.

On the evening of the grand opening, Chuck, Ed, Nikolaj, and Igor greeted the prestigious guests as they arrived and showed them to their dedicated seats at long tables in the restaurant, while guests of secondary importance stood in line outside, waiting for the doors to officially open. Their vigil was prolonged because Nemtsov was running late.

Then the occasion went straight to hell with the arrival of an uninvited Zhironovsky, who belligerently forged through the front door and demanded to be seated as a primary dignitary. With him was a bald and bloated American, Michael Bass, who had done some public relations work for the casino and whom Zhironovsky had retained as his publicity manager. On his own initiative, Bass had brought Zhironovsky, no doubt thinking that the opportunity to rub elbows with the gray cardinals would enhance his image. Nor, I'm sure, could Bass himself resist the chance to be seen on television.

Zhironovsky got so loud in his insistence on being seated immediately and prominently that Nikolaj let him have his way. Here, however,

Nikolaj showed his cunning. He seated Zhironovsky and Bass across from Igor Ballo, who had the reputation of being thin on tolerance. Once seated, Zhironovsky tried to take over the occasion, which embarrassed Igor in front of his guests. He sat quiet, glaring alternatively and murderously at his upstart rival and at Bass, whom he knew had engineered this farce. Basking as they thought they were in the attention they thought was being showered on them, neither Zhironovsky nor Bass noticed Igor's darkened brow, an oversight that amounted to patent stupidity on both their parts. Anyone who knew Igor personally or who even knew of him was fully aware that you had to watch his moods like a cat watches a mouse.

Then Nikolaj received a call from Boris Nemtsov, who held Zhironovsky in raw contempt. Boris's motorcade had pulled up to the casino, and he had recognized Zhironovsky's motorcade parked out front. Outraged, he refused to join the dinner party inside as long as his nemesis was present. To remedy that crisis, he told Nikolaj that he was summoning some help. Minutes later, two black armored vans pulled up to the front of the casino. The people outside watched as the engines were turned off and the vans sat still, doors closed, in a foreboding silence.

Inside, Zhironovsky's inflammatory antics and Bass' smug self satisfaction ignited Ballo, who took his glass in hand, raised it high, and brought it down with force on Bass' skull. The shards bit into his bald pate and rivulets of blood flowed down his face. He let out a horrified scream; then his obese carcass crashed to the floor. Stunned, he gathered his hands and his knees under him. Then, recovering his wits, he jumped up and fled, screaming bloody murder, out the front door, into the street, into the glare of the waiting television cameras.

This commotion broke the silence of the vans. The rear doors opened and spewed out at least a dozen hooded men dressed in black fatigues and carrying submachine guns. They snapped the butts to their shoulders and turned on their laser sights. Now the crowd was penetrated by the eerie red beams reaching out like extended fingers to touch on targets. At that moment, Nikolaj emerged from the casino and held up one hand. The men paused. Nikolaj then gave a wave and the men stood down. They waited for a minute and climbed back into the vans.

The front page of the next issue of *The Exile* carried a picture taken of Bass just after he had emerged onto the sidewalk, with his fresh head wound. His eyes were bulging grotesquely, and his face looked like a professional boxer had used it for a speed bag.

"Wow," I said when Ed had finished the story. "So, tell me about Chuck."

"Well, his name is really Carlos," Ed explained. "He's from somewhere in Oklahoma and has a brother named Aaron. He's a pretty good guy."

"Is he married?"

"No, but he just met a girl that he's pretty serious about now. She was a Sheriff's Deputy or something like that in California. It's funny, but she looks a hell of a lot like his ex-wife."

"Does he party, or is he the Simon Pure type of guy he plays on TV?"

Ed grimaced and started to say something. But then he cut himself short and looked around nervously.

"What?" I asked. "C'mon, Ed."

He leaned toward me and changed the subject. "You'll have to check out the girls working in the disco."

Later, I'd learn that the girls who worked in the club's disco were prostitutes who were selected by the club's management, which routinely brought girls in for auditions for these unenviable positions. I'd also learn, from a feature expose in *The Exile*, how young girls aged nineteen and under and desperatcly poor in the "reformed" economy of post-communist Russia were forced into prostitution in Moscow and then kept like slaves, herded by the dozen into shabby, one bedroom apartments and paid less than subsistence wages, if at all.

Ed and I finished our meal with little further talk. I excused myself and decided I'd walk outside and have a cigarette by myself. First, however, I went to the men's room. As I was leaving, the attendant handed me a towel. On his hand, between his thumb and forefinger, I saw a small tattooed image of a teardrop. The mafia's ranks extend deep indeed, I thought.

Outside, I leaned against the wall, lit a Winston, and welcomed the bite of the raw wind. It quickened my circulation against the jet lag that was making my brain feel like a dull mass. I thought about Chuck Norris.

As a teenager, I had seriously studied Gung Fu, the southern Chinese discipline of Kung Fu, with my small circle of friends. We spent hours taking instruction from Victor Cheng, an accomplished master who ran a dojo in Houston. After experimenting with several styles, I came to specialize in the Art of the White Crane. What I appreciated most was the mental training that was necessary to master the art.

As most other Gung Fu enthusiasts, my friends and I loved to watch Bruce Lee and David Carradine. Lee's films, however, were terminated by his early death, and Carradine fell victim to low TV ratings. I first saw Chuck Norris in Lee's *Return of the Dragon* (1973), where Norris plays a mafia assassin who is sent to Rome to dispose of Lee's character, who makes quick work of Norris. Later, I learned that Norris had been the world middleweight karate champion from 1968 to 1974. I became a fan when I saw *Good Guys Wear Black* (1978); thereafter, I rushed to the theater to catch each of his new movies.

Now, outside this Chuck Norris enterprise in Moscow, I reflected on how ironic it was that he had played a casino security guard at odds with the Hong Kong mob in *Forced Vengeance* (1982). I had no way of knowing it at the moment, but in the course of my stay in Moscow an especially bitter irony would become attached to two other of Norris' movies—*Missing in Action I* (1985) and *Missing in Action II* (1988). As events would force the issue, it would be Chuck himself who'd be missing when action from him would be needed.

As I was finishing my cigarette, I saw a black Mercedes sedan slowly making its way down the alley toward the casino. Then a steel door located several feet away from the casino entrance opened, and six security men, each similar in size and demeanor to the ones who had greeted me earlier, walked out and met the Mercedes as it came to a stop. They formed two parallel lines from the back door to the casino entrance. One of them opened the back door, and a huge man wearing sunglasses stepped out onto the sidewalk. His shoulder length black hair was slicked back, bandit style. A thick, black mustache covered his upper lip. He wore an Armani suit and a scarf that added a European flair. By huge, I mean that he was in the order of three hundred pounds. And he didn't look to be fat. In fact, he moved with menacing, lethal grace. He entered the casino, and the security men remained outside, standing at guard.

I figured the big man had to be Nikolaj Nikolaivich, one of Chuck's partners. He certainly fit the description I had heard of him. I recalled being told that he had won a karate championship while he was living in the US

I finished my Winston and returned to Ed's table. A few minutes later, Nikolaj's massive frame occupied the entrance to the restaurant. He looked around, saw Ed, and came up to our table. Close up, I could see that he had a perfect tan. He sat down and took off his sunglasses. His eyes were dark, almost black, and inscrutable.

Ed introduced me, and I extended my hand, which he took and crushed effortlessly as I said, "Good to meet you, sir."

He talked with Ed, as I listened, too tired to think of much to say, for about thirty minutes. Then Ed excused himself to go to the men's room.

Nikolaj smiled slowly as he looked me straight in the eye. I noticed that his upper lip was twitching under his mustache. His eyes lowered, and I could tell he was wondering about the ring on my right hand.

"So, you're one of those guys," he said.

I told him I was.

"I also understand that you're an ex Green Beret," he said. "And that you also received a commendation medal for the Grenada Rescue Operation while you were a paratrooper."

"Right again," I replied. "You've been doing some homework on me."

He smiled again. "I like to know who's who. I was the one who had to arrange for your visa to get here. By the way, you should know that you're red flagged on the government computers as a possible spy."

"Makes sense," I said. "I did some work in Angola back during the communist revolution there."

He retracted his smile and stared at me, his mustache quivering with the twitchings of his upper lip. I looked down at his monster hands. In his left hand, he was holding and furiously fingering a set of Syrian worry beads, also called prayer beads. On his right hand, I noticed a massive ring that looked hundreds of years old. Its two-inch base, which had been forged from silver, bore the crest of the Roman Orthodox Church on both sides. Set into the silver was the largest flat ruby I've ever seen— either across a counter or in any books. Secured to the ruby's face was a large golden crest that I recognized as the emblem of the Romanovs. If he had received the ring as a family heirloom, he was, I realized, Russian royalty, a descendant of the Russian imperial family. That would mean he was related to Catherine the Great, one of the most loved and admired of Russia's rulers during the czarist period that came to an end with the Bolshevik revolution of 1917, when many members of the royal family fled Russia to escape assassination by Lenin's Cheka. If this were Nikolaj's heritage, it was likely that he grew up as one of the leaders of the Russian aristocracy living in self-imposed exile and waiting for the chance to re-establish their ascendancy.

"So, you're a Romanov," I said quietly.

He smiled again, briefly. "You're a smart one, aren't you? Just remember the story about the curious cat." With that, he fell silent again, keeping intense eye contact.

I thought about the new face Russian politics had taken since the fall of the Berlin Wall. I was aware that the Russian Orthodox Church had re-established some of the hold it once had among the population at large and among political adepts. Church-endorsed candidates were, I knew, prevailing in elections. I also knew that many Russians had little confidence in the ability of an elected official to pull Russia out of the chaos into which it had fallen. The growing sentiment was that only a supreme imperial ruler would be able to save the country from self-destruction. That would explain why so many of the most recently elected governors and commissioners were descendants of royalty. It would moreover explain why Nikolaj was so solidly connected.

He broke the silence by asking what had probably been on his mind for the last few minutes. "So, what *really* brings you to Moscow?"

"I'm looking for asylum," I replied and laughed, to indicate I was joking. I was hoping to see that he had a sense of humor. Also, I wanted to feel out whether he knew anything about the attention I had received from the FBI back in Louisiana. My answer didn't seem to amuse or surprise him. His upper lip stopped twitching, and I got the feeling that he was well versed in my relationship with the FBI.

"The building is near Red Square," he said, whether seriously or not, I couldn't tell.

"What building?" I asked, feeling off balance.

"The one you go to and ask for asylum," he answered, now smiling again.

Ed returned to the table, sat down, and engaged Nikolaj in talk about business matters. Marginalized, I finished my meal in silence.

I worked the rest of my first week in Moscow on the Chuck Norris Hollywood Stars Studio, but the project fell to pieces financially owing to lack of commitment from some of the Russian participants. Ed then brokered a deal between Chuck, Nikolaj, and him, on the one hand, and the two owners (one an Israeli and the other an East Indian) of the Planet Hollywood Moscow franchise, on the other. This franchise owned a restaurant on the first floor of a large building in Moscow. The basement was occupied by a retail mall. The deal involved removing the mall and replacing it with a casino.

I then worked on trying to coordinate design and construction of the new casino. Several problems arose, however, and it became apparent to me that project development was going to move slowly, if at all. Also, I found myself footing the bill for business trips back and forth from the states, frequent long distance calls, and for development of design documents, which Ed seemed to think could be drawn up for free, on a napkin. By January, I was feeling severely pinched and decided to confront Ed outright on the issue of reimbursement. A nasty argument followed, in which he took the position that he had met his commitments by paying for my first two business trips. I got extremely angry at this rediculous attempt to change the facts in a pitiful attempt to cover his butt. When I originally came to him, I had desperately needed a paying job to pay the bills, not a winter vacation in Russia. This was especially bold of him considering that he had me working on Russian projects, over the phone, before I had even set foot on Russian soil.

We both fumed for several minutes. Then Ed calmed down and came up with what he thought might be a solution. "You know, the casino doesn't have a general manager right now. Why don't you go see if Nikolaj thinks you might be good for the job?"

I wasn't encouraged. I had heard that the employees of the Beverly Hills Casino—the Chuck Norris enterprise—weren't getting paid. "What good is a new job if I'm not going to get paid there either, Ed? The point I'm making is that I'm just about out of money right now."

"Chuck's going to straighten all that out when he comes back again," Ed said. "Anyway, I'll bet that they'll pay you if you take on general manager. In fact, I'm going to call Chuck and talk to him about it. It would be good for us to have you as our eyes and ears in the casino. After all, what choices do you have back in the states?"

Ed knew that I was between the proverbial rock and hard place. I knew it too. "I guess I don't have much choice right now," I answered. "I'll go see Nikki, but you make sure Chuck straightens out the pay situation, Ed. I mean it."

"I promise you he will," Ed said.

So one evening in mid February, I walked across the alley (by now I was installed in the apartment) to the casino. As I approached the entrance, I looked up at the sign, at the image of the couple dancing, at the gentleman in a black tux and the lady in a sleek black ball gown. I then looked at the white, ornately scripted "Beverly Hills" and at the gold lettering on a red background, "A Chuck Norris Enterprise." I thought about Chuck's partner, Nikolaj, whom I'd be seeing in a few moments. I knew he wasn't the easiest person to talk to—that he was very skillful at keeping you ill at ease, ever giving the impression that what he was saying was at best a dim indication of what he was thinking. And I thought about my experience in foreign employment. I had learned long ago that you have to be very careful about whom you work for overseas—that it's always the safest bet to work for a venture with American partnership. Among American expats there was a long standing, unwritten code that you did not screw over your *cumpadre*.

I told the apes who met me inside the entrance that I was here to see Nikolaj. Slowly they stood aside to let me by. I walked to the back of the casino, through the steel security door labeled "Private," and crossed the hall to the steel door to Nikolaj's fortressed office. I buzzed the doorbell and looked up at the security camera so that he could see my face on his monitors. The door lock clicked into the open position. I opened the door and walked up the stairs. Nikolaj was sitting at his desk. He motioned for me to take a seat.

For a while we chatted, then I broached what I had come to talk to him about. He smiled openly, not in the least surprised that I was asking for the job of general manager of the casino. "You know, John," he said, "I have an even better idea. Chuck and I have another company, Chuck Norris Casinos International, Limited."

He handed me a white business card with the logo printed on the top. I looked at the card and noticed the office locations—one in Florida and another in Beverly Hills. First we have the Chuck Norris Hollywood Stars Studio, I thought. Then this place, the casino. Now also this international company. Chuck's a juggernaut to be reckoned with. "What does this company do?" I asked.

"We're looking at building new casinos—maybe in Egypt and maybe in Tbilisi. That's in Georgia," Nikolaj explained. "Sound interesting?"

"It does. Think I could be of any help?"

Nikolaj stood, looming over me where I was sitting. "I'd like you to come on as vice president and help with new projects. But, while you are in Moscow, I want you to manage the casino."

"What's my salary?" I asked earnestly.

"Eight thousand a month will be okay," he stated, in a tone that told me there was no margin for negotiation.

Under different circumstances, I would have pushed the envelope for a better package. Right now, though, eight thousand a month was exactly eight thousand a month more than I was getting. I stood, extended my hand, and said, "Deal."

He took my hand and, smiling, crunched my knuckles. "Go and have dinner, why don't you. I'll tell Chuck and Ed you're on."

Ed called about a half-hour later. I took the call at the cashier's podium in the restaurant. "Congratulations," he said. "Nikolaj told me the good news. I've already spoken to Chuck, and he's excited. We both really like it that you'll be working for Chuck Norris Casinos International. That'll make a lot of things possible."

I thanked Ed, at the same time wondering whether Chuck was excited enough to see to it that payroll obligations would be met or whether he'd prove to be a convert to Russia's version of equal opportunity employment—the kind that eliminated your need for a wallet, a bank account, or an investment portfolio.

Sounding pontifical, Ed said, "Now, John, you know to watch things for Chuck and me. We're both depending on you. We want to know what's going on at all times. Chuck has a lot at stake."

I gulped hard, shocked. I was sure that Nikolaj had all the casino phones bugged and that he routinely played back the recorded conversations. And here was Ed, impressing on me how important it was that we ensure Chuck's best interests, entirely unaware that he was comprising me on Nikolaj's own killing ground. I had to fudge my reply. "I'm going to do the best I can for everyone," I quickly said.

"So, John, we're square now, right?" Ed asked.

Some *cumpadre* you are, Ed, I thought. "Yeah, Ed, just make sure you do your job with Chuck. You know what I mean by your job? Or do I have to make it clear?"

"No. You got it, kid," he answered and then hung up.

Right, I thought. I've got what? Fuck all until I get it.

It was about 1130 hours when I arrived back at my hotel room. The phone was ringing as I opened the door. It was Cary Feldman, calling to update me on recent developments in the investigation. Steve Irwin was now off the case, and Cary was now talking with three prosecutors, Jim Letten, Mike Magner and Peter Strasser. In time, I'd come to admire Strasser for his pit bull tenacity.

I asked Cary what he thought of the prosecution team. "They seem pretty factual and straightforward," he said. "And they want to talk to you. They want to meet with you in New Orleans."

"Did they say anything specific about what they want to talk about?"

"That's really why I'm calling. They want to talk to you about a possible immunity deal. They'll pay your round trip ticket if you'll come back and get together with them on this. John, if you can get it, I recommend that you take it. These guys intend to prosecute with a vengeance. If you're reading any of the stories coming out of Louisiana, you can see this business is getting nasty."

I paused a moment and thought over what Cary was suggesting. I wondered whether I could trust what the prosecution team had suggested to him. Or was it bait to get me where I'd be accessible? "Cary, do you trust these guys? I don't want to land back in New Orleans just to be handcuffed at customs."

"I trust them," Cary said. "In fact, I feel pretty good about this."

I asked him when I'd need to be in New Orleans. He replied that it'd be best if I could make it back in about three days. He'd make the travel arrangements. He had already looked at flights and knew that I'd be arriving in the evening. He'd reserve me at the Hyatt, and we'd meet there for dinner.

I thanked him for calling, hung up, and walked about my room, taking deep breaths, thinking fast. Immunity would certainly solve a few problems back home. Also, going stateside now would give me a chance to see Susan. I was wretched with missing her; and, if the immunity deal could be worked, there was something I needed to make final.

The next evening I met with Nikolaj in his office at the casino and told him I needed to return to Louisiana to take care of outstanding personal business before I could start my new job. I told him I'd need to be away for about a week. He didn't mind in the least. "I want to congratulate you," he said.

I pretended to be confused and asked, "What for, sir?" But I wasn't confounded in the least. The casino owned the apartment I was living in, and I was positive that its phone was monitored.

"You know," he answered. "I'll look forward to seeing you when you get back."

I thanked him and left his office with the uneasy feeling that there wasn't much of consequence happening or being said anywhere in Moscow that Nikolaj didn't know about.

Two evenings later, weary after the long flight across nearly half the world, I was sitting with Cary in the restaurant of the Hyatt in New Orleans. First we ordered. Then, in the manner that I had come to expect from him, he got right to the matter at hand. "I'm going over myself in the morning," he explained. "The process is called Queen for a Day. I tell them what you know. I do my best to make you look attractive to them. The deal is they can't use anything I tell them against you later. If they like what I say, they'll advise that you be given immunity."

I asked him if the process called for a leap of faith on our part.

"It's the procedure, John. Period. We're either on or off. It's your call."

I told him I was on. He asked me to think hard on whether there was anything I hadn't told him that could be of use to us. I thought about my missing tapes and wished I had them now. I told Cary there was nothing more I could think of.

"Okay. Then try and get a good night's sleep," he said. "You're going to need to be at your best."

With my mind sluggish but my body on full alert, the twin symptoms of jet lag and nervousness caused sleep to elude me until early morning. Briefly, I drifted off, into a dream where I found myself standing on the edge of the roof of a skyscraper, looking at a cassette tape that was hanging in the air in front of me. When I reached out, it would withdraw just beyond my grasp. If I extended my reach, leaning myself out as far as I dared, it would retire even farther. Over and over I tried, each time risking plunging to a certain death. The frustration woke me up. I looked at the alarm clock and saw that it was almost time to meet Cary downstairs for breakfast.

He ordered only coffee and toast. "That's all you're having?" I asked. "Got work to do," he said. "You look rough."

"Not as rough as I feel," I said and gulped down a glass of orange juice.

He finished his coffee, stood, and said, "Get some sleep then. I'm over to the government office on my own this morning. Meet me here for lunch. Be sure you're rested."

By noon I felt much better, after four solid hours of death-like sleep and then a hot shower. Cary was waiting for me when I came down for lunch.

"It's not enough for them," he said as I took a seat.

I thought about my dream. "I have nothing more I can tell them, Cary. I wish the hell I had those tapes."

"So do I. They'd come in more than handy. You sure you've looked everywhere?"

I told him I had searched everywhere I could think of, that the tapes were, as far as I was concerned, something that I'd see only in my dreams.

"Well, John," Cary said, "they could be bluffing, to see if you're holding out. Let's ride it out. I'm supposed to go back and talk to them some more after we finish here. Wait in your room to hear from me."

He was gone only an hour before he returned to the hotel and called me from his room. "You've got it, John. They're going to give you immunity."

I asked him if he knew why they had done a turnaround. "No idea," he said. "Makes no difference, really. If I were you, I wouldn't be looking a gift horse in the mouth. Anyway, hope you're bright eyed. We need to get over there now. They're expecting us."

Cary took me to the sixth floor of a private building that the FBI was leasing. There, we were escorted into a large meeting room where agents Santini, Swikert, and Hemphill were sitting with three men I didn't recognize. I took comfort from the absence of Assistant US Attorney Steve Irwin. Cary introduced the three men as prosecutors Jim Letten, Mike Magner, and Peter Strasser. As we moved quickly through the paperwork into the debriefing, I could see that these prosecutors were intent only on the facts. None of them seemed bent on an exercise in self-aggrandization. To the contrary, they were as serious as a heart attack about carrying out their jobs. Strasser, in fact, impressed me as having the intensity of a bloodhound on a trail laid with the fresh scent of Edwin Edwards. I could almost see Edwin lunging his way urgently through obscure backcountry bayous, driven by the ever-nearing baying of a search-and- find animal that could taste his sign even in water.

I felt good, seeing the real government of my country in action, and felt even better the next morning, in Baton Rouge, testifying before the grand jury. I had done the right thing, for the right people; and now I could look forward to doing another right thing, for myself and for Susan, the right person in my life.

First, I picked out and bought a diamond ring; then I flew to Lake Charles. Susan met my flight and took me to her house. As soon as we were in the living room, I told her to sit down, on the couch. Then I went suppliant, on one knee, and asked her if she'd mind changing her last name. She smiled, brilliantly, at the same time that tears gathered in her eyes. She said, "If you mean changing it to Brotherton, which is what you'd better mean, I only want to know what took you so long."

We were married three days after my testimony, aboard my boat, which Rick Shetler arranged to have anchored at the same seawall where I had first seen Susan. The ceremony was performed by Susan's second cousin, Judge Greg Lyons, and attended, in addition to Rick, by Susan's family and, of course, Eddie Austin, who claimed he had seen this day coming the moment I had noticed Susan among the Contraband Days crowd. It felt great to be back among close friends, and it felt wonderful to be married again, to be able to look forward to a life with Susan, who'd be joining me soon after I arrived back in Moscow.

Susan and I had given a lot of thought to the question of whether we should bring Taylor with us. Our plan was to let him stay with his father (who had been asking for an extended visit for a long time) in Houston for a few months, while we tested the waters in Moscow. If we liked what we saw, we'd then bring Taylor over and enroll him in a private school.

While I was in Lake Charles, I met Huck, a friend of Susan's who had learned to speak Russian in the military and who expressed interest in going to Moscow, to work in Chuck's disco as its manager. I contacted Ed and got his approval. Huck, who'd arrive in Moscow toward the end of April, almost together with David Tucker, a Floridian whom Danny had recruited, was excited. The month or so that he'd be spending in Moscow, however, would give him a near lethal overdose of adventure.

My time home was all too short. I had told Nikolaj that I'd be back in about a week, which left Susan and me no chance to take much of a honeymoon. We agreed that we'd take the first occasion to do it right, and late in the afternoon of March 2 my Lufthansa flight again descended toward the runway of Sheremetyevo 2. This time, despite the overcast and the wind-driven snow, I felt more buoyant as the wheels touched town. Out loud, I sang the lyrics to "Back in the USSR" and ignored the curious-to-outraged looks of the other passengers.

The next day, I arranged to rent the apartment, located near Red Square and the Kremlin, where I'd live with Susan when she arrived. (Later, when David would arrive, he'd move into the apartment I had been sharing with Danny.) That evening, I checked in with Nikolaj, who was abundant with congratulations, all curiosity about my wedding ring, and full of anticipation to meet Susan—"this woman," as he put it, "who's made a lucky man out of you." For the moment, I thought his childlike curiosity about something so small and simple as my wedding ring was endearing, especially in a man of his size and physical power.

He was also brimming with enthusiasm about business prospects. First he said I'd be conducting new business for Chuck Norris Casinos International right off, that we'd be starting by going together to Egypt, to check out potential casino sites for Chuck's company in Cairo and in Sharm-El-Shiek, a resort community on the southern tip of the Sinai Peninsula, which dips into the Red Sea. Next we'd be going to Tbilisi, Georgia, for about a week to also scout new casino sites.

The prospect of visiting Georgia, formerly known as the Georgian Soviet Socialist Republic, excited me. I knew it had the dubious distinction of being the birthplace of Joseph Stalin and that it was also the home of Eduard Shevardnadze, James Baker's counterpart in the Gorbachev government during the gulf war and now Georgia's president. (I knew Eduard's grandson personally; he was a regular at the Beverly Hills casino.) Baker and Shevardnadze were close friends, and the American secretary of state had visited Georgia in the spring of 1992, while Shevardnadze was acting as interim President, following the ousting of the despot Zviad Gamsakhurdia. Baker's reports of the open hospitality of Georgians and of the beauty of the little republic, bordered by Turkey, Armenia, and Azerbaidzhan to its south and by the Black Sea to its west, were glowing. I also knew that Tbilisi, set in the valley of the Kura River and framed by the Greater Caucasus to its north, the Lesser Caucasus to its south, and the north-south oriented Surami Range to its east, was one of the most fascinating cities in the world, offering a mosaic of sites representing almost every major religion.

We'd be going to Georgia, Nikolaj said, almost as soon as we returned from Egypt. Susan would be in Moscow by that time, and I asked Nikolaj if he and Chuck would mind it if Susan and I grabbed an opportunity to take a short honeymoon. He agreed readily, speaking for both Chuck and himself.

The trip turned out to be an all-in-all great time, everything I had bargained for and a few things I hadn't. On the first morning, Nikolaj, Susan, and I walked out of our hotel to meet the escort that would be driving us around for our site visits. Waiting for us were two Russian Volga sedans, each riddled with bullet holes. One of the Volgas had a huge hole in the windshield, directly in front of the driver's seat. I looked in through the hole and saw that the drivers seat itself was liberally blood-stained.

I looked at Nikolaj, who was smiling widely. "They were part of President Shevardnadze's motorcade until two weeks ago," he said. "After he was ambushed by guerrillas, he switched cars with these guys," he added, pointing to our drivers, who were standing outside the Volgas.

I looked at the drivers, then at Nikolaj. "They're Georgian tax officers," he said. Then he tossed his head back and laughed. "Bet Shevardnadze had a hard time hiring a new driver."

We spent the next two days inspecting empty buildings and taking pictures. Just before we planned to return to Moscow, it occurred to us that we had overlooked getting Susan a visa that would allow her to re-enter Russia. Because she was on her first visit to Russia, she had only been able to obtain a single entry visa. To give the Russian consulate enough time to complete the paperwork, Susan and I would need to remain in Georgia a few more days, while Nikolaj went back to Moscow.

To help us look after our needs, we were assigned an escort, a young Georgian (in his late twenties) named Beka. He was on the short side and so slender that he was almost outsized by the automatic pistol he always carried in a makeshift holster tucked into the back of his overly large trousers. He turned out to be a typical Georgian, a warm hospitable host. On our sightseeing tours, he would stop and introduce us to his several friends, who all wore the same type of pistol in the same type of holster. I couldn't understand what they said in their native Georgian, but from the little Russian I overheard I gathered that Beka had distinguished himself as a hero in the war for independence that the republic had recently fought against Russia.

On one of our excursions, Beka stopped by the congress to intro-duce us to the speaker of the house, a close friend of his who accepted some of my American cigarettes with enthusiasm. One evening, he took us out into the country to eat at a restaurant that was frequented by other war heroes, some of whom were now high-ranking politicians. Arm locked in arm, we recited one toast after another over repeated rounds of vodka until our legs went to jelly. As we were leaving, Beka's friends embraced us heartily, slapping us on the back and insisting that we return. The next day, despite our hangovers, we drove out into the mountains that pre-sided over old Tbilisi, to the eleventh- century monastery where the Geor-gian monarchs had been buried. Susan and I found the fantastic cathedral to be suffused in mystery.

We couldn't have dreamed of a more exotic honeymoon. The morn-ing we picked up Susan's visa, Beka drove us to the airport and insisted on walking with us all the way to the boarding gate. Each time we passed through a metal detector, his pistol caused the alarm to annunciate. But no one took notice. They all knew Beka. Finally, Susan and I each hugged Beka and exchanged the three kisses on the cheek, in the best Eastern European tradition of heartfelt friendship.

Back in Moscow, after we had settled into our apartment on the Moskva, Susan lucked into a job opportunity in short order. One evening, we ran into Michael Bass at the Beverly Hills casino. He had just launched his *Metropolitan Magazine*, a monthly featuring high fashion and goings on in elite social strata, and needed an advertising salesperson. Susan more than met his requirements, and he offered her the position. Because the magazine was so new—its first issue would be out shortly—most of the advertising revenue would consist not of cash but of bartering—for example, meals at restaurants and clothes from retailers. For the first few months, Susan's commissions on her sales were also to be worked out in bartering, an arrangement that Susan would later deploy as the equivalent of a derringer in her garter.

CHAPTER 21

THE HEIST

＊

I had now been working for Chuck Norris Casinos International, Limited and for the Chuck Norris Beverly Hills Club for over three months without having been paid. As for Danny, he had been on regular payroll initially but hadn't received a paycheck in over two months. It was the same with David—though he too had been paid partially a few times back when he had started. Huck hadn't, as I hadn't, received a cent since day one.

In my own case, the term over which I had provided gratuitous service was straining my financial picture. If it continued much longer, I'd certainly lose my home in Lake Charles. As it was, my credit cards had already been cancelled. Susan and I were, moreover, sharing what money we had with Huck, who otherwise would have been in dire straits.

Tonight, however, this situation would be overturned, according to Ed, who had begged us to be patient and not to leave, promising us time and again that Chuck Norris would rectify our outstanding salaries first thing when he arrived in Moscow. Today, Chuck was arriving; and to-night he'd be attending a gala dinner celebration at his casino. Tonight, Ed promised, Chuck would take the necessary steps.

So today I was in enough of an upbeat mood to probe another of

Stalin's contributions to Moscow's architecture—the network of tunnels that ran beneath the entire city. Since I had arrived back in November, I had been curious about these tunnels; and I knew that one lay under the casino. But I had been reluctant to investigate, deterred perhaps by the gloom that had been hanging in my mind during the severe winter. Also, the tunnels carried such sinister associations that few people were willing to talk about them. I had managed to find out that their labyrinthine layout was unmapped and that they had been built, supposedly, as bomb shelters by forced labor—by political dissidents or other detainees who had fallen into Stalin's disfavor. Their actual functionality would be evident enough, I had been told, after a brief tour, if I could work up the nerve to take one.

The tunnel was accessible through a thick steel door in the basement part of the casino. The door was about seven feet tall and four and a half feet wide. It opened onto a landing that was about six feet by six feet. From the landing I took a sharp turn to the right and went down a steep flight of steps to another landing. I turned again, to the left this time, and went down another set of stairs to a narrow hallway. At this point, I figured that I had descended about twelve feet below the level of the basement door. The hallway led me roughly twenty-five feet to another steel door—this one about six feet high and three feet wide. I worked the door open and stepped into the tunnel, which ran to my right and left.

In the dim lighting, provided by bare bulbs (the few that weren't burned out) set into fixtures that hung every forty feet or so from a strand of electrical wire running along the ceiling, I could tell that the tunnel had been constructed from concrete, entirely hand-troweled. The passageway was about fifteen feet wide and eight feet high. The floor was rough and cluttered with debris. The air was damply chilling and so thick with dust that I had to hold a handkerchief over my mouth. Breathing in fact was so difficult that I decided I'd make this a short recon and come back sometime later with an improvised breathing mask.

The tunnel seemed to stretch into infinity in either direction. I chose one and started walking, suppressing the urge to constantly cough. About every thirty feet, on each side, I saw steel doors that opened to small rooms that had no lights, wiring, shelves, or water. I gathered that they were solitary-confinement cells hidden from public view. I hadn't gone far before I came upon a series of doors that had been welded shut. Looking at the silent doors, wondering about what remains lay in internment behind them, and feeling the cold, clammy, dust-rich air, I began to understand why these cells were a non-topic. As I walked back toward the door to the stairs, it occurred to me that the casino had appropriated some of the cells as free office space.

I went straight to the men's room and carefully washed the dust and grime from my hands and face and brushed my suit off as best as I could. I started toward the restaurant, intending to take a table and to wait for Susan to arrive for dinner, but noticed that it was empty of patrons, except for two people—Michael Bass, whom I knew well, and Umar, whom I knew of well—and a near platoon of body guards. The heavies were attending Umar, who was having what looked like a dinner meeting with Michael. Umar was, I had heard, a Moscow-based venturer who was, you could say, capitalistic in the purest sense: in all his business dealings he looked after his own interests scrupulously.

He was strikingly handsome, in his late thirties, with perfectly cropped, jet-black hair, tonight covered by the black baseball hat he was wearing. Sitting with one leg leisurely crossed over the other and patiently listening to Bass' latest line of bull, he looked like he belonged more at a Baccarat table in Monaco than at a corner table in Chuck Norris' Beverly Hills Club here in Moscow. Seeing him wearing the black hat irritated me. In my view, the black hat was a symbol of functional authority, properly worn by the drill instructors at Fort Benning. I didn't think it belonged on Umar's head.

As I took a seat at one of the tables, Umar's security men glared at me as if I had stepped inside the sanctum of a sacred circle. I stood and returned the glare, thinking, You want to look? Then take a good look— at the only Green Beret in this room. In the time I had spent in Moscow, I had seen more than enough goons and was tired of getting the look from them. They had, of course, the advantage in greater numbers; and they had firepower, which I lacked entirely. But to me the badass staredown meant I'll go at it with you one on one, hand to hand. And if it came to that, I'd be more than happy to accommodate any one, two, or three of them. I got up from my table, walked to the service bar, took a bottle of water, and returned to my seat. I wasn't going to miss Michael Bass's show for anything.

And what I was seeing was vintage Bass. He was waving his hands around, trying to make some point or other to a not even mildly interested Umar. Small beads of sweat perched atop Bass's shaved head, and the "Uncle Festerish" wrinkles and folds on the back of his head and neck were undulating, fluid like.

I figured Michael was excelling at either of the two things he did best—getting himself into or out of deep shit. With Umar, getting in was not a hard thing to do, and there was no getting out. I thought a moment of what had, I heard, gone down between Umar and Paul Tatum, one of the first American carpetbaggers who had tried to hustle Moscow after the fall of the Berlin Wall. Tatum was attempting to open up a new Radisson Hotel franchise. In constructing one of the city's most beautiful hotels, he courted Umar as his partner. The hotel was a great success right from its opening.

The way I heard it told, Umar then acted on his guiding principle of self-interest. Paul came to work one day to find that his key no longer fit the door to his office. When he asked for an explanation, he was thrown bodily out into the street. Unable to take this gentle hint, he tried to make a press spectacle out of his shabby treatment by sleeping every night in front of the hotel lobby. For his effort, early one morning he received a few ounces of lead, in the form of nine-millimeter rounds, in his head and was laid to a dirt nap.

Now here was Michael Bass, holding forth, speaking his words trippingly on his slippery tongue, maybe to placate an angel of death. I had to wonder how Bass managed to keep himself out of Birchwood Forest, a several square mile thicket in Moscow that was used as a resolution ground for delicate issues.

When Umar was finished listening to whatever Michael was urging, he rose, summoned his guards, and walked out of the casino, with Bass following, still imploring.

Alone now in the restaurant, I thought about the night ahead. Chuck Norris would have arrived by now. He was staying at the Sovietsky Hotel and should be showing up here soon with Ed. I was eager to meet Chuck, if only to see the payroll issue settled. Danny came over to tell me it was time to open the casino. "Tonight's the night," he said as he walked up to my table.

"The night for what, I wonder?" I asked and laughed.

"The night we get paid, I hope," Danny replied without laughing.

"Then tonight can't happen soon enough," I said, looking toward the casino entrance and then following Danny into the casino itself. Susan hadn't arrived yet, so I'd wait for her before I had dinner.

Susan showed up in about an hour and took a table in the restaurant. I went over to join her. Within a few minutes, some of the doormen came in, all abuzz with excitement. Chuck's entourage was here. I walked out the entrance to take a position out front, to greet Chuck and the guests that would be arriving with him. I saw that two cars, carrying armed security personnel, had preceded the van in which I knew Chuck, his girlfriend (from California), his personal bodyguard, and Ed were riding. Two chase cars pulled up behind the van. Their doors opened; and at least six security men emerged and formed parallel protective rows between the van and the entrance, where I was standing.

The door to the van opened. Chuck's bodyguard stepped out, slowly surveyed the scene around him, then looked inside the van and nodded. A hugely muscled black man who had earned a thirteenth-degree black belt in karate (the highest level, held by only a handful of sensei in the entire world), the bodyguard was aptly nicknamed Action Jackson.

Chuck stepped out and also gave the scene a quick look over. Then he reached inside for his girlfriend, who emerged holding his right arm. Ed followed; then came another man whom I didn't recognize. He was older, maybe in his early sixties, and distinguished looking, with short, curly gray hair. I stepped aside as the two columns of security men, followed by Jackson, preceded Chuck, his lady, the older man, and Ed into the restaurant and ushered them to a specially appointed table. Chuck, his lady, and Ed sat at one end of the table, the older man at the other. Then the guards positioned themselves in a perimeter. The show of force was, I thought, pathetic here in Moscow, where it would have been only out of good-humored tolerance that the gunmen of the Russian mafia allowed this security corps to remain standing. Even Jackson himself would have been defenseless against a thick enfilade of nine-millimeter rounds.

Ed walked up to Susan and me and asked, "How's the action tonight?"

I told him a lot of people had shown up, hoping to meet Chuck.

"His facelift looks pretty good, doesn't it?" Ed asked.

"Whose?" I asked in turn. I didn't know what he was talking about.

"Chuck's," he said.

I looked at Susan, who was peering over toward Chuck's table, trying to get a good look at him. "I didn't know he had gotten a facelift," she said.

"Neither did I," I added.

"It's actually his second," Ed said. I noticed that he was looking back and forth, at me, then at Chuck's table, trying to get Chuck's attention. As soon as Chuck looked over toward him, he waved, left us, and went to take his seat. His fawning attitude toward Chuck gave me a sinking feeling. He seemed to be nearly obsessed with looking after Chuck's convenience, despite the entourage that was charged with this duty.

Susan, I could see, was still staring, goggle eyed, toward Chuck's table. "Is he that good looking?" I asked.

"Who?" she asked back.

"Chuck. Your eyes are bulging, honey. I'm feeling a sting of envy here."

"Chuck? Good looking? Cute maybe, with those chipmunk cheeks of his. Forget Chuck. Don't you see who's at the other end of the table? I can't believe it. It's Jed Allen. Jed Allen, he's here. Amazing! Now he is good looking."

I had to agree. "Who's Jed Allen?"

"Who's Jed Allen? John! He was Don Craig on Days of Our Lives and C.C. Capwell on Santa Barbara."

"Really?" I replied, glad that Ed wasn't here. I didn't think he'd enjoy hearing a good-looking woman demote Chuck to second in prominence at the VIP table here tonight.

"I'd love to meet him. Can I? Please?" Susan asked.

I noticed that there were two empty seats next to Jed. I walked over to Action Jackson and asked him if he'd mind. "My wife'd be thrilled to meet Jed Allen," I explained.

He looked at me, over at Susan, at Chuck, then said, "Sure, if *that's* what you want."

I told Susan to take the seat next to Jed. He was pleased to meet us, and we enjoyed a lively conversation with him during the dinner. Actually, we had him all to ourselves. Everyone else at the table was hanging on every word Chuck uttered.

Occasionally, I looked at Ed and could see that he was basking in the presence of Chuck and his girlfriend. I couldn't overhear any of their conversation, but it didn't look as if it were touching on any serious matters. When they were finished, Chuck nodded, and his corps stood and took up protective positions. Then Chuck, his girlfriend, Jackson, and Ed stood. As they were walking toward the entrance to leave, Ed looked over at Susan and me and waved for us to come over and meet Chuck.

Susan and I thanked Jed for his company and walked up to Ed, who made the introductions with overwrought pomp. "Good to meet you, John," Chuck said, extending his hand. "I've heard a lot of good things about you, and I appreciate the job you're doing for me here."

He introduced himself to Susan and then looked around the room. "How about a picture of us together?" he asked. Immediately, Ed fetched the one of the roving photographers.

"A rose between two thorns," Chuck said, smiling for the photographer, also reaching around Susan's back and patting me on my shoulder. I took the gesture as indicating he had meant what he said about being appreciative of my job performance.

We stood together, with Susan in the middle, while the photographer took the shot. Then Chuck told us how happy he was to have met us and said goodnight. He turned, nodded to Jackson and his security men, and together they walked out of the casino. Ed took a quick look at me and then followed Chuck. As Jed passed us, Susan said, "Goodnight. And thanks again."

"Thank you. I enjoyed it," he replied.

Danny, David, and Huck came over and stood with Susan and me. Huck looked at me, his eyes wide and hopeful. "So, did Chuck do anything about our payrolls?"

"Not a fucking thing," Danny replied, disgusted. "Fuck that son of a bitch. He ain't shit."

We worked the rest of the evening without speaking to each other. We had seen enough, and there was really nothing to be added to Danny's assessment. The plain fact was that we were near broke, without enough money between us to buy even one of us a plane ticket home.

I woke the next morning early, after a restless night, and decided to use my time unpacking a few boxes that Susan and I hadn't as yet attended to. Also, I needed a bath, an undertaking in the order of a megaproject in this apartment, which lacked hot running water. To fill the bathtub even halfway, I'd need to heat about one hundred coffee kettles of water, one by one, a process that took up to two hours. I understood the fetid smell that pervaded the crowded subways and wondered how long it would take me to abandon the daily bath that I had always regarded as one of the essentials of a minimally civilized life.

First, I made a cup of instant coffee and sat a moment, looking out my window, at Red Square. Then I opened a box and began removing its contents. Toward the bottom, I found a box of items I had gathered before I had vacated my Players office in Lake Charles. In the box, I saw a black Memorex tape cassette with names and dates I had written on both sides. I looked at the names—Edwards, Shetler, Players, Coushatta—and realized I had found one of the tapes that I had scoured my home for the night I discovered I was being tailed by the white car.

Excited, I started going through the items I had taken from the box. I found a pair of black Army fatigue pants. The right pocket was bulging. I opened it and removed three more of my tapes. I wanted to run through them immediately, to refresh myself. But I didn't have a tape player in my apartment. Danny, however, did; and I had no doubt he'd let me borrow it. I dressed and headed for the metro station, to take the subway to his apartment, which was across the alley from the casino.

Later, back in my apartment, with the tapes running, I was amazed about how brazen Players had been in their participation in one scheme after another. It would be hard for anyone to listen to the conversations without believing that the company had been openly extorted. Their culpability would be plain to the FBI, if they were to listen to the tapes, I thought. I tried placing a call to Cary Feldman, but had to settle for leaving a message on his voice mail. And I had to be discreet. I knew that Nikolaj's goon squad was recording my calls, and I wanted to keep Nikolaj's knowledge level at minimum. There was no telling what would prompt him to order active measures.

Then I thought of something that Assistant US Attorney Peter Strasser had explained to me back in New Orleans. If Players found themselves up against the wall, he had said, they might try to depict me as a rogue operative, a loose cannon who had engineered the illegal deals on his own, without their knowledge. These tapes, I knew, would give the lie to that plea, would stop Players cold in their tracks if they tried to use me as a human shield.

Not only that, I could now see to it that there would be virtual hell to pay within Players; I only needed to decide who was going to do the paying. And that was no problem. It would be Pat Madamba. I inserted one of the tapes, held the speaker of the phone up to the player, and dialed his direct line, at his office at the Players headquarters in Atlantic City. When his voice mail message was finished, I turned the player on and let it run, wishing I could be on hand the next morning to watch him wet his pants as he listened to the message. When the tape had run through a few nasty conversations, I turned it off and hung up, assured that I had thrown a spanner into any plans that Players might have to massage the truth.

Exhilarated over having delivered some measure of payback to Players, I decided to take the night off. With Susan working late, I'd go back over to Danny's and see if I could get him into a fun-loving mood. I put the tapes in my carry bag and headed again for the metro.

"Great minds think alike," Danny said, as he opened his door and looked me over, no doubt taking note that I was wearing blue jeans and not a suit. He too was in jeans and was also wearing his stupid looking gray golf hat—in all, his favorite partying costume.

"I'm authorizing a night off for both of us," I said as I stepped into his apartment. "Can't see what difference it makes. Anyway you look at it, we're not getting paid."

In reply, he held up a sixty-five dollar bottle of Jack Daniels and used it to wave me in. After a few shots each, we decided it would be more practical to conserve his high-priced whiskey by going over to the casino disco. "I don't see why Chuck should mind paying for our drinks," Danny said. "It's about all he's good for."

I laughed, grabbed Danny by the arm, and pulled him toward the door. "Tonight, drinks are on Norris whether he minds it or not."

It was a quiet night at the casino—none of the Russian mafia regulars and very few other patrons other than a small group of drunken Russians sitting together at a table and playing grab ass with the staff prostitutes. Danny and I took a table in the middle of the floor, ordered a round of drinks, and sat back, listening to the skull-piercing mix of Spice Girls and Russian techno pop, played at a level that would make you deaf within an hour.

I looked around at the near empty disco, then said, "Danny, get ready for a very special brand of rock and roll."

"Rock and roll, I like that," he said.

"Not everyone likes this. The ones who like it the least have to dance to it anyway," I said, taking one of my tapes from my bag.

"Whatever," Danny said, as I got up and walked toward the DJ booth.

Played over the loudspeakers at 100 decibels, the recorded conversation sounded worse than nasty. One voice boomed out, "I'll personally kill the son of a bitch!"

That, I could see, riveted the crocked Russians as well as Danny; but I didn't tell him about its background. Nor did I mention anything about being under immunity.

When the side of the tape had finished, I retrieved it from the DJ, who went back to playing the Russian techno. Danny and I relaxed and drank slowly until 0200. Then I said good night to him and commandeered one of the casino's limos to drive me to my apartment.

Over the next few days, Ed constantly reassured us that Chuck would resolve the matter of our overdue pay. Chuck and his entourage visited the casino and enjoyed a lengthy dinner gala again. This time, however, Chuck sat down with Nikolaj and they spent quite a bit of time conversing with each other. As they talked, they both broke out in laughter several times. I watched as the entire staff buzzed with hope, anticipating that this travesty was indeed, possibly, coming to an end. No results were forthcoming, however; and, finally, three nights after the night we had taken off, Danny became utterly fed up. To keep him from making a scene that might get him in trouble with the goons, I left David in charge of the casino and walked him over to his apartment for a few drinks and a vetting session. Neither of us said much, though, as we nursed a few more rounds of his Jack Daniels. After an hour or so, I decided to leave and go back to my apartment. I was too despondent to go back to work. I stood in Danny's doorway and said, "Try to keep your pecker up. We'll think of something."

Danny just looked at me and poured himself another drink. I remember that image of him well because it was the last time I ever saw him.

When I arrived at the casino for work the next evening, I saw David standing out in front of the apartment he shared with Danny. David came up to me and asked, "Have you seen Danny?"

"No," I answered. "Why? Isn't he here? We have to work tonight."

David looked worried. "He was here late last night. But when I woke up early this morning to use the bathroom, the steel door was wide open. I looked in on Danny's room and he was gone."

Now I was worried. I knew that Danny was careful in everything he did and that he'd never leave his door wide open even when he was awake. On several occasions, in fact, I had seen him make sure the door was shut tight after he had closed it. It was a precaution that made sense. At the casino, we had both pissed off several of the Chechen mafia types by refusing them credit.

David took me up to the apartment and I inspected it thoroughly, looking for anything unusual in addition to the wide-open door. Everything else looked to be in order, however. For a moment, I hoped that Danny had gone off exploring Moscow, which he did often. But I couldn't dismiss the darkening feeling that something wasn't right here. The wide-open door nagged me. Around his apartment and at work, Danny was, I knew, a creature of habit. That he would leave the steel door open just didn't make sense to me.

Hoping for the best, I went to my office to prepare for opening the casino tonight. As soon as I sat down at my desk, Nikolaj's bookkeeper and unofficial snoop, Liz, came in and asked, in her typically accusatory tone, "I don't suppose you've seen Danny?"

Tonight, worried as I was about Danny, I didn't need this shrew in my office, making her customary serpentine insinuations about everything she saw happening around her. At the best of times she got under my skin with her *I'm going to find out something bad and tell Nikolaj* bearing. Even her looks irked me. The first time I saw her I thought that when she was a child someone must have pulled hard enough on both of her ears to stretch her pie-shaped face all out of proportion. I hadn't known her long before it became clear that the spite she held for almost everyone around her was an expression of her own self-hatred. The child of a native Russian father and a mother who had been a career CIA employee, she had been brought up in Phoenix and had probably never fit in with any peer group. Whatever the root cause of her dour personality, she functioned perfectly in the casino as a seamless extension of Nikolaj's often sadistic nature.

One of the duties she most enjoyed, for instance, was telling the staff—many very young mothers with children—why they couldn't be paid. That she had no regard for the fact that the victimized staff were left unable to feed themselves or their families made me all the more irritated that Chuck Norris allowed this situation to persist. Not infrequently, when one of the young mothers didn't report to work, the other girls would tell me that she was sick and that her baby was starving. At a moment like that, even though I was a former US paratrooper, I felt ashamed of being American—by virtue of having to share that status with someone like Chuck Norris.

I looked at Liz, standing smirking in front of me, and said, "No, I haven't seen Danny. Have you?" Then I looked down at my desk, hoping she'd go away.

"I'm here to get the cash from the safe," she said. "We had a good night last night. There should be $24,000."

She was referring to the procedure by which Danny or David would count out the money the casino had made each night after closing and place it in the safe here in my office. Then Slava, the Russian casino supervisor, would prepare the tally sheet which drastically understated the earnings. This sheet would serve as the basis for calculating taxes owing to the government. At the same time, the actual earnings would be documented on a slip of paper and left with the goons at the security entrance. Liz would collect the slip the next day and use it for her bookkeeping. Also, each day she'd come to my office, retrieve the cash from the safe, and take it to a safe that was concealed in Nikolaj's office.

I had long ago made it clear that I wanted no personal part in this illegal procedure. I did have one of the two known keys to the safe. Danny had the other. From what I knew, there were also three other undocumented keys; but I didn't know who held them.

I swung my chair around and put my key in the antique keyhole. I reached in and pulled out the moneybag. It was empty, except for some small change. Before I could get my hand out of the bag, Liz was on my phone, dialing Nikolaj's number. "The money from the safe is gone," I heard her say, "and Danny's missing too."

Though Liz was about six feet away from me, I could hear Nikolaj screaming back to her in Russian. She hung up and went to his office, no doubt to call him back and continue their conversation in private. Now I was beyond being worried about Danny. If he had taken the money, he was as good as dead, on direct orders from Nikolaj.

Within a few minutes, Liz returned to my office and hovered over the front of my desk. "Nikolaj says that Danny is probably dead. Either that or he's been taken for ransom. He also says that no Americans are to leave until he gets here." She then picked up the phone, called one of the goons near the entrance, and repeated Nikolaj's mandate in Russian.

Panic grabbed me. I knew that if Danny had in fact been kidnapped, and that if he wasn't dead yet, he soon would be. In this part of the world, abductors were not in the habit of returning bodies, dead or alive.

Within minutes, the phone lines started lighting up crazily, and the goons outside were dashing all over, obviously waiting for an unhappy Nikolaj to arrive. Outside, I heard the squeal of tires braking on the asphalt. I had no doubt that it was Nikolaj's Mercedes. A moment later, Nikolaj burst through the front entrance and marched down the hall, using his huge forearms to blast aside anyone who was even nearly in his way. He stopped a moment in my doorway, raised his sunglasses, and looked at me, his eyes dark and hard. Then he turned and walked back toward his office. I heard the sound of his steel door slamming shut behind him.

For the first time in ages, I felt the *Happiness is a warm gun sensation* spread through me. I longed for the familiar feel of an M16 in my hands. I knew this rifle so well that I could strip it down, clean it, and reassemble it with my eyes closed. I also knew how to apply it in a combat situation. I was pretty sure that out there in the casino I'd be up against Heckler-Koch MP5s, probably the world's most formidable urban assault submachine gun. But, with one thirty-round magazine slammed up into the receiver of an M16, I could even those odds.

The fact of the matter right now, however, was that I had only my hands and my wits for weaponry. The best I could figure to do was call Ed at the Sovietsky and see if he and Chuck could get over here fast.

"I can't fucking believe it," Ed said, after I told him about Danny's vanishing act and the missing money. "Do you think he's still alive?"

"If he's lucky," I answered. "You and Chuck need to get over here fast as possible. We need damage control."

For a moment, Ed was silent. Then he said, "Well, Chuck's beat. We've been working all day on the PR for his new Russian movie project. He just turned in."

I went numb. Here was Ed worried about his darling Chuck being worn out when David, Huck, and I, his American employees, were under orders not to leave his casino, with the means of enforcement being a thick hail of automatic fire.

I asked Ed to reconsider. I didn't see how asking Chuck to come over and cover for his men would put him out of sorts.

"Send a limo for me," Ed said, "and I'll be right over."

As soon as I hung up the phone, the leader of Nikolaj's goon squad entered my office, followed by Liz. We called him Oscar because his real Russian name was so hard to pronounce. He was at least six foot four and wore his snow-white hair close cropped, military style. He was dressed, as always, in a black tuxedo, with a white shirt and a black bow tie—one of the standard uniforms of casino henchmen. The sides of his jacket bulged from the twin guns he carried in nylon, quick-draw holsters.

It was plain that right now I'd have to make an exception to my routine policy of avoiding Oscar. In guttural Russian, he ordered me to take him over to Danny's apartment. I nodded and motioned for him to precede me. I followed close behind, with Liz in tow. This way, if he made a sudden move to turn on me, I'd be able to strike before he could bring his firepower to bear.

Danny's place was impeccable, in accord with his anal temperament. His toothbrush and toothpaste were in the bathroom cabinet; his clothes, especially his suits, were perfectly pressed and hung in the order of his preference, from right to left; his travel bags were in the corner of his bedroom and his CDs were in a neat row on the top of his dresser. But something on the dresser drew my attention. It was his contacts, neatly placed in their holder. I knew that Danny never went anywhere without his contacts; he'd be blind as a bat.

I heard Liz mutter "Kidnapped, probably Chechens" to Oscar. I felt sick to my stomach. The Chechen mafia had the reputation of collecting their ransom money and then phoning back with directions to a shallow grave or dumpster.

Oscar, Liz, and I returned to my office, where Oscar posted himself in the doorway. Out in the hallway I heard quick but heavy steps that I knew to be Nikolaj's. He debriefed Oscar and Liz in Russian, excused them both, pulled a chair in front of my desk, and sat down. For seconds, he was silent, fingering his worry beads, his upper lip moving under his mustache—a mannerism that I knew indicated he was upset and thinking darkly. In a whisper that sent shivers through me, he said, "Looks like Danny may have been kidnapped. He hasn't passed through any of the passport checkpoints. I know that much. So he's still in Moscow. All we can do is wait for the call."

He got up slowly, turned and walked to the door, but then turned back and bent his stone cold eyes on me. "One thing bothers me, though," he said.

"What's that?" I asked.

He stopped working his worry beads. "I was told that Danny was watched as he put the money in the safe and closed the door. I was told that he left then and never came back to the office. I'm trying to reach the guard that was on duty, but there's no record of Danny coming back in the logbook." He stood a moment longer in my doorway, carefully studying my reaction. Then he turned and went back to his office.

It didn't take a mind reader to guess what he was thinking. Again, I longed for the weight of the M16 forearm in my left hand and for the feel of my right index finger on the trigger. The selector, of course, would be on full auto, rock and roll.

A half-hour later, Susan arrive, having finished her workday at *The Metropolitan*. I expected her to be upset by the situation, especially considering that she was now included among the Americans who were under orders to remain in the casino. But she took the news calmly, showing more concern for me than for herself.

I was about to take her out to the restaurant when Ed arrived. I told him to sit down and asked Susan if she minded sitting at a table in the restaurant by herself for fifteen minutes or so.

When we were alone, Ed let out a long sigh.

"Glad you're here," I said. "We've got to clear this situation up but quick."

But his mind was elsewhere. "How do I tell Chuck about this?"

I stood, walked around my desk, and stood over Ed. "It's not important how, Ed. What's important is that he get over here and put a lid on this, not to mention getting us paid."

He looked away from me, out my doorway. "I don't know. Chuck's already a little ticked at me. He feels I scheduled too many press conferences today. We had to cancel some of them. I told you he's worn out. Right now he's sleeping."

Again, he looked out my office door. "Oh, by the way. I brought his bodyguard, Action Jackson, with me. Could you make sure one of the girls takes care of him? You know what I mean?"

I knew exactly what he meant. I also knew the backgrounds of the down-and-out young girls who had been recruited, from poor rural areas, to work as prostitutes here at Chuck's casino. Almost all of them were under twenty and many were as young as seventeen. They had been lured to Moscow by promises of glamorous careers as models and were then forced into prostitution in order to earn enough money to eat. They barely earned enough to do even that, and there was no going back home for them, not once their honor had been sullied by their trade. I had no intention of making one of these girls available to Chuck Norris' bodyguard. In the time I had worked here, they had come to trust me to do my best to look out for them; and I wasn't about to let them down. Moreover, I was outraged that the thought had even crossed Ed's mind, once he knew the crisis David, Huck, I, and now Susan were facing.

"I'll see what I can do," I said to Ed and asked him to leave. Then I joined Susan for dinner while Ed and Jackson went to the nightclub. Every now and then, Ed would appear at the entrance to the restaurant, his expression begging me to do what was needed to make Jackson a content man. Instead, over a two-hour period, I covertly sent the girls to the bathroom, one at a time, with instructions to then go directly home for the night. As it turned out, Ed and Jackson also went home for the night, with Jackson's needs outstanding.

Around 0300, Nikolaj came out of his office and walked up to me, where I was standing near the roulette tables. I could tell from the hardness of his eyes and the twitching of his upper lip that his mind was busy with thoughts I'd prefer not to see translated. "I'm leaving in a few minutes," he said. "It'd be a good idea for none of you Americans, including your wife, to do anything unusual. That includes trying to leave Moscow. It'd be useless. I'd know as soon as you tried. By the way, we're going over all of the recorded phone calls now."

I knew he wanted me to pick him up on the "we're," to ask him whom he meant by it. Instead, I stood saying nothing, just looking at him and nodding briefly.

"According to security," he said, "Danny was leaving his apartment every morning for an hour or so."

That explained why I had to wake Danny up each evening in time for him to get ready for work. Again, I said nothing to Nikolaj.

He stared at me for a moment, then said, "We have indications that the money in the safe was just the tip of the iceberg, so to speak. Looks like there may be hundreds of thousands of dollars, maybe even millions involved. That'd explain the rotten numbers we've been getting here over the last few months."   I thought I knew what accounted for the less than impressive numbers, at least on one set of records. But again I remained quiet.

"I want to ask you something," Nikolaj said, his black eyes now drilling into me. "I'm getting reports that Danny was regularly meeting with a Russian man and woman at several restaurants around town. Maybe you know who they were?"

I didn't know what he was talking about and told him so.

He smiled again, but only briefly. "This is turning into a Big Boris and Little Boris matter," he said, referring to Yeltsin and Nemtsov. "Yeltsin is pissed off about this whole thing, and we're going to start a conspiracy investigation. We'll find who's involved. They'll be taken out to Birchwood Forest and shot."

He turned to go but then stopped, looked back at me, and asked,

"Anything you want to tell me now, Johnny?"

I knew this was no time to let him intimidate me. "Anything like what, Nikolaj?"

"Nothing really," he replied. "Just thinking out loud. You know how I am." With that, he turned again and left for the night.

And he left me with food for troubled thoughts. I realized that if he were to deliberately default on the protection payments to the Russian mafia, and that if he were to blame the casino'ssupposed inability to pay on a conspiracy among the casino's American employees, Susan would find herself a widow in short order. A contemptible strategy, to be sure, but also, I had to admit, a cunning one. In effect, he'd be bartering a few American lives and be saving Chuck's casino a lot of money in the process.

I stayed in my office another hour and then decided that I had put up with enough stress for one night. At the front entrance, Susan and I secured one of the limos. I knew the driver, whom I called Victor 1 (to distinguish him from Victor 2, the other driver who was, coincidentally, also named Victor) and asked him to take us to our apartment. We drove a few blocks and then the driver gradually slowed. "What's up?" I asked.

"Militia, a roadblock," he answered.

I looked up ahead and saw that we were being waved over. I also noted that the militiamen were dressed differently tonight. They were wearing flak jackets and had AK-47s slung on their shoulders. Usually, they only carried sidearms. I looked closer and saw that the AK-47s were not the standard, long-barreled Army issue. These were the short-stocked, carbine, urban assault model, with a large flash suppresser on their muzzles, making them look more like cannons. I also noted the thirty-round banana clips. I wondered why the militia was loaded out for a firefight at close quarters but then recalled that Yeltsin was stepping up enforcement as part of his campaign against street violence.

Two officers walked up to our limo. Victor 1 looked back at me, and I nodded my head to signal that we would fall back on a routine we had prepared long ago.

One of the officers came around to Susan's door and knocked on the window. She opened the door.

"Give me your visas!" he barked in Russian.

Susan looked at me, confused. I looked back at her, then at the officer. "I don't speak Russian, sir," I lied. "English? Do you speak English?"

He didn't, of course, know a word of English. After several attempts at communicating what he wanted in Russian, he gave up and motioned for the other officer to talk with Victor 1. In accord with our routine, Victor would do the negotiation. This way, if one of the militia officers were in a foul mood and decided to have him taken to the local station, I could show up and spring him for a few hundred dollars. If I, an American, however, were taken in, the cost of my release would be astronomical.

Victor 1 turned to us, pointed at the officer standing by Susan's door, and said, "Visas." "Oh, that," I replied. Susan and I handed over our visas while Victor got out of the car to talk to the other officer.

I looked over at Susan and saw that she was rigid, looking at me with huge eyes, terrified. Then I looked at the officer who was closely examining our visas. He was bent over slightly, with the flash suppresser on the muzzle of his AK-47 pointing directly at Susan's ear, only an inch or so away. I leaned over and looked out, trying to see if the selector was on its safety position. But I couldn't get a clear view of the top of the pistol grip, behind the trigger guard. "Sit still, honey," I said. I didn't want her doing anything that would alarm the officer into making any quick move. If his AK-47 wasn't on safety, and if he had a round chambered, the rifle could fire accidentally and make quick work of my wife.

Victor 1 came back to my window and signaled, with his fingers, the price we were being asked to pay—two hundred and forty rubles each (about eighty US dollars). I reached in my wallet and gave him the money while the two officers looked off into the distance. Actually, I didn't begrudge them the bribe. I was enough of a world citizen to know when I was helping someone who only earned the equivalent of pennies to feed his family.

We arrived at our apartment building to find that the elevator was working for a change, a big enough break considering that we were both exhausted and would otherwise have to climb fourteen flights of stairs. Outside our apartment, I asked Susan to step back well down the hallway as I opened the double set of dead-bolted exterior and interior doors. I asked her to remain in the hall while I checked the living room and the bedroom, to make sure no one was lying in wait for us. As I was walking toward the bathroom, I looked toward the back door, to my left. This door, which could be secured from the inside by three large, steel sliding bolts, led to a back set of steps that had at one time been used by maintenance staff. I never used the door and was always careful to check that the bolts were in place.

Now, however, I could see that each of the bolts was slid back, open. Someone had been in the apartment while Susan and I were out working, and whoever it had been had taken little trouble to cover their tracks. That realization bothered me. Had it been Nikolaj's goons? At first, I didn't think so; they would, I figured, be careful not to leave traces— unless they wanted me to know that they could access my living quarters whenever they pleased.

I started to make a closer inspection. First, I looked to where I had stashed the small amount of cash I had left and found it still there. Then I pulled the bag where I had stored my tapes out from under the bed. The bag was empty.

In a panic, I turned the apartment inside out. But the tapes were obviously gone; they had obviously been the objective of what the Russians call an *obysk*. But Who? I asked myself. I thought about the FSB, the reorganized version of the KGB. Why would they want to extort me? I wondered. Do you think it was Nikolaj's men, or maybe your own government? I knew my phone was tapped and that the apartment was probably crawling with bugs, and it wouldn't have surprised me in the least if some manner of co-op agreement were in operation. But why the tapes? I wondered. And what use could they serve?

I knew I had a sleepless night ahead of me and was especially grateful that Susan would be beside me. I needed her company.

The next day, I woke up a few hours after Susan had left for work and went through the motions of preparing a bath. Then I dressed and left for the casino.

Standing in front of the casino, when I arrived, were six men in urban camouflage fatigues, each wielding a submachine gun, each also looking to be on intense alert, ready to open fire at the least provocation. I noted that the magazines were inserted through the bottom of the pistol grip and thus recognized the submachine guns as Uzis, designed to permit accurate, nine millimeter fire, at up to six hundred rounds per minute, from the hip in tight quarters. I also noticed that Nikolaj's black Mercedes was the only car in the parking lot.

I knew that the Uzi was a popular weapon among security personnel and special law enforcement agencies and thought that the casino might be under siege by the tax police (Russia's version of the IRS), known to be heavy handed in their collection methods. But it occurred to me that Nikolaj's network would have given him ample heads up if a raid were coming his way.

As I approached the entrance, Sasha, the casino's administrator, came out the door, nodded quickly in my direction, and walked away, down the alley, stepping double time. Now I knew something was afoot. It was only 1700, and I never knew Sasha to leave work before 2300. I had always thought that Nikolaj had charged him with monitoring me for the first part of my shift.

I entered the casino and was immediately confronted by at least twice the normal number of goons. Two of them motioned with their heads that I should go back the way I came. I didn't care to debate the point.

I walked across the alley, went up the flight of stairs to the apartment that David and Danny had shared, and knocked on the steel door. David answered and invited me in.

"Looks like the shit's coming down hard," he said.

"I don't like it, whatever it is," I said. "I feel naked, being unarmed."

"Well, I don't know what's going on either," David said. "Danny's probably dead, and I think we should get our asses out of here."

I motioned to him to speak carefully and looked around the apartment, to remind him that it was probably bugged. We both walked over to the window and looked down at the men in urban fatigues, still standing at attention at the entrance.

A few moments passed, and I saw Umar walk out the front entrance, followed by Nikolaj's goons, who took up protective positions to wait for Nikolaj. Then Nikolaj came out, walked over to his Mercedes, and was chauffeured away, his driver accelerating quickly.

Seven identical white Lincoln Continentals, each with dark tinted windows, pulled up in a line from the hidden positions they had taken down the alley. This, I knew, was Umar's security entourage. I had heard that he was obsessive in looking after his safety. He didn't trust limousines and insisted on thoroughly bulletproofed Continentals. And he never rode in the same one twice. Now, he walked down to one of the last cars, around to the driver's side back door, and opened it and climbed in. Within a few seconds, however, he emerged from the passenger side back door, walked up to the middle car, and got in, using the rear passenger door.

Clever, I thought, as I watched the men in fatigues fill the remaining cars. The line up then pulled away. At least now I had an explanation for the unusually uniformed and armed men. But it did nothing to put my mind at ease. I thought of Danny. If he wasn't being held, his execution squad was on the way. If he was a hostage, his captors were about to buy the farm. Nikolaj certainly knew how to resource his operation. Umar's work, I had heard, was quick and unerring. I wondered whether Nikolaj had asked Umar to do anything about me. I thought of Susan being widowed, being left alone, here in this strange city, so far from home. I thought of Norris, chasing around on self-aggrandizing PR missions. Then I thought about the open bolts on the back door of my apartment and about my missing tapes. Suddenly, I found myself in a frame of mind where either nothing made sense or everything made sense. I preferred the nothing. The everything added up to a picture I didn't want to think about, not unless I could come up with a positive course of action.

CHAPTER 22

YELTSIN AND THE
SMASHING PUMPKINS

✳

At 0300, I left David in charge of the casino and went to my apartment. I was so tired that I hardly noticed Susan asleep beside me as I crawled into bed.

A ringing sound woke me the next morning. Still half asleep, I reached over for Susan and found her side of the bed empty. She had, I realized, already gone to work. I wondered what time it was and where the sound was coming from. I shook my head clear and reached for the phone.

"John, it's me," I heard Danny say.

I was fully awake now. I knew that the call was being recorded, but I needed information from Danny. "Keep it basic," I said. "The money?"

Danny started to explain. "I was tired of Norris not paying us."

"Basic," I said. "Where is it? With you?"

"Yes," he replied.

"Where are you?"

"In the states."

"How did you get out... never mind. My tapes? With you?"

"Yes. I needed all the security I could get. Sorry."

I felt anger surge in me. "Thanks, pal. To cover your own butt, you put Susan and me in a world of shit here. And I mean the worst sort of shit."

He seemed surprised that he had put me in any danger and wanted to explain himself further. But I couldn't afford to let him continue. I gave him a phone number in the states and told him to call it in a week. And I made it as clear as I could that he was to be careful with the tapes—that they were a lot more important than he could even begin to guess. Then I hung up and got out of bed. I wanted to see Nikolaj right away, to let him know about Danny's call, so that he might call off his terror machine. As I opened my clothes closet, I thought, Danny, you've got no idea of what you've done.

I found Nikolaj in his office, looking no more friendly than usual. I explained that Danny had taken the money but mentioned nothing about the tapes. Nikolaj looked me straight in the eye, as he did the first time I met him. But he didn't smile. And I could see his upper lip moving under his mustache. I was in no frame of mind to offer him a cent for his thoughts. I sat back and waited.

He continued looking at me for what seemed like a full minute. Then he said, "It's bullshit. I don't believe it. He probably called from Russia and he wants us to think he's not here. It doesn't matter where he really is, though. We'll find him. I'll have him brought to me. He'll regret the day that he was ever born."

His upper lip stopped moving, but his eyes remained fixed on me. I thought a moment about what he had said, about its implication, about how far his reach could extend. He frowned and continued staring at me. Seconds passed and he said nothing; and I knew it would be smart for me to leave him alone with his thoughts.

From my office, I called Ed and explained what had happened to the money, again leaving out any mention of the tapes. Then I asked him if he would be coming over to the casino.

"I don't know yet," he replied. "It's pretty hectic over here. Chuck's making arrangements to leave now."

I didn't want to believe I was hearing what Ed had said. "Leave? He's leaving? But nothing's been straightened out over here yet. You said he'd see to it we got paid."

Ed sighed. "Well, he's getting ready to leave. What can I say? You know, Chuck's only an investor in the casino."

I hung up, pissed off, thinking, So this place is called "Chuck's Casino," and I'm working for Chuck Norris Casinos International? Chuck Norris this! Chuck Norris that! Nothing but hype to get North Americans over here, thinking we're working for an above-board company? But when there's trouble? Chuck's suddenly nothing more than an investor? So much for this as a Chuck Norris Enterprise. So much for Chuck Norris. Action hero? Hero? Hero my ass!

I remembered the "Missing in Action" movies in which Chuck Norris played a one-man Delta Force team whose self-appointed mission was to infiltrate Cambodia to retrieve MIAs left behind after the official pullout from Vietnam. I could see the expression of triumph on his face, at the end of one movie, as he marched the MIAs he'd saved into a press conference being held by a mealy mouthed politician who was trying to deny that the MIAs existed. I thought also of what Major Howard had said— "You will cherish as a sacred trust the lives of the men with whom you will serve." And I said to myself what I'd be willing to say anytime: *Whatever heroics he apes on the silver screen, the real Chuck Norris leaves his own behind.*

Then I thought of Ed, how with him it had been Chuck this and Chuck that right from the outset. He had recruited us, he had said, to work over here for Chuck. Bullshit, Ed! I thought. Chuck's deserting us, and you're knocking yourself out to cover his ass, leaving our asses exposed as hell.

Disgusted, I walked out of my office, sat down on a couch just outside, and lit a Winston. I could see a procession of strange looking men coming in and out of Nikolaj's office. I had no doubt who they were— spooks, government agents, and underworld strongmen. Apparently, Nikolaj didn't care about what I had told him about Danny and was forging ahead with his campaign to put the grab on what he claimed were the conspirators.

I was about to go back into my office, when I noticed a man come through the security entrance. As were all the goons, he was tall, well built, and athletic looking. But he was also different. His hair was blonde and cut very short. He wore olive drab slacks, a kaki dress shirt, and black rubber-soled shoes. His watchband was nylon with a bezel cover strap. His belt was military style—black cotton webbing with a black metal buckle. He wore small-rimmed sunglasses.

I was sure he wasn't a spook. No spook would wear a watchband like that; it'd be a dead giveaway. He wasn't a goon either; the watchband was too low class. I figured that he was one of the government's elite "cleaners." If I was right, Yeltsin had personally sent one of his most qualified resources.

As he walked up the hall toward Nikolaj's office, the goons standing around outside fell silent and nodded to him. They either respected him or were scared witless of him. Nikolaj clicked the lock open before he was anywhere near the door.

He closed the office door behind him, and I sat on the couch, waiting. After fifteen minutes, the door opened and the blonde cleaner stepped out into the hall. He stood a few seconds with his back toward me, then swiveled around, lowered his sunglasses with one hand, and looked right at me. I looked back. We held eye contact for a moment; then he slowly turned and walked down the hall to the exit.

I went over to the restaurant, found Huck and David, sat with them, and ordered dinner. I explained that Danny was still alive and had made it back to the states, what Ed had told me about Chuck just being an investor, and that he had pulled out on us. I told them we were on our own now and that we'd have to look out for each other. They were as pissed as I was, and we ate quietly, with no interest in our food. The aftertaste of betrayal had killed our appetites. Then they went to their work areas, to get ready for the night's business. They had no choice, really. Had Nikolaj seen one move that roused his suspicion, he would have struck quickly. I felt like leaving the casino but thought better of it. I didn't want to start any trouble—not right now, anyway. Also, I wanted to catch Ed if he happened to stop by.

I went back to my office, sat at my desk, and was thinking of lighting another Winston, when Nikolaj appeared in the hall outside my door. He stood looking at me a moment and then took a step toward my office. But he didn't come in. His awesome mass seemed to fill the doorway completely.

"I'm leaving now," he said sternly.

I nodded and pulled out a cigarette and lit it.

"And, Johnny," he said, "no one gets any casino credit tonight. You are not to issue any markers to any players tonight. None. Period."

With that, he turned and walked down the hall to the security exit. I noticed that I could once again see out into the hall though my open door.

I thought about the order he had given me and hoped that no one important would show up. I went out to the casino and instructed all the managers and bosses to withhold credit tonight and to let me know if any problems arose. Then I retuned to my office.

About an hour later, my hopes were dashed. David came rushing into my office to tell me that Mr. B (a name I'll use for convenience here), one of the Chechen mafia's top bosses, had arrived.

"He's in the disco right now and he's going through the vodka shots pretty quickly," David said.

Mr. B was a regular at Norris' "investment" casino, and I always made a point to greet him personally. He seemed to appreciate this attention. From what I had seen, I was the only person in the casino to whom he ever gave a smile. For now, however, I'd stay in my office and hope for the best.

"Keep an eye on him and let me know what's going on," I told David. "I don't want him to know I'm here."

David was back in half an hour. "He's had about twenty shots now and he's playing roulette. He's betting heavy and getting loud. "

I told David to watch him closely. I sensed an ambush taking shape here. Nikolaj always knew when Mr. B would be stopping in, and Mr. B often requested credit. I thought a moment about the style of the Chechen mafia. Though Chechnya is at a considerable distance from Moscow, and though it is on the outs with the formal Russian military, it nevertheless controls, through cunning application of force, at least a third of the commerce that takes place in Moscow. The shock troopers of the Chechen mafia differ from their counterparts in the Russian mafia in that they depend less on firepower and more on stealth—typically on knife work within arm's length. Where one of the Russian mafia's ex KGB operatives would open up on you with his submachine gun on full automatic, a Chechen adept would move close and open a sucking chest wound. You wouldn't feel the blade enter; you'd only feel your life slipping away.

David returned in fifteen minutes, this time with Slava, the Russian casino supervisor, who looked a nervous wreck.

"He wants credit," David said.

"Can't do it, guys," I answered. "Nikolaj's orders. No credit tonight. Period. Tell him as nicely as you can."

They returned in five minutes, with Slava looking like he was beyond being a nervous wreck. In Russian, he said, "He wants $10,000 credit. And he means it. If he doesn't get it, he says he'll call his men to come in and kill everyone in the casino. He means it. He'll do it. He will kill all of us. We have to give him credit. Please?"

I told David and Slava to calm down a moment and dialed Nikolaj's car phone. It was turned off. I called Nikolaj at home and only got his answering machine. Then I told David and Slava that they'd have to go back and tell Mr. B that the policy tonight, from the boss, was no credit. I had no doubt about what Nikolaj was up to and decided it was time that Susan and I got the hell out of Moscow.

Within minutes, David and Slava were back. "He wants to talk to you, John," Slava said. "He knows you are here and he's demanding that you come out and talk to him."

"How many vodkas has he had?" I asked.

"We count thirty-two now," David replied.

I saw no point in leaving David and Slava in the line of fire, not when Mr. B knew I was in and wanted me. Also, I had thought of a tactic that might unspring Nikolaj's ambush.

I walked to the casino and saw Mr. B sitting in one of the chairs at a closed Blackjack table. He was holding his cell phone in one hand, ready to dial. I walked over and greeted him. In reply, he looked straight at me with his black, piercing eyes.

"Sir—" I started to say.

But he cut me off. "John, I wanted $10,000 credit, but I've changed my mind. Now I want $50,000. Don't even think about telling me no."

I had to credit Nikolaj for being clever. He knew I wouldn't disobey his orders. He also knew that if I refused Mr. B I'd be killed the minute I walked out of the casino. But I didn't intend to buy the farm tonight.

"Mr. B, I have an idea you might like," I said. "What if I give you $50,000 in chips? If you win tonight, I keep the winnings. If you lose, we're even. After all, you only want to play. Right? I know that a man of your importance doesn't need casino winnings from a joint like this to pay the bills."

He smiled, slightly and slowly, as he thought over my suggestion. Maybe he realized I had foiled what Nikolaj and he had possibly been planning; perhaps he was just amused. I couldn't tell. "That's fine, John," he said. "I just want to play and not be bored."

We shook hands. Then I went to the cage, pulled out the chips, and handed them to him. Within an hour, he had gambled the chips away. But he was happy. He honored our agreement and left, with no trouble.

The next morning, from my apartment, I called Ed at the Sovietsky and told him I wanted to get out of Moscow. "Chuck didn't do shit for us, and I'm tired of working for him, or his investments, or whatever the hell you're calling it now. Fact is I'm broke. I can't pay child support, and I'm losing my house back home. Not to mention that that I'm having all I can do here to stay alive, with Chuck's partner playing secret agent amateur hour. I've had it. This Russian deal's been nothing but a disaster."

Ed replied that he was leaving tomorrow and suggested that Susan and I go with him. He'd pick up the tickets. He also suggested that I go over to the casino and submit a resignation. "I'll be over later," he added. "I've got a friend that just bought a company in Houston. I'll make sure he gives you a job. I'll lend you some money until you can get back on your feet. I promise. You and Susan should pack your things and come over here to the Sovietsky. I'll send Chuck's van over to get your bags. Call me back after you tell Nikolaj."

Susan and I kicked into action packing. We only had two suitcases each. We laid them out on the bed and stuffed them with all the clothes that would fit and with the few precious keepsakes and pictures we had brought with us to Moscow. We decided to dispose of everything else, especially anything that would leave a trace that Nikolaj could use to find us. I gathered up every piece of paper that had my name, address, or phone number on it, burned it in the sink, and washed the ashes down the drain. We pushed everything else we hadn't packed down a garbage chute that emptied into a communal dumpster in the basement. Finally, we wiped the entire apartment clean of fingerprints. When we were done, I told Susan to wait for the van Ed was sending to take her to the Sovietsky.

I kissed Susan, left the apartment, and decided against taking a limo over to the casino. Instead, I walked down to the Teatralnaya metro station in Red Square. I wanted to see it again before I left Moscow. Built in 1940, this station was my favorite of Moscow's metros, each renowned for its architecture and decoration. In the Taetralnaya, I especially admired the ceramic panels celebrating the art forms characteristic of the different states of the former Soviet Union.

As soon as I approached the entrance to the casino, one of the security men called up to Nikolaj's office to report that I had arrived. I went straight to my office and wrote my resignation. I had to word myself carefully, for fear of further rousing Nikolaj's already fired up temper. While I was signing my name, Liz walked into the office and asked "What's up?" in her usual smart-ass manner.

I answered that I needed to see Nikolaj, to hand in my resignation. But the meaning of what I had said didn't seem to register. Either that, or she didn't care one way or the other. "He's not seeing anyone right now," she said flatly. I handed her the letter and asked her to take it to him.

A few minutes later, my phone rang. "Johnny, come on up to my office," Nikolaj said. His tone wasn't inviting.

I heard the door lock click open as I got to his door. He was sitting at the end of his long desk, looking in a box. I walked over to him. "I just traded for some pretty neat stuff here," he said. He reached into the box and pulled out something wrapped in a handkerchief. He removed the handkerchief and held up a derringer. "Look at it," he said, handing it to me.

I took it and opened the cylinder to see if it was loaded. Nikolaj watched, smiling. I took the handkerchief from his hands, wiped my fingerprints off the derringer, then picked it up with the handkerchief and handed it back to him. "Thanks all the same," I said.

I could see that he wasn't pleased that I hadn't taken the bait—that I hadn't assumed the weapon was loaded and tried to use it, that I had cheated him of a reason to frame me for attempted murder. I took a seat at the table adjacent to his desk. He looked down at my letter.

"They told me you'd try to leave," he said softly.

"They, who?" I asked.

"The guys looking into the conspiracy. They said you and Susan would soon try to leave town."

I stood to impose the point I needed to make. "What, because that makes us guilty of something? Cut it out, Nikki. Danny's in the US, and he says he took the money. I'm broke. I haven't been paid since I've been here. I just want to go away from this place and forget it all ever happened."

"I'll see what I can do," he said, standing to indicate he wanted me to leave. "Get a bite to eat in the restaurant. I'll be down later."

There was nothing more I could say, and I had no appetite. I left his office, went out the security door, and walked toward the front entrance of the casino. I wanted to visit David, in his apartment, to see how he was doing. As I approached the entrance, however, three of the security men blocked my way. I realized that I was now being held hostage in Chuck's so-called investment casino, that I was now a POW of sorts. I again resolved that I would, if I got out of this alive, find a way of telling Norris what I thought of someone who played a superhero on the screen but who in fact, it seems, deserted his own men.

I returned to my office, called Ed, and told him I was being forced to stay in the casino. "Nikolaj's playing some kind of game here. He wants to escalate this thing with Danny, make it look like it's bigger than it really is."

Ed told me that Susan hadn't arrived yet. I asked him to get her settled in when she got there and to let me know if he heard anything further. Feeling trapped, and not wanting to be alone, isolated, I went to the restaurant and took a seat—although I wasn't hungry.

Huck and David saw me and came over to sit at my table. But when they saw Nikolaj enter the restaurant, they went back to work. Without even a glance at me, Nikolaj walked over to a large table where several guests were seated and joined them for dinner. I watched him for a full hour, during which he ignored me. Impatient, I walked up to where he was sitting. He backed his chair away from the table and turned it so that he was facing me.

"Nikki, can I leave now?" I asked.

"John, my guys think it's best for you to stay in Moscow a little longer. They want you to stay until everything's looked into." He started to turn back toward the dinner table.

"How long will that be?"

Again, he turned to face me. "I don't know yet. I've already talked to Ed. My guys will let you leave the casino and the limo will take you over to the Sovietsky. Go talk to Ed about it."

Ed was finishing his packing when I arrived at his palatial suite at the Sovietsky. He told me Susan had arrived and gave me the number of our room.

I sat down on his bed and asked, "What's going on, Ed?"

He closed one of his suitcases, snapped it shut, walked over and looked out the window, and then turned to me. "You have to stay in Moscow for a little while longer. Just until the investigation is finished."

Just until? I thought. "Ed, a little while longer and I'll be dead. It's his guys. Do you know who his guys are? Ed, Nikki's the one starting all of this crap." Though it would have been more than relevant, I didn't see fit to add that Ed had every reason to appreciate what I was getting at. Back in Louisiana, Players had offered my head, so to speak. But then, it had only been my professional reputation that was at stake. Now the stakes were far more serious.

Ed held his hands palms out, in a calming gesture. "Nikki gave me his word that he wouldn't let anything happen to you."

I got up from the bed and started pacing around the room. "His word? I wouldn't risk my life on his word. Would you? It's my life we're talking about here, Ed. "

Ed lowered his hands to his side and looked at his packed bags. "We have to believe him." Then he changed the subject. "I also guaranteed him that I would cover any money you might be liable for. You know I'm still owed $200,000. And I still have all the money out on the slots and arcade games I sent over here for the Planet Hollywood deal."

I stopped pacing and took a deep breath. I had to. I was getting angry, and I knew I had to keep a grip on myself. "Damn you, Ed. You want to talk money when I'm telling you this bloodthirsty bastard wants to see me killed? Money's no good to me if I'm dead. Besides, you're confused about who owes who. You're just giving him an excuse to take your money too."

Ed lowered his eyes to the floor. "I don't think we have a choice. You have to stay. I checked Susan in and took care of the room tonight. I'll have someone from the studio call over and make sure the room and meals are taken care of tomorrow."

I took another deep breath. "I like the way you say we, Ed. You know what I got on me? About forty dollars. How long do you think that'll last Susan and me?"

Ed looked at me for a moment but then looked back at the floor. "I'll call every day and make sure everything's going okay. Take care, kiddo. It'll be all right."

I walked to the door, opened it to leave, but stopped. "Say whatever you have to, Ed, to make yourself feel good. You're not the one who'll be in a nameless grave in Birchwood Forest." Then I left, closing the door behind me with force.

The room that had been reserved for Susan and me was farther down the hall. It was tiny, the smallest hotel room I had ever seen.

"It'll do for tonight," Susan said when she saw my expression.

I told her I had bad news, that we wouldn't be leaving with Ed tomorrow morning, that I couldn't say for sure when we'd be leaving. For a moment, I thought she was going to start crying, something I'd never seen her do before. But she embraced me and said, "I'm with you, honey. Whatever it takes. Whatever happens."

Knowing I wasn't alone made me feel better—but not much.

The next morning, just as it was getting light, we watched out our window as Ed got into the cab that would take him to the airport. As soon as the cab pulled away, Nikolaj called and told me that I should let Susan leave. "She needs to go now," he said.

I knew he wanted to get Susan out of the way, to isolate me and have me killed. This way, it would be simpler for him. He could dispose of me and cover for it easily. But it'd be harder if he had an American couple killed. There'd be questions, and the press would want answers. I looked at Susan and repeated what Nikolaj had said.

She reached for the phone, yelling, "Tell that worthless piece of shit that I'm not leaving my husband behind in Russia to be killed!"

Overhearing that, Nikolaj grunted and hung up. But he called again about ten minutes later, telling me that he had put a tap on the phone line and warning me not to try to call anyone who could stir things up.

I thought of calling the Reverend; he'd certainly agree that Susan and I were in deep shit. But I decided to hold off for now, to wait until I had a concrete idea of when I'd try to get out of Moscow. That way, Nikolaj would have less time in which to react.

The following day passed with no contact from Nikolaj. I guessed that he was trying to figure out some way of getting Susan out of the way or that he was hoping she'd get fed up and leave. As for the investigation he claimed was underway, no one came knocking on my door asking questions.

Early on the morning of the next day, the hotel manager informed me that we would no longer be permitted to sign for meals. Then, later in the morning, we received a call from the hotel staff asking for payment for our room and for meals we had signed for so far. I was told that no one had called to make arrangement for the charges.

Indignantly, I answered that I was with the Chuck Norris casino, that the hotel management should know that the charges were to be taken care of. That backed the management off until about 1130, when a staff person called, telling me that we could stay in the room but that our meal privileges were canceled until payment was arranged.

"Looks like Nikolaj is trying to starve you out of town," I told Susan.

She laughed. "Then we're both going to lose a lot of weight. I'm not going anywhere without you."

Close to noon, we heard a knock on the door. I positioned myself next to the wall, not in front of the door. "Yeah," I said.

"John," I heard Huck say.

I opened the door and saw Huck wearing a pair of sunglasses and a hat. "Nice disguise," I said. "Come on in."

He stepped just inside the door. "I'm making a run for it. I went out the back window of my apartment. There was someone watching at the front. I'm going to try and get to the airport. I still have the open return from my flight over here. I think I've got a chance."

"What about David?" I asked.

"He's still at the casino. But it's getting weird there. He's in a lot of trouble, I'm afraid."

I asked him if he knew for sure that he hadn't been followed here.

"I can't be sure. I don't think so. I went here and there in the metros. But I know I took a chance. So I'm going to split, before they have a chance to figure it out."

I wished him luck and shook his hand. Susan came over and hugged him. Then he said goodbye, stepped out into the hall, looked up and down, and walked away.

Early in the afternoon, Ed called from the states. I was surprised that the phone hadn't been cut off for non-payment of charges. But then it occurred to me that Nikolaj had perhaps ordered the hotel to keep the phone in operation so that he could monitor any calls I made or received. Ed said he was surprised that we hadn't heard from the studio and that arrangements hadn't been made to cover our expenses. I asked him for the name and number of a contact at the studio, but he couldn't (conveniently, I didn't doubt) remember the name. I asked him for a credit card number to which we could charge our room and meals. I pointed out that I hadn't been paid in eight months and that my cards had been cancelled. But he didn't want me to use one of his accounts. He promised that he'd try to work out arrangements through the studio.

Totally out of faith in anything to do with Chuck Norris, I hung up and told Susan we'd have to go as long as we could on the forty dollars we had between us.

"So much for the great Chuck Norris," she said.

I laughed. "You mean Chuck the Great?"

"How about Magnum Chuck?" she replied and smiled in the way that never failed to dazzle me. Susan and I left the hotel to go to a nearby food store. As soon as we stepped out the front entrance, the cleaner I had seen visiting with Nikolaj in his office pulled up to the curb in a BMW coupe. Again, he pulled his sunglasses down slightly and looked at me, a slow smile crossing his face.

I ignored him and led Susan around the corner to the store, where we spent the last of our money on food and bottled water. Nikolaj, I realized, was resorting to one of the most ancient of siege tactics—starve the garrison. But he was deploying it as a diabolic psych op. Susan might not leave if she had anything to say about it; but if our detention ran much longer, I'd have to ask her to leave. In fact, I'd have to make her leave. I couldn't watch her starve slowly, day by day.

Our water supply was especially critical. If that were to run out, we'd have to use the tap water to hold off dehydration. No one in Moscow drinks city water; it's worse than in Mexico City; it's a sure way to bring on fever and diarrhea, which would be fully as dehydrating as going without water.

By the end of day three of our forced stay at the Sovietsky, I figured that Susan and I could hold out together for two or three more days, at best. I thought again of the Reverend but again judged it best to wait until the last minute to call him.

Early on the morning of day four, Nikolaj called. He wasn't happy that Huck had made it out to the airport. I sensed that he was mad at himself for not having alerted his contacts at the airport to be on the watch for him. He threatened to come over to the hotel and to himself put a bullet in my head and to send some resources from Brighton Beach, New York, to kill Danny, wherever he was in the states. Susan, he insisted, had to leave now.

I looked at Susan. "Don't even suggest it," she said.

I told Nikolaj that Susan didn't feel like going anywhere without me. He hung up.

By day five, we had run out of water and nearly out of food. I had given up on expecting a call from the studio and had gotten used to incessant calls from Nikolaj. I had to credit him for his cunning. Instead of threatening me, he appealed to my love for Susan. He asked why I wanted to put her through this ordeal and insisted that I'd let her leave if I really cared more for her and less for my own ass.

Susan for her part didn't need to hear what he was saying. She knew. Each time he called, she yelled, "Tell the scumbag I'm staying right here with you!" When he heard that, Nikolaj would grunt or snort and hang up. Apparently, Susan had access to his ego.

Early in the afternoon, Huck called to let us know that he had made it home and that he had contacted Ed, to let him know Susan and I were in desperate straits, and that he had called David's parents in Florida. Later in the afternoon, Ed called and tried to explain that he was doing everything he could think of to get us released. I had to cut him off too, realizing that every call would provide Nikolaj with critical intelligence.

On day six, we ran out of food. Susan was already starting to get ill from drinking water from the tap. I couldn't stand watching her suffer and was going to tell her she'd have to leave. She was standing in the bathroom, bent over the toilet, vomiting. I approached the door to talk to her, but she read my mind and slammed the door shut. I sat on the bed and waited. I knew she'd have to go and that I'd have to find a way of getting her to agree.

I was thinking of how I'd handle myself on my own, when she opened the door to the bathroom and came out smiling. She looked like hell except for that smile. If I knew I loved her before, I didn't know how much until now. And I also knew that I'd be slamming myself against a concrete wall asking her to leave me here alone.

"Let's show that bag of shit how smart we are," she said, her tone full of fight. "I have an idea."

I got off the bed, walked over to her, and hugged her.

"*The Metropolitan* still owes me some commissions," she said. "I just thought of that. Cali's restaurant is just a few blocks, and they owe Metropolitan money in barter for their advertising. I'll call Michael Bass and see if I can take my commissions in food from Cali's."

I thought it might work and started to pick up the phone. But Susan took it from me. "If that fuckhead is listening, I want him to hear me this time."

She made the call, and Bass agreed to call Cali's immediately and try to put the arrangement into place. The word was out on the street about us, he said, and he wished us luck.

Susan and I dressed to go to Cali's. As soon as we stepped out of the hotel, two huge goons dressed in black picked us up. They followed us to the restaurant but were careful to stay a few hundred feet behind.

As we approached Cali's, I could see that it was a California style bar & grill. Despite my uneasy stomach, I could almost taste the food. I also had to laugh at the irony of it: it might easily turn out that I'd be executed in Moscow, with my last meal having been American.

"There's a bar and tables inside," Susan said, "or we can sit on the patio outside. I'd like outside. I need some fresh air."

The patio had about thirty small tables. We took one as near as possible to the door to the bar. Our two companions chose a table near the street. I smiled at them as they sat down.

After we finished our first full meal in four days, we sat drinking one coke after another. The restaurant owner came out to our table and sat down. He knew Susan well because she had sold the Cali's account. She explained our situation.

"I wish you luck," he said. "You're welcome to eat here, all you want. But don't get me involved. I have enough of my own troubles with my own set of guys."

We told him we understood his position and that we appreciated his offer.

"By the way," he said, "the Smashing Pumpkins are playing in Moscow tomorrow night. We're holding the after-concert party here. We're only allowing a limited amount of guests, but you're both welcome to come. Especially if you'll help us put up balloons."

Susan's eyes brightened and she smiled. I could see that even the two goons watching us from their street side table were impressed. They didn't smile, but their eyes went wide. "Sure," Susan told the owner. "We'd love to come for the party. Since this is our only way to feed ourselves, we'll be here for breakfast, lunch, and dinner too."

Early the next morning, our seventh day as hostages, Nikolaj called very early, before we were awake. He wanted to know when Susan would be leaving. "You want to tell him?" I said to her, handing her the phone.

"Not in my lifetime!" she yelled into it without taking it from me.

Moments later, the phone rang again. It was Ed, calling to tell me that he was all out of ideas on how to help us. I hung up without saying a word.

We spent most of the day at Cali's, sitting on the patio, watching our two escorts watching us. They kept their distance but followed us whenever we left the restaurant.

In the evening, we went to the party and had a great time, despite the stress we were under. We helped put up the balloons, sipped Jack Daniels, and socialized with Billy Corgan and the Smashing Pumpkins after they had finished their dinner.

The next morning, the phone rang early, again before we were awake. I was expecting that it would be Nikolaj and was ready to tell him to kiss my ass. I was getting sick of his threats. It was Huck, however. "David's safe," he said. "He made it to the American Embassy."

I knew this news would really put a hair across Nikolaj's butt, but I no longer cared. He couldn't threaten me with anything worse than what I had already heard from him. "How'd he pull that off, Huck?"

"I called his parents in Florida and told them how to get in touch with him at the casino. They called him there and said his grandfather had passed away. His grandfather had died some time ago, so that tipped him off. Then they asked him if he knew where the American Embassy was. He got the clue, and he knew the embassy was only a block away. So he ran for it before Nikolaj could figure out he wasn't going to his apartment."

I thanked Huck and hung up, thinking, Eat those words Nikki! As if in response, the phone rang. I knew it was Nikolaj.

"So David got away," he said. "You guys think you're pretty slick. Not you though, Johnny. You, you son of a bitch, you're not going to live through the night."

"You have a good life, Nick," I said and hung up.

"What now?" Susan asked, alarmed.

I told her about David.

"So it's just you and me here, now," she said.

I hugged her to me. "You and me, honey. But I've had enough. It's time for nuclear war. At least I'm going to try. If I can do it, I'm going to make this asshole regret that he jacked with a real soldier."

Susan hugged me tighter. "John, you're not going to fight him and his men alone. You'll get killed."

I pulled away and reached for the phone. "I'm not going to do it alone. I've got a holy friend, remember?" I dialed the number that I had memorized long ago, in Houston.

"Hello, sir," I said when the Reverend answered.

"Young man?" he replied. "I'm hearing some things that disturb me. I've been hoping you'd call."

"You said if I was ever in deep shit, sir."

"You are now if my understanding is correct. Listen. Don't talk. Get a sheet of paper and fax me a sit rep. Names, phone numbers, and details.

But do it fast. Get it on the fax line before it can be monitored. Then call me in two hours, 0900 your time." The Reverend gave me the fax number I needed and hung up.

I used hotel stationary to write out the sit rep, brought it down to the reception desk, and told the female attendant to send it immediately. When the machine had cycled the sheet of paper, I asked for it back. I was relieved that she said nothing about the charge.

After two hours that lasted an eternity, I dialed the Reverend's number.

"Young man," he said, "you are definitely in some deep shit. This Nikolaj wants to have you run into a wall."

"Right, sir. It would definitely save Chuck's casino some money if they told the Russian mafia they can't pay them because of a conspiracy by the American employees to steal the casino blind."

"That could be part of it. It's probably as much a matter of his having gone so far with this conspiracy hype that he'd be pounding nails in his own coffin if he tried to back off it now. So you're the only American left to serve up to the mafia as a blood price. Also, don't forget that Chuck's casino owes *you* money. And you know too much about how the place is run."

"Got to hand it to this Nikolaj for efficiency. He wants to kill two birds with one stone. The trouble is both birds are me, pardon the humor."

"Never mind that for now, young man. I know the Sovietsky from the old days. It's almost a straight shot to the airport."

"What do you have in mind, sir? Do you by any chance have an old friend or two here?"

I heard the Reverend snicker. "That's what I've been doing since I got your fax, talking to old friends. I also called Ed Fishman. He said he'd pay for my long distance calls. Will he?"

"Probably not. If he won't, you know I will."

"Okay, young man. This Nikolaj may think he's a heavy hitter, but he's about to step up to the plate in the big leagues for the first time. In fact, I hope he's listening. An old friend of mine will call him tonight, and you can be sure he'll shit his pants. You can also be sure that he'll have a lot more than you to be worried about. But I need you to do something."

"Yes, sir. I'll do whatever you say."

"You need to get in touch with someone in the states who'll stir up a ruckus in the American Embassy there in Moscow. We need some important people, maybe even some spooks, mad-dashing around asking questions about you. You still have some political contacts in Louisiana, right?"

"I do, sir. I'll get right on it."

The Reverend's voice took on a fierce tone that I had never heard in him before. "When I'm done, Nikolaj will *want* to let you go. He'll want to so much that he may even offer you a ride to the airport. So when you get the chance, get to the airport as fast as you can. But call me first, young man. Don't forget that. I don't care about the time. You be sure to call me. Got it?"

"Yes, sir. I will. I won't forget."

"It'll probably be tomorrow. So try to get a good night's sleep tonight, you and Susan. I'll talk to you then"

Susan was sitting on the bed, trembling. "Someone's going to get killed here. I know it," she said.

"Maybe, honey," I said. "This is a strange war we're fighting." Then I told her what the Reverend had instructed me to do.

"My mother," she said. "She knows more people back there than you and I put together. I'll call her now."

Later, I would learn that Susan's mother, Darlene Smith, contacted Jan Becker, at United States Senator John Breaux's office, and that Ms. Becker started making calls, on behalf of Senator Breaux, to the embassy. Also, as I read later in a news feature, the senator took the measure of faxing a letter to the embassy, expressing concern for Susan and me.

About an hour after Susan's talk with her mother, Nikolaj called, incoherently ranting about spooks and the CIA. "Goodnight, Nikki," I said and hung up.

Susan and I were now exhausted, with no appetite. We decided to go to bed early. First, however, I moved the room's one dresser against the door. The night passed slowly, and we only slept in short intervals. Any noise in the hall or outside in the street brought us wide awake.

As it was getting light, we heard a heavy knock on the door. I told Susan to go into the bathroom, and I called out, "Who's there?"

"We got something for you. Something you want," I heard spoken in English, with a Russian accent.

I pushed the dresser away from the door and inched it open. Outside, I saw two of Nikolaj's goons. One handed me an envelope. Then they turned and walked down the hall.

"What is it?" Susan said from behind me. She hadn't gone into the bathroom.

I sat down on the bed and opened the envelope. It contained two plane tickets, a small amount of US currency, and a note. The note read: "Here are two tickets for the next flight out of Moscow and enough money for a cab to the airport and to get something to eat. You don't have much time before the flight takes off. Once you are out of Russia, your visas will be cancelled. Please leave and don't come back."

I handed the note to Susan and let her read it. When she had finished, I said, "Let's get dressed and get going. We don't have much time. Put anything critical in your purse. We're leaving the luggage."

Then I dialed the Reverend's number.

"We're heading for the airport, sir," I said when he answered. "I want to thank you for helping us."

"I'm thinking you'll need some more help, young man," he said. "You'll bloody well recognize it when it gets there. Nikolaj's not the problem now. The problem now is the people who'll be pissed off because he let you go. They may know by now, but maybe not. Get Susan and you out of there and could be you'll get a head start. That'll be a lot if you can make the most out of it. But any way we look at it, a lot of this'll have to be up to you, and you need to know what you're up against, if you don't already."

"I know, sir. These goons were once KGB."

"And they haven't changed since Lenin. They're still Bolsheviks.

Purity of arms is something they've never heard of. There's a world of difference between the way they kill and the way you were trained. That's your edge. Keep smart. Be tactical. Just get Susan and you on the plane."

"They should be easy to spot."

"If they're there, they will be. You've probably seen how big they are. They make my bricks look like dwarfs. You know the size is to scare you. And you know about the black suits and ties, the uniform. In the crowd, they'll have a harder time tracking you than you'll have spotting them. Don't underestimate their readiness to use force. They'll be armed to the teeth, most likely with Heckler and Koch—."

"I know, the MP5. I've been trained on it. But I'm not afraid of them, sir. I'll use the crowd against them. The 9mm is high velocity. It'd be like a harvest if they opened up."

"Exactly. You're ready, young man."

"I am, sir."

"Okay, you may not need to hear this, but I'll say it anyway, in case you do."

"Go ahead, sir."

"Remember who you are, Sergeant, and give them an overdose of it if you have to."

"I won't let you down, sir."

"You won't let yourself down, John. God bless, and get yourself back here."

"Talk to you soon, sir," I said as I hung up, realizing that he had used the rank I had earned in the 82nd and my first name, instead of his customary "young man."

As I placed the phone down, I thought of the legacy that the 82nd Airborne Division, the "All Americans," had gathered since it was formed in 1942. Whether behind the line of Rommel's Atlantic Wall on D-Day, where it had closed with the Wehrmacht's elite Waffen SS and Panzer divisions, or in the Northern Frontier Region of Saudi Arabia, where its Division Ready Battalion had stood alone, armed with little more than their M16s, to face Saddam Hussein's heavy tank divisions, the 82nd had been relied on to fight an enemy that outnumbered it.

Then I saw myself collecting butt time in the C-130 Hercules as it approached the Fryar Drop Zone at Fort Benning. It's the first day of my last week of the Basic Airborne Course. Behind me are all the simulations—the parachute landing falls and the qualification drops from the 34-foot and the 250-foot towers. Because I've made my way to the top of my class, I'm assigned the seat next to the door separating the known confine of the transport from the unknown medium outside. I'll be the first in my stick to make a real jump—something for which all the training and all the worrying cannot prepare. I'll be the model for the others that'll be lined up behind me. If I fail, I'll disgrace myself, my class, and the blackhats who have guided me toward this defining moment.

The Jumpmaster opens the transport door, and I watch the light that will turn green in just a second. So little time to understand so much. You can watch action movies and root for the heroes; you can drink with your buddies and talk about being brave. And you can go home and go to sleep, knowing you don't have any real tests to worry about. But not if you're going to belong to the 82nd.

I hear the Jumpmaster bark "Stand up!" and then "Get ready!" I look out the door into the rolling horizon between air and earth. I feel a ball of heat deep in the pit of my stomach. Is this what it feels like to be afraid? Will I fail now? Will I sit back down and take the transport back? And will I cower from every test I'll face from here on in my life?

The light turns green and the Jumpmaster yells, "Go!"

"John," I heard Susan saying, "I'm ready."

"Let's go," I said.

I opened the door of our room and stepped out into the long hallway.

CHAPTER 23

BLACKBIRD

You cannot choose your battlefield,

God does that for you.

– Stephen Crane, "The Colors"

✴

Our driver slowed, pulled up to the curb outside the terminal for Sheremetyevo 2, and stopped. I stepped out, looked back, and saw the black Volga sedan, also slowing.

"Ready?" I asked Susan.

She nodded. I took her hand and helped her out onto the sidewalk. She still looked pale, and I could feel her hand trembling. I pushed her ahead of me toward the entrance doors to the main lobby area. I wanted to get us inside and into the crowd as fast as possible. And I knew we had to move quickly. Our plane would be leaving in twenty minutes; and we needed to get through the three military checkpoint stations up ahead. Are they up there too, the mafia? Is there anything in this country that *isn't* mafia? I wondered. Again, I pushed Susan ahead of me, past the Militia Police and through one of the entrances.

I took a quick look over my shoulder to see if the Volga had parked.

It was sandwiched in the moving traffic, and I could only see the driver sitting in it. But on the edge of the crowd I saw two men looking toward Susan and me. The Reverend was right; they were huge—about my height, but easily two hundred and forty pounds each. Their necks were short and thick; their hair was close cropped, burr-head style; and they were stone faced. I could see no expression in their eyes. What I could see were the bulges in the jackets of their black suits, from the weapons they were carrying. If they were going to use them, I knew it'd be with the selectors on full auto, not on semi-auto or three-round burst.

One locked his eyes on me and then nodded to the other. Together they forced their way into the crowd. One of them pushed aside a young lady who was in his way, forcing her to drop her carry-on bag. He kicked the bag aside and continued toward us.

My senses went on full alert. I kept Susan ahead of me, my hands on her waist; if there was going to be an attempt to eliminate me here, I didn't want to see stray rounds ripping through her. I fought down the urge to run. "Walk briskly and play the crowd," I whispered in Susan's ear.

I looked back again and could see that the two goons had gotten a little closer. I couldn't let them get within arm's length. If they did, they could split Susan from me; and I'd be an available target. I had to weigh my chances now, quickly. You'd like to be alone, wouldn't you? I thought. Damned right you would! You'd know what to do then. But you're not, not now. It's not just you against them—not that simple.

One advantage I knew I had was terrain knowledge. I had been through this terminal so often that I could find my way to the checkpoints blindfolded. Another thing maybe—Susan. As long as she had been with me, there had been no overt attempts on me. But I had already concluded that the rules had changed, now that I was making a definite run for it.

Maybe we had more than a fighting chance if the Reverend was sending help. "You'll bloody well recognize it when it gets there," he had said in what had sounded to me like a bad imitation of a British accent. Had he said it that way deliberately? Why? But I didn't have time to wonder. I had to keep Susan and me moving.

To our left was the desk where the customs disclosure forms were stacked in untidy piles. Ahead was the checkpoint one station. I took Susan by the arm and pulled her to the desk. All the forms were in Russian. I grabbed one for myself and handed another one to her. "Make it quick," I said, "just the truth. Say we have nothing but the clothes we're wearing."

Susan put her hand on my chest, lightly. "I love you," she whispered.

"I love you, too," I told her. "We're going to make it. Let's go!"

The line in front of checkpoint one was long and moving slowly. The control officer was inspecting customs visas and passports carefully, but he was also looking out over the line up of people approaching him. When his eyes stopped on me, he started moving people past him more quickly. By sheer concentration I forced myself not to look around, not to do anything that would indicate I was nervous.

When there were only two people in front of us, the control officer looked down at the documents I was holding in my left hand. The blue on the covers of our passports was, I knew, a giveaway that we were Americans.

"Passport and visa!" the officer said in Russian, as I stepped up to him, with Susan beside me. He looked our documents over slowly, then asked, "Any goods to declare?"

As I was about to say *Nyet*, a superior officer stepped up to him, took the passports and visas, and looked at them momentarily. He then handed the customs forms to the other officer to stamp and commanded "Pass!" in Russian.

"Spaseeba," I said, using the Russian for "thank you," as I grabbed our documents and stepped through the checkpoint, wondering why the superior had intervened.

I moved Susan ahead of me, into the roped off lanes leading to the next checkpoint. I had to really move here. This line was slow also, and I had a sense that I was being approached from behind. I could almost feel a knife driving into my kidneys, immobilizing me. I heard "Next!" yelled in Russian and grabbed Susan, broke from the line, and headed us directly to the free officer behind the counter.

"Sorry, sir," I said. "Our flight leaves in about fifteen minutes." I started to ask "Please?" But he cut me off.

"Passport, visa, and tickets!" he demanded, in English, extending his right hand.

He looked at our documents, then at us. "What was the nature of your stay in Russia?"

"Business," I answered.

"And what is the nature of your embarkment?"

"Our what?" I asked, confused.

"Your embarkment. Your departure. Why are you leaving?"

"We're going back to the states to take care of a few financial matters. Just a short trip," I answered.

"Your bags?" he asked. "You have no bags?"

I felt Susan's hand grip my arm.

"A quick trip, as I said," I answered. "We have what we need there. We won't be there long."

"I see," he said, looking me over again. "Are you ill? You don't look well. You're sweating. Your documents are damp. Is there trouble?"

"No trouble, sir. Maybe a touch of your Russian flu, but I'm okay, really."

The mention of the dreaded Russian flu killed his interest in us. "Please move on," he directed and then called "Next!" in Russian.

We hurried toward the long line in front of checkpoint three, the passport check booth. I glanced around to see if I could find where the goons were now. I could see only one of them, still well behind us. The crowd was too dense for him to move quickly. But ahead I saw the other one standing outside one of the rooms just left of the booth. I felt like a pheasant being chased by the guns behind me into the guns waiting ahead of me. Another time, asshole! I thought, as I saw the one ahead of me walk into the room. I couldn't read the Russian on the sign fixed to the door. But I was sure that the room was used by security for interrogation.

The line was moving quickly. In moments about twenty people had been processed. Now we were fourth from the front. So close! So close! I thought. If they're going to take me, it'll have to be now.

The door of the room to the left opened, and a young man stepped out and started toward me through the crowd. His eyes, expressionless, locked with mine. He had an unkempt, disheveled look. His tweed jacket was worn and loose fitting; his white shirt and gray slacks were wrinkled; his black loafers were scuffed and dull; and his hair came down to his ears and hung in bangs over his forehead. He looked like a picture right out of the sixties. But he moved quickly, looking to be in a graceful hurry. With no effort, he wove his shoulders to one side or the other to avoid collisions as he kept moving toward me.

"Mr. Brotherton," he said in a clipped British accent, "my name is Malcolm Evans[†]. Our time is bloody well short. I want you to do exactly as I say."

I watched the queue move forward. There was only one person in front of us. I looked at Evans, thinking, I bloody well recognize you, sir. I asked, "What do you want me to do?"

"I need your passport and visa, now."

I handed him my documents. "What about Susan's?"

"Not hers. Seems you're the man of the hour." He was almost laughing, but not in amusement. He turned sharply and walked back to the room to our left. He didn't look back as he closed the door behind him.

Susan looked at her watch. "We're going to miss the plane. We're not going to make it," she said.

I put my arm around her shoulders. "All we can do is wait, honey. Whatever's going to happen is going to happen now."

We were at the head of the line, with about thirty people queued up behind us. The officer in the booth waved us forward. He was wearing the olive drab uniform of the Regular Russian Army.

"I'm scared, honey," Susan said. "What do we do? What if we don't—"

[†] This person's name has been changed for the purposes of this book.

"You go," I said, gently guiding her forward. "You have your passport and visa. Go up to the booth. Act casual. Now, Susan! You have to!"

For a moment we held hands. Susan briefly closed her eyes, took a deep breath, then took one step forward. But she wouldn't let go of my hand.

"Go, Susan!" I said. "Go! You have to."

"I love you," she said as she released my hand and walked up to the booth. With a quick look at me, she handed the officer her documents.

I heard loud voices from the interrogation room to my left and then, ahead, the sharp report of the rubber stamp as the officer marked Susan's passport. She walked through the passport checkpoint and then stopped and waited for me.

The officer in the booth waved me forward. I didn't know what to do. In five minutes the plane would be leaving, and I could hear the people in line behind me complaining. I walked to the booth and stood looking at the officer.

"Your passport and visa!" he commanded in Russian.

"I don't have them."

"What?" he barked. "You are here without them? Why are you—"

He was interrupted by another officer who appeared at the side of the booth. The two conferred, whispering and glancing at me. Then they walked behind a partition off to the side. I looked toward Susan. She was still standing waiting for me. The color had completely gone from her face.

Another officer walked up to her and said, "You cannot stay here." He took her elbow and tried to push her toward the boarding gate.

But she wouldn't move. "I'm not leaving without my husband," she told the officer and twisted her arm from his grip.

"Move! Now!" he ordered, this time gripping her by the shoulders, turning her away from me, and shoving her down the corridor and toward the gate.

I felt rage and frustration bolt through me at once. But Susan held her balance, turned back, and again stood looking at me, her face twisted.

The officer started toward her. Susan quickly walked away, obeying his orders. I could see her shoulders heaving, and I knew she was crying. She turned the corner and was gone.

I felt alone. So you've been tricked. And now you're open. She's alone up there, too. Will they make her get on the plane? Will she do it?

In my mind I could hear Major Howard—"Be loyal to that which is true to you." That'd be Susan, I knew, no matter what happened. If they grab you, I told myself, you're going to have to fight now. That's all you got left to do. But you can show them how it's done. You can damn well do that all right.

The door to my left opened. A young woman in uniform walked out, toward the booth where I was standing. Her face was stern, and she moved with precision, as if close-order drill was her routine way of walking. She faced me, smiled abruptly, mechanically, and handed me my passport and visa. Then straight-faced, her smile gone, she said, "Mr. Brotherton, have a pleasant flight." Before I could thank her, she placed a "Closed" sign on the booth, turned sharply, returned to the interrogation room, and shut the door behind her.

Susan was waiting in the corridor beside the boarding gate doors. She had stopped crying, but she was still trembling. When she saw me, she ran toward me. At the same time, the attendants started to close the doors.

"Wait!" I yelled, grabbing Susan and running toward the gate. "We're on that damn flight!"

I took Susan's ticket, then her arm, and pulled her down the aisle to our seats. Without a word, she sat by the window and covered her face in her hands. In a few moments she stopped trembling. She took a deep breath and turned to me. Tears welled in her eyes. I didn't know if I could stand it if she started crying again. But she didn't.

She sat straight up. "Can you tell me what happened to you back there?" Her voice was clear and unbroken.

"I don't really know," I said. "All I know—all I want to know—is that we're on this plane. We're getting out of here."

The plane pulled away from the gate, turned down the runway, and accelerated. As we lifted from the ground, I heard the landing gear retract. I always noticed that sound during takeoff—it had so many associations. Now, it meant we were off Russian soil.

"We're safe," I said as I kissed Susan.

"Thank God," she said, kissing me in return, at first urgently, her mouth pressed hard against mine. Then her lips relaxed. She rested her head on my shoulder, and I could feel the tension go out of her.

"Yes, thank God," I said. "Thank God. Thank the Reverend. Thank Senator John Breaux. And thank you. Thank you for waiting. Thank God I have you."

She lifted her head and looked at me. "We don't have any money, do we?"

"We're lucky if we have four dollars," I answered.

"Then we are lucky," she said playfully.

"Lucky, really?" I said.

"Well, they serve free drinks on international flights, don't they?"

"They do, honey. Thank God for that, too."

She tilted her head back slightly, and I could see lights dancing in her soft brown eyes. "So we'll land in the states with nothing, and we'll get to start over," she said, her lips suggesting a smile—the beautiful smile that had riveted my attention the night I first saw her, walking along the seawall near the Lake Charles Civic Center, while I was drinking with Eddie. I felt the same rush from my chest, the same pounding in my heart, the same alive sensation that I felt then.

I kissed her perfect face. "We'll be all right. We've got each other."

"I have what I want," she said. "I have John Brotherton."

Hearing her say that and feeling her close beside me, I felt like singing. So I did. I sang, "All we need is love—"

"All we need is love, love," she sang back to me, not missing a note.

"Love is all we need."

EPILOGUE

There's always a price.

– James Webb, *The Emperor's General*

＊

On May 9, 2000, Candy Edwards sat in the spectator's gallery in the federal courthouse in Baton Rouge while her husband, Edwin Edwards, stood to hear the jury's verdicts in the nearly five-month trial that had resulted from the FBI investigation into Edwin's associations with the casinos that had received licenses during his fourth term as governor of Louisiana. When the foreman finished reading the jury's consensus, Candy leaned forward, placed her head in her hands, and sobbed quietly.

She wasn't shedding tears of relief. After six days of deliberation, the jury, which had been narrowed down to eleven participants, had found Edwin guilty on seventeen counts involving extortion, racketeering, conspiracy, and money laundering.

Edwin faced the verdicts with dignity, showing that he was man enough to accept the consequences of his daring run at living as a law unto himself. And he gave those who had been Edwards watchers—some of them friends, others enemies, and many just admirers from the sidelines—a grand display of his flair for the dramatic. He quoted the ancient

Chinese proverb "If you sit by a river long enough, the dead bodies of your enemies will float by you" and then commented, "I suppose the feds sat by the river long enough." Over the five-years that I worked as an executive in the casino industry, I came to know Edwin well enough to wonder if he was really saying, "If the feds were any good at what they do, it wouldn't have taken them this long to do it." And over the short period of time that I dealt with the federal prosecution team, I learned that they were indeed more than good at what they do.

Candy Edwards can look forward to having an even greater reason to weep. The Honorable Frank J. Polozola, Chief Federal Judge, Middle District of Louisiana, is expected to pass one of the harshest sentences—if not the harshest sentence—to be imposed on a former state governor. Press accounts are speculating that Edwin will do his best to obtain a reduced sentence; but then the Honorable Frank J. Polozola is known for the severity of his judgments.

Back in May, just after the jury had stated its verdicts, Edwin said, "I regret that it ended this way, but that is the system. I have lived seventy-two years in the system, and I will live the rest of my life in the system." Theoretically, Edwin's sentence could come to a total of two hundred and seventy-five years. Certainly, he now faces several years, perhaps the remainder of his life, in the penal system, as a consequence of having run afoul of the justice system—that a consequence of his having lived so long and so recklessly in his own system.

And thus came to its end the reign of the King of Louisiana, who can now look ahead to the humbling status of being an inmate in a federal institution of one sort or another. It wouldn't surprise me in the least if his old campaign sticker ("Vote for the crook—it's important!") became a collector's item of inestimable value. By the cruelest of ironic twists, the members of the tenacious prosecution team urged the jury to vote for the crook precisely because they thought it was important.

The events that led to the conviction and sentencing of Edwin Edwards cast a shadow over nearly every one of the major characters in this book. Take, for example, Rick Shetler, who acted as the bagman for Edwin and Stephen in their schemes to extort money from Players, confessing that he personally had funneled over a half million dollars to them. Though Rick testified for the prosecution under a leniency deal, the ushering of Edwin and Stephen to justice gutted him emotionally.

In my mind's eye, I see two pictures of Rick. In the first, taken in happier times, his face is glowing with congeniality, and he's smiling openly, warmly, showing the big, generous heart I often saw in him. In the second, he's standing on the steps of the courthouse in Baton Rouge, where the press caught him on his way to testify against Edwin. It would take a seasoned eye to recognize in both pictures the Rick Shetler I knew. In the one taken on the courthouse steps, he's emaciated, his face looking caved in. He is, in short, a wreck. As I said to myself when I saw the photo on the front page of *The Lake Charles American Press*, "He's looked better."

I offer Pat Madamba as another casualty—and a deserving one at that, I strongly feel. These days, I hear, he's not as busy as he'd like to be, to put it mildly. I imagine that it'll take a long time for the shadow hanging over him to dissolve.

I also offer Players International itself, which was forced to wear infamy like a punitive hair shirt. Because of its participation in Edwin's schemes, Players had leveled on them the largest monetary sanction ever imposed on a casino operator in the United States. A newly appointed and sharkish Louisiana Gaming Commission ordered Players to pay $10.2 million, to sell its assets to an unrelated third party, and to depart the state, to never attempt to do business there again. (Later, the commission demanded that Players cough up another $600,000—of this, $300,000 to be paid by Howard Goldberg himself.) As a spin off benefit to the people of Louisiana, the assets that Players was required to unload were purchased by Harrah's, one of the largest, best managed, and most credible casino operators in the world.

Incidentally, the tapes that Danny abducted from our apartment in Moscow also figured in Players' descent into ignominy. As I understand it, Danny, when he returned to the states, called Ed Fishman and tried to use the tapes as leverage to obtain a paying job. In response, I'm told, Players consulted their attorneys, who advised Ed to warn Danny off and to demand the tapes. Players then turned the tapes over to the feds, who heard them out and turned nastily on the company. The way I heard it, the content was so incriminating that it persuaded Rick Shetler to accept the leniency deal and nipped in the bud (to say the least) any intention Players may have had to cover itself by depicting me as a rogue operative.

For me, Edwin's shadow extended all the way to Moscow, where it merged with the shadow cast by the gunmen of the Russian mafia. As you've seen in this book, Susan and I ran a tight race against certain death and won just barely, with help from the venerable Reverend, acting on a moment's notice from me.

And, in one sense or another, that shadow remains over me today, its darkening fingers still touching essential aspects of my life. Primary among these is the welfare of my son, Derek, now seventeen, and my daughter, Macie, now eleven. As they embark upon young adulthood, carrying the load of a broken family as their heritage, they both seem to be bearing up in a way that makes me proud. But I have to recognize that appearances in young people can be a mask and that Derek and Macie will need all the love, support, and vigilance that I can give them. There can never be enough of that.

I for my part, at least, realize that—although Kathy continues her jihad against me. In my first months back, she refused to let me see my son and daughter. Broke to the point of not having a car, I borrowed my stepfather's pickup truck and drove to Lake Charles several times, trying to meet and come to terms with her. Once I was able to get some money into her hands, she began waffling on one agreement after another, admitting that she wanted to mire me so deeply in legal proceedings that I wouldn't have time to line up employment.

Of course, the Austin protocol was at my avail, backed by one of Eddie's recently acquired associates, Kathleen Delaney, who countered Kathy and her attorney so effectively that the judge finally mandated that Kathy not only allow visitation but that she also personally deliver Derek and Macie to me. I owe a huge thanks to Kathleen for her legal and moral support at a time when I was harassed on several fronts.

In this book I have taken aim at several situations (e.g., the internecine nest within of the former Players organization) and personalities (primary among these the on-screen role that Chuck Norris typically apes). Lest you think that I'm indulging in overkill regarding Chuck Norris, I want to make it perfectly clear that he abandoned five fellow Americans in Moscow—that he headed back stateside, leaving Danny, David, Huck, and me unpaid and exposing us as well as my wife to what is likely the most organized and ruthless killing machine on the face of the earth.

I now and then monitor The Beverly Hills Casino on the Internet and have noted that it was still being advertised as a "Chuck Norris Enterprise" as recently as October of 2000. From time to time, for the pure amusement of it, I stomach my way through Chuck's postured heroics as Walker, Texas Ranger. The anthem that opens the program—sung with Chuck in stiff-backed, confrontational posture, uniformed in his Texas Ranger hat and long coat, facing the horizon and the challenges to law and order that lie ahead for him—claims that Walker will always be behind you, the implication being that he'll come at you showing his front side. As I've shown, Norris wasn't behind me or my American associates in Moscow when the situation got perilous.

Whenever I think of Norris, I can't help contrasting his pullout from Moscow with the risks that Carl Paige took to come to the aid of the foundering *L'Envie*, which was nearly overwhelmed by the thirty-foot waves that tropical storm *Beryl* churned up in the Gulf of Mexico (described in Chapter 10). Chuck Norris knew who I was, and he also knew my wife. I have a picture, taken at the Beverly Hills Club, in which Chuck is standing with Susan and me, giving the camera his best smile. Carl Paige knew only my voice over the VHF and the danger we were in. Chuck Norris was facing no real personal risk in Moscow. Carl Paige was having all he could do to keep his fishing boat running, with the engine throwing out lube oil as fast as he could supply it. You will recall that he was just about to head in when he received our distress call. Yet his response to our crisis was, "My best friend died out here last year... No way I'll let that happen again." When I pointed out that his own situation was precarious, he replied, "Right...I reckon it don't look so good for the home team. But I ain't leaving you in this. Can't do it. I'm skinning back and coming on full."

To the full, Carl Paige measured up to the standard set by Major

Robert L. Howard, my training officer in the Green Berets. As a platoon sergeant in Vietnam, Major Howard, though injured so badly he could only crawl, refused to leave any of his men wounded on the battlefield. In the face of an attacking force of two companies, he moreover crawled from position to position and rallied his withered platoon so effectively that it was able to repulse the enemy for over three hours, until rescue helicopters were able to land. Even then he refused to board until he had supervised the safe loading of his men. On Carl Paige and Major Howard, the combat fatigues of the Airborne would be a genuine uniform; on Chuck Norris, in my opinion, they would be no more than a costume.

I get an especially big kick out of the episodes in which Norris, as Walker, intrepidly takes on the Russian mafia. If you want a startling example of a diametric contradiction between image and actuality, consider this. When I returned to the states, I wrote a demand letter to Norris' attorneys and Ed Fishman that brought several responses. One was a nasty reply that was copied to Nikolaj Nikolaivich. Another was an open threat.

This threat, by the way, was my biggest reason for writing *A Fistful of Kings*. When the Reverend met me in Belize, he saw straight to the soldier in me. Later, when he came to Lake Charles, he counseled me to think military in crisis situations. And in my room at the Sovietsky, just before Susan and I made our run for the airport, he told me to remember who I am and to give the gun-toting goons of the Russian mafia an overdose of Sergeant John Brotherton. Regarding any threats to my security (or to the well being of anyone close to me), I point out that the overdose that the Reverend advised is in place and ready for application. *De oppresso liber* ("Freedom from oppression," the mandate handed to soldiers who wear the Green Beret) is a code for which I make no apologies.

The Reverend, incidentally, remains one of my closest friends. We talk over the phone at least once a week and make sure to spend time with each other at least once a year. Whenever I see a chance presenting itself, I try to get him to explain exactly what he did to help Susan and me in Moscow. By now, though, you know the Reverend pretty well—well enough that you have as much as I've been able to get from him by way of an answer to my question.

I don't want you thinking that my intent here has been to level judgment from a moral summit. If you've read my story thoroughly—the epigraphs at the beginning, the Preface, and the march of events through the chapters—you will have seen that I myself have been my own primary target.

At the outset, I said that this is very much my own story, and it has been in the sense that it has depicted my sorry lapse into a dark night of the soul, a chapter in my life during which I lost sight of who I really am, during which I allowed myself to become a victim, lured by a worldly-wise value set into a "slough of dispond." You've noticed, I hope, that my title has drawn on the image of a deck of cards—an image that is potent in its import. I remember the story in which an infantry grunt, lacking a Bible, explains to a chaplain how he's been using a deck of playing cards as a prayer book. We also commonly think of a deck of cards as signifying something resembling destiny, what life has in store for us. To borrow "The Soldier's Prayer Book," the deck that the unknown rifleman kept in his rucksack, I'd like to suggest that my narrative has shown what a higher power had in the cards for me, the path in which I was intended to walk but from which I strayed, only to be brought to my own true ground by the course of events. "There is," Hamlet says, "a divinity that shapes our ends, rough-hew them how we will."

I often wonder whether I had deafened myself to the still, small voice to which scripture urges our attention and that is supposed to tell us God's plan for us. I wonder too about the several hints that were perhaps laid along my errant way—the friends who attached to me not because I was a highly paid and placed executive, but because I was, as they saw me, a basic, nuts-and-bolts, down-to-earth, honest person. In the end, I was brought low—as I'm told God does to us when we ignore his message—down to almost nothing in the way of what I had so highly valued. But, at that pass, I learned that I really had everything. I had Susan, who had earlier put her finger on my heart and told me that what I had there is what counted for her. She couldn't have cared less that I had only four dollars in my pocket. In fact, if you've held the keen ear I asked for in the

Preface, you should have noticed that she saw being broke as an opportunity, a chance to start over with what both she and I most needed—me restored to my best self.

One of the first things I had to confront when I got back to the states, as poor almost as a threadbare pauper, was what I was going to do for a living. I didn't give the casino industry even a moment's thought and wouldn't have taken a job in that sector no matter how lucrative, no matter how perk-filled the package. I knew where I belonged—the construction industry. I got together with a few old friends and joined their small construction firm, which we have worked together to build into a still small but lean and honestly competitive force in our market.

Through the tough months I faced when I returned from Moscow, Susan stood by me as staunchly as she had during our incarceration in the Sovietsky. We seem to fall more in love with each other each day, and I'll never take for granted what she means to me as my soul mate. So I hope in the last analysis you'll join me in celebrating my heroine—my Beatrice. (When I think of it, my first sight of Susan on the seawall in Lake Charles must have been every bit as resonant as Dante's first meeting with Beatrice on the Ponte Vechio.) I thank you for undertaking my story, and I offer you my hope that your life is, as mine is now, full of things for which you give thanks.

* * *

Can You Solve
The Brotherton Puzzle?

The first person that solves the book's mystery will receive an all expense paid vacation for 2 to Las Vegas, Nevada. The rules of the contest are:

- Only one person will win the contest.
- This contest is void where prohibited.
- Contestants must be 21 years of age, or older, to qualify.
- Vacation origin must be within the continental United States.
- Anyone with personal knowledge or prior associations with any of the book's characters will not be eligible to win.
- All disputes will be settled at the sole discretion of the author. By entering the contest, you agree to be bound by this provision.

To win, you must do the following:

1. Provide 30 mystery clues on a separate sheet of paper and attach it to this contest form.
2. Attach proof of book purchase to this contest form.
3. Fill in the answer to the mystery in the space provided on the next page.
4. Fill out the personal information requested on this form.
5. Put the form and attachments in an envelope and mail it to:

> The Shears Group, Limited
> Contest Entry Department
> 6942 F. M. 1960 East #133
> Humble, TX   77346-2704

6. You may bypass sending in this form by logging on to www.afistfulofkings.com to answer the mystery on the Internet web site. If you choose to answer the mystery in this manner, you will still be required to mail in proof of age and proof of purchase to the address listed above.

Official Entry Form

I think The Answer To The Mystery Is:

_____

_____

_____

_____

_____

_____

_____

_____

_____

_____

_____

_____

_____

Name_____

Address_____

City _____ State _____ Zip _____

Email _____

Phone _____

Where did you purchase the book? _____

Book Order Form

Would you like to order a copy of *A Fistful of Kings?*

Check with your local book retailer first and ask them to order it.
You can then fill out this form and send it to the address listed below.

Name_____

Address_____

City _____ State _____ Zip _____

Email _____

Phone _____

Where did you purchase the book? _____

    Cost of book - $29.95 each + Shipping & handling - $4.95 each
    Total number of books = _____ X $34.90 = $_____
    Texas residents add 8.25% - $2.87 for each book = $_____

Payment method:
_____ AmEx   _____ Visa _____ MC _____ Check (enclosed)

Credit Card Number _____Exp Date _____

Total Order $_____

Mail this form to:

The Shears Group, Limited • Book Orders Department
6942 F. M. 1960 East #133 • Humble, Texas 77346-2704

Book Order Form

Would you like to order a copy of *A Fistful of Kings?*

Check with your local book retailer first and ask them to order it. You can then fill out this form and send it to the address listed below.

Name_____

Address_____

City _____ State _____ Zip _____

Email _____

Phone _____

Where did you purchase the book? _____

    Cost of book - $29.95 each + Shipping & handling - $4.95 each
    Total number of books = _____ X $34.90 = $_____
    Texas residents add 8.25% - $2.87 for each book = $_____

Payment method:
_____ AmEx   _____ Visa _____ MC _____ Check (enclosed)

Credit Card Number _____Exp Date _____

Total Order $_____

Mail this form to:

The Shears Group, Limited • Book Orders Department
6942 F. M. 1960 East #133 • Humble, Texas 77346-2704